UNITARY SYMMETRIES
AND THEIR APPLICATION TO HIGH ENERGY PHYSICS

UNITARY SYMMETRIES

AND THEIR APPLICATION TO HIGH ENERGY PHYSICS

M. GOURDIN

Professor of Theoretical Physics
Faculté des Sciences d'Orsay

N·H
P C

1967

NORTH-HOLLAND PUBLISHING COMPANY
AMSTERDAM

JOHN WILEY & SONS, INC. - NEW YORK
(Interscience Publishers Division)

PUBLISHERS:

NORTH-HOLLAND PUBLISHING COMPANY - AMSTERDAM

SOLE DISTRIBUTORS FOR U.S.A. AND CANADA:

INTERSCIENCE PUBLISHERS, a division of

JOHN WILEY & SONS, INC. - NEW YORK

PRINTED IN THE NETHERLANDS

PREFACE

In this book we shall attempt to give an up-to-date survey of unitary symmetries in elementary particle physics. Unitary symmetries originated from the success obtained by isotopic spin symmetry. We shall study successively SU(3) internal symmetry, which is a clear generalization of SU(2) isotopic symmetry; then we shall come to problems related to SU(6) symmetry which tries to mix internal symmetry with an intrinsic spin symmetry.

This book is divided into two parts: one purely mathematical, the other purely physical. The mathematical developments are intended for physicists. They supply many results but very often omit proofs. Their main purpose is to give a correct language and as precise as possible an idea of the results obtained by mathematicians in this domain of group theory and of Lie algebra. From this point of view, the six "mathematical" chapters should permit easy localization and coordination of applications of group theory to elementary particle physics. The Lie algebra is presented abstractly in its intrinsic form – in our opinion, this allows a better understanding of the role played by structure constants. Only then do we come to the field of applications to Lie algebra physics, with the study of Lie groups of transformations. Up to now, linear, orthogonal, pseudo-orthogonal, unitary, pseudo-unitary and symplectic groups have been used in various models of elementary particles. This is why we chose to expatiate on the chapter called "Lie groups of transformations", and to treat it in a systematic way. Problems of topology are surveyed fairly quickly. However a few subtleties which are of great importance in physics were paid attention to, and some particular points emphasized. We then study the standard form of semi-simple Lie algebra and the classification of simple algebra due to Cartan. The theory of representations is next presented in the particular case of compact groups for which all representations are equivalent to unitary representations. This unitary character is fundamental for the conservation of probabilities in physics. Finally, the last chapter of this mathematical part is devoted to a study of tensor algebra, Young diagrams, and products of representations. The tensor method is one of the most interesting from the point of view of explicit computations which one cannot fail to encounter in physics; moreover it does not necessitate too important a mathematical background.

In good logic, we should have placed all the mathematical chapters foremost. As the book is intended for physicists, more often than not prejudiced against pure mathematics, we have considered the psychological aspect of this question and chosen to treat these six mathematical chapters as an appendix, which it is not indispensable to study in detail in order to do useful work with the physical part. So we deliberately avoided any lyric style and gave a very succinct account of the facts. We were also urged to write these mathematical chapters (apart from the pedagogical aim) by the desire to set in their proper light many impressive papers of physics which, when deprived of their mathematical contents familiar to specialists, appear astonishingly poor and devoid of interest, except of documentation.

Eleven chapters are devoted to physical applications of unitary groups. Seven of them are related to SU(3) and four to SU(6) symmetry. At the head of each of these two parts, we thought it necessary to write a chapter supplying the technical notations and main mathematical properties used. These chapters are obviously directly constructed from the mathematical appendix; but they can spare the reader from reading that appendix.

The origin of any application of group theory to elementary particle physics is the study of isotopic spin symmetry. The SU(2) unitary group is too well known in quantum mechanics and in nuclear physics to be studied again here. We have taken for granted that the reader is familiar with the properties of this group and with the consequences of isotopic symmetry, these two postulates serving as a starting point for our study of unitary symmetries. SU(3) symmetry is an internal symmetry, which is assumed to commute with the Poincaré group, and in this sense it is a mere extension of isotopic symmetry. The rules of the game are then mathematically well defined even if their physical justification is not always satisfactory. We study this symmetry of strong interactions and its violations in medium-strong, electromagnetic and weak interactions. The latter domains appear to be far the most fruitful and furnish a fairly large number of predictions which can be compared sometimes with experimental data.

There was a question deliberately left aside: that of the dynamical origin of SU(3) symmetry. Many authors studied it more or less rigorously or satisfactorily. This problem, which is highly interesting and fundamental when one wishes to gain a better understanding of symmetries, has been so far treated only by very disputable methods such as the approximations currently made in bootstrap theory; it is hard to know whether partial results that can be obtained have any value going further than the framework of approximations. For lack of competence in these domains we abstained from treating them, preferring not to give questionable and unrigorous comments.

The SU(6) problem has become a fashionable problem which is as yet immature. The considerable effort which has been devoted to it for eighteen months, the positive and negative results obtained, make it an arduous task to bring any comprehensive survey quite up-to-date, especially if this survey is to have a reasonable lifetime (at least for the duration of printing the book). On these grounds we were brought to adopt a cautious attitude and to make a choice which may well become outdated in the light of new results. The difficulties have been pointed out in the three chapters devoted to SU(6) symmetry, and we wish to apologize for being sometimes incomplete or partial. In particular, the attempts to formulate relativistic extensions of SU(6) symmetry were simply quoted and not discussed. The mathematical tools needed have been included in the mathematical chapters, but the results obtained to-date did not seem to us to justify a detailed study which might have not been clear and convincing enough. On the other hand, the techniques of currents-algebra were developed with some care, due to the important success obtained, although some of their theoretical bases are not yet well-established.

The origin of this book is a series of lectures given at "Faculté des Sciences" at Orsay in the frame of "Troisième Cycle" of Theoretical Physics, and conferences given in other laboratories, especially at the "Matscience Institute" in Madras, at "Faculté des Sciences" in Bordeaux, at Stanford University, and at Nordita (Copenhagen). The author is glad to take this opportunity to thank Professors A. Ramakrishnan, R. Vinh Mau, L. Schiff, J. Hamilton and C. Möller for their hospitality which helped him to give these notes their present shape.

December 1965 MICHEL GOURDIN

CONTENTS

CHAPTER VI

WEAK INTERACTIONS

CHAPTER VII

NON-LEPTONIC WEAK INTERACTIONS

CHAPTER VIII

THE UNITARY GROUP SU(6)

CHAPTER IX

THE SU(6) MODEL

CHAPTER X

LIE ALGEBRA OF CURRENTS

CHAPTER XI

PHYSICAL CONSEQUENCES OF SU(6) SYMMETRY

CHAPTER XII

LIE GROUPS AND LIE ALGEBRA

CHAPTER XIII

LIE GROUPS OF TRANSFORMATIONS

CHAPTER XIV

TOPOLOGICAL PROPERTIES

CHAPTER XV

LIE ALGEBRA OF THE SEMI-SIMPLE GROUPS

CHAPTER XVI

REPRESENTATIONS

CHAPTER XVII

TENSOR ALGEBRA OF THE LINEAR GROUP

CHAPTER I

THE UNITARY GROUP SU(3)

1.1. Lie algebra

1. The Lie algebra A_2 is simple and the root diagram is a regular hexagon.

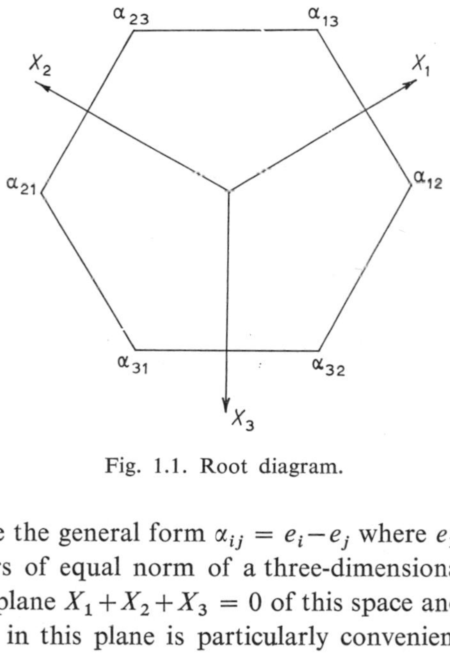

Fig. 1.1. Root diagram.

The roots α_{ij} have the general form $\alpha_{ij} = e_i - e_j$ where e_1, e_2, e_3 are three orthogonal vectors of equal norm of a three-dimensional space. The root diagram is in the plane $X_1+X_2+X_3 = 0$ of this space and the use of triangular coordinates in this plane is particularly convenient.

2. The Cartan tensor is a regular tensor normalized so that $g_{\alpha-\alpha} = 1$. From this condition it follows that the roots are normalized in the following way:

$$(\alpha, \alpha) = \tfrac{1}{3}$$

and all the non vanishing structure constants have the same modulus equal to $1/\sqrt{6}$.

3. The Lie algebra has the dimension 8 and the Cartan subalgebra the

dimension 2. We will use for this last subalgebra three generators H_1, H_2, H_3 of sum zero:

$$H_1+H_2+H_3 = 0.$$

The commutation relations of the Lie algebra in its standard form are then given by:

$$[H_i, H_j] = 0 \qquad [E_{ij}, E_{ji}] = \frac{1}{\sqrt{6}}(H_i-H_j)$$

$$[H_i, E_{ij}] = \frac{1}{\sqrt{6}}E_{ij} \qquad [H_j, E_{ij}] = -\frac{1}{\sqrt{6}}E_{ij}$$

$$[E_{ij}, E_{jk}] = \frac{1}{\sqrt{6}}E_{ik} \qquad [E_{ji}, E_{kj}] = -\frac{1}{\sqrt{6}}E_{ki}.$$

4. We have three subalgebras of the type E_α, $E_{-\alpha}$, (α, H) isomorphic to a Lie algebra A_1:

$$\sqrt{6}E_{12} \qquad \sqrt{6}E_{21} \qquad \tfrac{1}{2}\sqrt{6}(H_1-H_2)$$

$$\sqrt{6}E_{23} \qquad \sqrt{6}E_{32} \qquad \tfrac{1}{2}\sqrt{6}(H_2-H_3)$$

$$\sqrt{6}E_{31} \qquad \sqrt{6}E_{13} \qquad \tfrac{1}{2}\sqrt{6}(H_3-H_1).$$

Another interesting subalgebra is the subalgebra so(3) associated to the real unitary transformation. This algebra of type A_1 is defined by the three linear combinations:

$$\sqrt{6}(E_{12}-E_{21}) \qquad \sqrt{6}(E_{23}-E_{32}) \qquad \sqrt{6}(E_{31}-E_{13}).$$

We must remark that the three generators in this case are exterior to the Cartan algebra of A_2.

1.2. Fundamental representations

We have two contragradient three dimensional representations noted for simplicity 3 and $\bar{3}$. We now construct the matrix representations of the Lie algebra A_2.

1. The highest weight of the first fundamental representation has the

following components:

$$L = \tfrac{1}{3}(2e_1 - e_2 - e_3)$$

and can also be written, in terms of the roots as $L = \frac{1}{3}(\alpha_{12}+\alpha_{13})$.

The three equivalent weights are obtained from L by the Weyl's reflections and they have the general form:

$$m_i = \tfrac{1}{3}(\alpha_{ij}+\alpha_{ik})$$

where i, j, k is the set of the three numbers 1, 2, 3.

We then immediately deduce the relations:

$$m_i + m_j = -m_k \qquad m_i - m_j = \alpha_{ij}$$

and:

$$(m_i, \alpha_{ij}) = -(m_j, \alpha_{ij}) = \tfrac{1}{2}(\alpha_{ij}, \alpha_{ij}) = \tfrac{1}{6}.$$

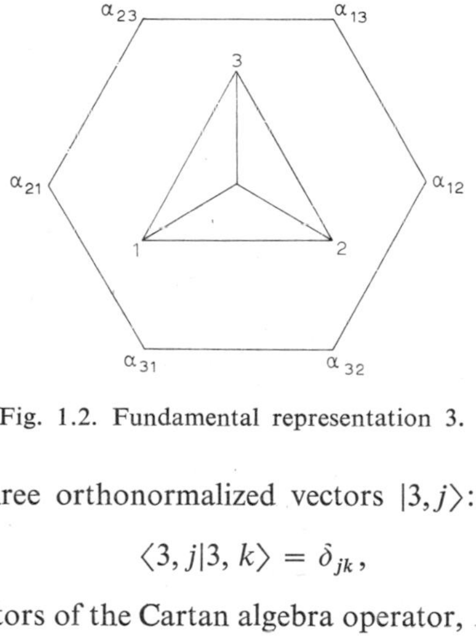

Fig. 1.2. Fundamental representation 3.

2. We define three orthonormalized vectors $|3, j\rangle$:

$$\langle 3, j | 3, k\rangle = \delta_{jk},$$

which are eigenvectors of the Cartan algebra operator, H, with the eigenvalues m_j. By definition of the weights, we obtain the following representation of the Cartan algebra:

$$H = \sum_{j=1}^{3} m_j |3, j\rangle \langle 3, j|.$$

Each component of the Cartan algebra H_k has the explicit form:

$$\sqrt{6}H_k = \tfrac{2}{3}|3, k\rangle\langle 3, k| - \tfrac{1}{3}|3, i\rangle\langle 3, i| - \tfrac{1}{3}|3, j\rangle\langle 3, j|.$$

3. The only possible transition with the operator E_{ij} is to go from the

weight $|3, j\rangle$ to the weight $|3, i\rangle$ and we obtain the representation:

$$\sqrt{6}E_{ij} = \omega_{ij}|3, i\rangle\langle 3, j|.$$

The arbitrary phase ω_{ij} is restricted by the commutation relations to satisfy:

$$\omega_{ij}\omega_{jk} = \omega_{ik}$$

and the general form of ω_{ij} turns out to be simply $\omega_{ij} = \exp i(\varphi_i - \varphi_j)$. It is possible to include the phase φ_j in the state $|3, j\rangle$ and to obtain finally the simple form:

$$\sqrt{6}E_{ij} = |3, i\rangle\langle 3, j|.$$

4. An explicit matrix representation is then the following:

$$|3, 1\rangle = \begin{vmatrix} 1 \\ 0 \\ 0 \end{vmatrix}; \quad |3, 2\rangle = \begin{vmatrix} 0 \\ 1 \\ 0 \end{vmatrix}; \quad |3, 3\rangle = \begin{vmatrix} 0 \\ 0 \\ 1 \end{vmatrix};$$

$$\sqrt{6}H_1 = \tfrac{1}{3}\begin{vmatrix} 2 & 0 & 0 \\ 0 & -1 & 0 \\ 0 & 0 & -1 \end{vmatrix}; \; \sqrt{6}H_2 = \tfrac{1}{3}\begin{vmatrix} -1 & 0 & 0 \\ 0 & 2 & 0 \\ 0 & 0 & -1 \end{vmatrix}; \; \sqrt{6}H_3 = \tfrac{1}{3}\begin{vmatrix} -1 & 0 & 0 \\ 0 & -1 & 0 \\ 0 & 0 & 2 \end{vmatrix};$$

$$\sqrt{6}E_{12} = \begin{vmatrix} 0 & 1 & 0 \\ 0 & 0 & 0 \\ 0 & 0 & 0 \end{vmatrix}; \quad \sqrt{6}E_{23} = \begin{vmatrix} 0 & 0 & 0 \\ 0 & 0 & 1 \\ 0 & 0 & 0 \end{vmatrix}; \quad \sqrt{6}E_{31} = \begin{vmatrix} 0 & 0 & 0 \\ 0 & 0 & 0 \\ 1 & 0 & 0 \end{vmatrix};$$

$$\sqrt{6}E_{21} = \begin{vmatrix} 0 & 0 & 0 \\ 1 & 0 & 0 \\ 0 & 0 & 0 \end{vmatrix}; \quad \sqrt{6}E_{32} = \begin{vmatrix} 0 & 0 & 0 \\ 0 & 0 & 0 \\ 0 & 1 & 0 \end{vmatrix}; \quad \sqrt{6}E_{13} = \begin{vmatrix} 0 & 0 & 1 \\ 0 & 0 & 0 \\ 0 & 0 & 0 \end{vmatrix}.$$

5. The two fundamental representations are contragradient. The two weight diagrams are symmetrical to each other with respect to the origin.

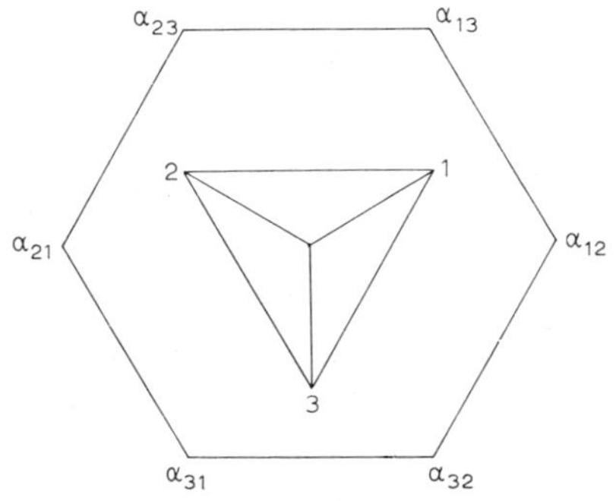

Fig. 1.3. Fundamental representation $\bar{3}$.

The weights n_j are labelled in such a way that $n_j+m_j = 0$. It follows from the general theorems that it is possible to find in the vector spaces of two contragradient representations two basis such that if X_ρ and X'_σ are the representations of the same operator one has:

$$X'_\sigma = -X^{\mathrm{T}}_\sigma .$$

6. We define three orthonormalized vectors $|\bar{3}, j\rangle$:

$$\langle\bar{3}, j|\bar{3}, k\rangle = \delta_{jk}$$

associated to the weights n_j. The Cartan subalgebra has the following representation:

$$H' = \sum_{j=1}^{3} n_j|\bar{3}, j\rangle\langle\bar{3}, j|$$

and from the relation $n_j+m_j = 0$ we deduce $H+H' = 0$.

7. For the generators E_{ij} we immediately obtain the simple expression:

$$\sqrt{6}E'_{ij} = -|\bar{3}, j\rangle\langle\bar{3}, i|$$

and an explicit matrix representation is then the following:

$$|\bar{3}, 1\rangle = \begin{vmatrix} 1 \\ 0 \\ 0 \end{vmatrix}; \quad |\bar{3}, 2\rangle = \begin{vmatrix} 0 \\ 1 \\ 0 \end{vmatrix}; \quad |\bar{3}, 3\rangle = \begin{vmatrix} 0 \\ 0 \\ 1 \end{vmatrix};$$

$$\sqrt{6}H_1 = \tfrac{1}{3}\begin{vmatrix} -2 & 0 & 0 \\ 0 & 1 & 0 \\ 0 & 0 & 1 \end{vmatrix}; \quad \sqrt{6}H_2 = \tfrac{1}{3}\begin{vmatrix} 1 & 0 & 0 \\ 0 & -2 & 0 \\ 0 & 0 & 1 \end{vmatrix}; \quad \sqrt{6}H_3 = \tfrac{1}{3}\begin{vmatrix} 1 & 0 & 0 \\ 0 & 1 & 0 \\ 0 & 0 & -2 \end{vmatrix};$$

$$\sqrt{6}E_{12} = \begin{vmatrix} 0 & 0 & 0 \\ -1 & 0 & 0 \\ 0 & 0 & 0 \end{vmatrix}; \quad \sqrt{6}E_{23} = \begin{vmatrix} 0 & 0 & 0 \\ 0 & 0 & 0 \\ 0 & -1 & 0 \end{vmatrix}; \quad \sqrt{6}E_{31} = \begin{vmatrix} 0 & 0 & -1 \\ 0 & 0 & 0 \\ 0 & 0 & 0 \end{vmatrix};$$

$$\sqrt{6}E_{21} = \begin{vmatrix} 0 & -1 & 0 \\ 0 & 0 & 0 \\ 0 & 0 & 0 \end{vmatrix}; \quad \sqrt{6}E_{32} = \begin{vmatrix} 0 & 0 & 0 \\ 0 & 0 & -1 \\ 0 & 0 & 0 \end{vmatrix}; \quad \sqrt{6}E_{13} = \begin{vmatrix} 0 & 0 & 0 \\ 0 & 0 & 0 \\ -1 & 0 & 0 \end{vmatrix}.$$

8. Two contragradient representations of SU(3) are equivalent with respect to the real orthogonal transformations of the sub-group SO(3). It follows that the Lie algebra so(3) previously defined has two equivalent matrix representations in two contragradient representations of SU(3).

In the actual case of the fundamental representations, we have obtained:

$$\sqrt{6}(E_{12}-E_{21}) = \begin{vmatrix} 0 & 1 & 0 \\ -1 & 0 & 0 \\ 0 & 0 & 0 \end{vmatrix}$$

$$\sqrt{6}(E_{23}-E_{32}) = \begin{vmatrix} 0 & 0 & 0 \\ 0 & 0 & 1 \\ 0 & -1 & 0 \end{vmatrix}$$

$$\sqrt{6}(E_{31}-E_{13}) = \begin{vmatrix} 0 & 0 & -1 \\ 0 & 0 & 0 \\ 1 & 0 & 0 \end{vmatrix}$$

which is the three-dimensional vector representation of the orthogonal group SO(3).

1.3. Adjoint representation

1. The adjoint representation is eight dimensional as the Lie algebra and the weight are the roots of the Lie algebra.

The adjoint representation can be constructed according to the product of the fundamental contragradient representations

$$D^{(3)}(1,0) \otimes D^{(3)}(0,1) = D^{(8)}(1,1) \oplus D^{(1)}(0,0).$$

The scalar representation $D^{(1)}(0,0)$ can be associated to the conserved hermitian form invariant, by definition, under unitary transformations.

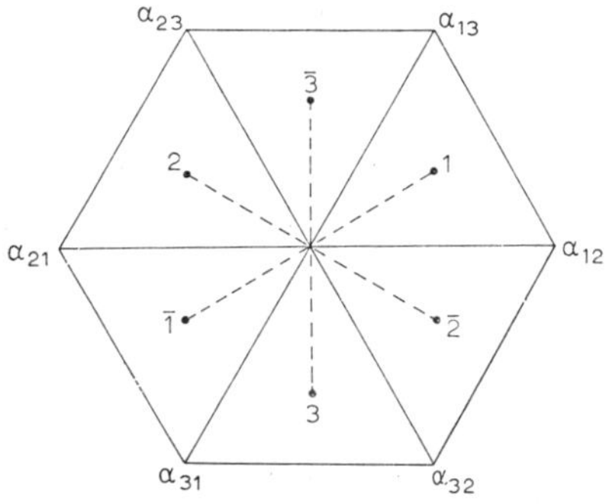

Fig. 1.4. Adjoint representation 8.

2. The vectors of the adjoint representation associated to a non zero root α_{ij} can be immediately written, up to an arbitrary phase, as a tensor product:

$$|8, ij\rangle = |3, i\rangle \otimes |\bar{3}, j\rangle, \qquad i \neq j.$$

In order to determine the two eigenvectors of the adjoint representation corresponding to the weights zero it is convenient to construct first the scalar associated to the invariant representation $D^{(1)}(0, 0)$. We immediately obtain:

$$|1\rangle = \frac{1}{\sqrt{3}} \sum_{j=1}^{3} |3, j\rangle \otimes |\bar{3}, j\rangle.$$

The general form of an eigenvector of the adjoint representation associated to the weight zero is then easily deduced from the previous result and is characterized by the zero trace condition:

$$|8, \rho^{\alpha}\rangle = \sum_{j=1}^{3} \rho_j^{\alpha} |3, j\rangle \otimes |3, j\rangle$$

with the restrictions:

$$\sum_j \rho_j^{\alpha} = 0, \qquad \sum_j (\rho_j^{\alpha})^2 = 1.$$

As expected we have only two linearly independent eigenvectors. It is useful to introduce some particular solutions

$$|8, \rho^{ij}\rangle = \frac{1}{\sqrt{2}} [|3, i\rangle \otimes |\bar{3}, i\rangle - |3, j\rangle \otimes (\bar{3}, j\rangle].$$

3. The adjoint representation of the Cartan subalgebra is easily obtained by using the non-zero roots α_{ij} as weights:

$$H = \sum_{i,j} \alpha_{ij} |8, ij\rangle\langle 8, ij|.$$

For each operator H_k we then have:

$$\sqrt{6} H_k = |8, ki\rangle\langle 8, ki| + |8, kj\rangle\langle 8, kj| - |8, ik\rangle\langle 8, ik| - |8, jk\rangle\langle 8, jk|.$$

The explicit representation of the generators E_{ij} is constructed by tensor product of the fundamental representations:

$$\sqrt{6} E_{ij} = |8, ik\rangle\langle 8, jk| - |8, kj\rangle\langle 8, ki| + \sqrt{2} |8, \rho^{ij}\rangle\langle 8, ji| - \sqrt{2} |8, ij\rangle\langle 8, \rho^{ij}|.$$

One easily checks that the coefficients are simply the structure constants.

4. The adjoint representation is equivalent to its contragradient representation as a general property of semi-simple Lie algebra.

It is then possible to find a bilinear form C which is invariant under unitarity transformations. Such a form corresponds to the scalar product of two vectors in the real vector space of the adjoint representation. The adjoint representation is a subset of all the 8×8 orthogonal matrices which leaves invariant the symmetrical bilinear regular form C. The adjoint representation is a subgroup of the special orthogonal group SO(8) and the Lie algebra A_2 a subalgebra of D_4. The symmetrical matrix C has the following expression

$$C = \sum_{i \neq j} |8, ij\rangle\langle 8, ji| + \sum_{\alpha} |8, \rho^{\alpha}\rangle\langle 8, \rho^{\alpha}|$$

where the sum $\sum_{\alpha}$ is extended to two orthonormalized arbitrarity eigenvectors associated to the weight zero of multiplicity two.

1.4. Topology

1. The universal covering group of the Lie algebra A_2 is the simply connected group SU(3). The center of SU(3) is isomorphic to Z_3 and can be represented in the fundamental representation $D^{(3)}(1, 0)$ by the three matrices:

$$\{I, jI, j^2 I\} \quad \text{with} \quad j = \exp \tfrac{2}{3} i\pi.$$

The center is generated for instance by the element jI.

The contragradient representation of this generating element is the complex conjugate matrix $\bar{j}I = j^2 I$.

For the irreducible representation $D^N(\lambda_1, \lambda_2)$, the generating element is now given by:

$$\exp \tfrac{2}{3} i\pi(\lambda_1 - \lambda_2) I_N$$

where now I_N is the $N \times N$ unit matrix.

The kernel of the homomorphism:

$$SU(3) \Rightarrow SU(3)/Z_3$$

must be represented by the unit matrix in all the representations of the factor group $SU(3)/Z_3$. It follows that the representations of SU(3) which are also representations of $SU(3)/Z_3$ are characterized by:

$$\lambda_1 \equiv \lambda_2 (3).$$

The adjoint representation satisfies of course this condition and generates, by tensor product all the irreducible representations of the factor group $SU(3)/Z_3$.

2. The eigenvalues of the operators $\sqrt{6} H_j$ of the Cartan subalgebra has been defined as the components X_j of the weights.

The components of the weights of the fundamental representations are not integer numbers. The three coordinates X_1, X_2, X_3 have a structure depending only of the representation and the same for the three coordinates because of the Weyl's reflections:

$$X_j \equiv -\tfrac{1}{3}(1) \quad \text{for} \quad D^{(3)}(1,0)$$
$$X_j \equiv +\tfrac{1}{3}(1) \quad \text{for} \quad D^{(3)}(0,1).$$

For the irreducible representation $D^N(\lambda_1, \lambda_2)$ the result is obtained by the tensor product:

$$X_j \equiv \tfrac{1}{3}(\lambda_1 - \lambda_2) \quad (1).$$

We then obtain the important result: the eigenvalues of the operators $\sqrt{6}H_j$ for all the irreducible representations of the factor group $SU(3)/Z_3$ are integer numbers.

3. The irreducible representations $D^N(\lambda_1, \lambda_2)$ can be divided in a direct sum of three classes following the values of the difference $\lambda_1 - \lambda_2$ which is also called the triality of the representation:

Class C_0	$\lambda_1 = \lambda_2$ (3)	triality 0
Class C_1	$\lambda_1 \equiv \lambda_2 + 1$ (3)	triality +1
Class C_{-1}	$\lambda_1 \equiv \lambda_2 - 1$ (3)	triality −1.

Only the representations of class C_0 are associated to a group which is $SU(3)/Z_3$. For instance, $D^{(3)}(1, 0)$ is a representation of class C_1 and the contragradient $D^{(3)}(0, 1)$ a representation of class C_{-1}. Generally the contragradient representation of a representation of class $C_{\pm 1}$ is a representation of class $C_{\mp 1}$. The set of classes is a finite group isomorphic to Z_3 with the multiplication table 1.1.

TABLE 1.1

	C_0	C_1	C_{-1}
C_0	C_0	C_1	C_{-1}
C_1	C_1	C_{-1}	C_0
C_{-1}	C_{-1}	C_0	C_1

Only the irreducible representations of class C_0 have the weight zero.

4. We have previously defined three subalgebra of the type A_1 with the sequences of generators $\sqrt{6}E_{ij}$, $\sqrt{6}E_{ji}$, $\tfrac{1}{2}\sqrt{6}(H_i - H_j)$. We now introduce three sub-groups SU(2) which are contained in both SU(3) and $SU(3)/Z_3$.

The situation is quite different for the Lie subalgebra so (3) of type A_1

also, defined by $\sqrt{6}(E_{12}-E_{21})$, $\sqrt{6}(E_{23}-E_{32})$, $\sqrt{6}(E_{31}-E_{13})$. The fundamental representations 3 and $\bar{3}$ become equivalent to the vector representation and only the orthogonal group SO(3) is a subgroup of both SU(3) and $SU(3)/Z_3$.

Finally, we have shown that the adjoint representation is a subgroup of the orthogonal group SO(8). It is easy to prove that such a result is true only for the factor group and not for the universal covering group:

$$SU(3)/Z_3 \subset SO(8).$$

1.5. Tensor algebra

1. The vectors of the fundamental representation $D^{(3)}(1,0)$ can be associated to first order contravariant tensors ξ_j,

$$\xi_j \Rightarrow |3, j\rangle.$$

The vectors of the fundamental representation $D^{(3)}(0, 1)$ can be associated to first order covariant tensors ξ^k,

$$\xi^k \Rightarrow |\bar{3}, k\rangle.$$

The vectors of the adjoint representation $D^{(8)}(1, 1)$ are then related to second order mixed tensors ξ_j^k of trace zero given by:

$$\xi_j^k \Rightarrow |8, jk\rangle \qquad \text{if} \quad j \neq k$$

$$\xi_j^j \Rightarrow \tfrac{1}{3}\sqrt{2}[|8, \rho^{ji}\rangle + |8, \rho^{jk}\rangle].$$

It can be useful in practice to consider such a tensor as a 3×3 matrix of trace zero.

2. More generally, the vectors of the irreducible representation $D(\lambda_1, \lambda_2)$ correspond to tensors of order $\lambda_1 + \lambda_2$ and of mixed character with λ_1 symmetrized contravariant indices, λ_2 symmetrized covariant indices and a trace zero:

$$\xi^{k_1 k_2 \ldots k_{\lambda_2}}_{j_1 j_2 \ldots j_{\lambda_1}}, \quad \text{with} \quad \xi^{j k_2 \ldots k_{\lambda_2}}_{j j_2 \ldots j_{\lambda_1}} = 0.$$

For instance, the vectors of the representation $D^{(10)}(3, 0)$ are described by third order fully symmetrized contravariant tensors and the vectors of the contragradient representation $D^{(10)}(0, 3)$ by third order fully symmetrized covariant tensors:

$$\xi_{jkl,} \Rightarrow D^{(10)}(3, 0) \qquad \xi^{jkl,} \Rightarrow D^{(10)}(0, 3).$$

3. A completely antisymmetrized contravariant or covariant third order

tensor is invariant under unimodular unitary transformations. It follows for instance that a first order covariant (contravariant) tensor transforms like an antisymmetrized second order contravariant (covariant) tensor. All the irreducible representations of SU(3) can then be associated to irreducible contravariant tensors. The irreducible representation $D(\lambda_1, \lambda_2)$ can be described by a purely contravariant tensor of order $\lambda_1 + 2\lambda_2$ with the symmetry character $\lambda_1 + \lambda_2, \lambda_2$:

$$\xi_{j_1 j_2 \dots j_{\lambda_1} l_1 l_2 \dots l_{\lambda_2}, m_1 m_2 \dots m_{\lambda_2}},$$

by using the invariant third order antisymmetric tensor ε_{klm}.

4. We now give a restrictive list of some useful irreducible representations of SU(3). In each case we indicate the smallest rank mixed tensor associated and we draw the corresponding completely contravariant Young diagram. Table 1.2 contains all the mixed tensors of rank from 1 to 4 and table 1.3 is restricted to higher rank tensors of $SU(3)/Z_3$.

TABLE 1.2

Rank	Irreducible representation		Triality	Mixed tensor	Young diagram
1	$D(1, 0)$	3	+1	ξ_j	
	$D(0, 1)$	$\overline{3}$	−1	ξ^j	
2	$D(2, 0)$	6	−1	$\xi_{jk,}$	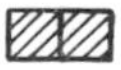
	$D(0, 2)$	$\overline{6}$	+1	$\xi^{jk,}$	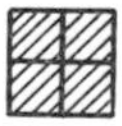
	$D(1, 1)$	8	0	ξ_j^k	
3	$D(3, 0)$	10	0	$\xi_{jkl,}$	
	$D(0, 3)$	$\overline{10}$	0	$\xi^{jkl,}$	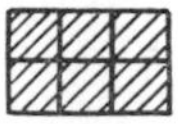
	$D(2, 1)$	15	+1	$\xi^l_{jk,}$	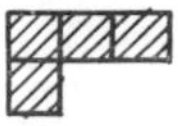
	$D(1, 2)$	$\overline{15}$	−1	$\xi^{kl,}_j$	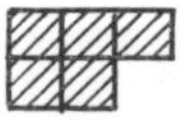

TABLE 1.2 (Continued)

Rank	Irreducible representation		Triality	Mixed tensor	Young diagram
	$D(4, 0)$	$15'$	$+1$	$\xi_{jklm},$	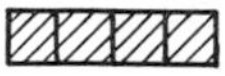
	$D(0, 4)$	$\overline{15}'$	-1	$\xi^{jklm},$	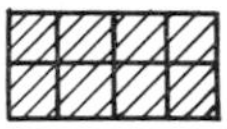
4	$D(3, 1)$	24	-1	$\xi^{m}_{jkl},$	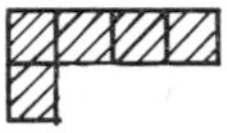
	$D(1, 3)$	$\overline{24}$	$+1$	$\xi^{klm}_{j},$	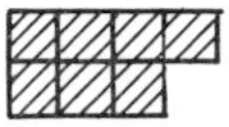
	$D(2, 2)$	27	0	$\xi^{lm}_{jk},$	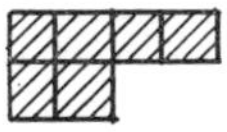

TABLE 1.3

Some high dimensionality representations of $SU(3)/Z_3$

Rank	Irreducible representation		Mixed tensor	Young diagram
5	$D(4, 1)$	35	$\xi^{n}_{jklm},$	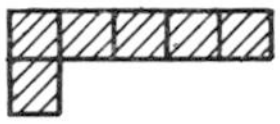
	$D(1, 4)$	$\overline{35}$	$\xi^{klmn}_{j},$	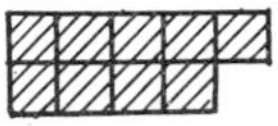
	$D(6, 0)$	28	$\xi_{jklmnr},$	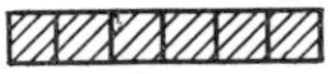
6	$D(0, 6)$	$\overline{28}$	$\xi^{jklmnr},$	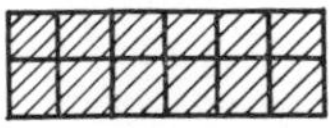
	$D(3, 3)$	64	$\xi^{mnr}_{jkl},$	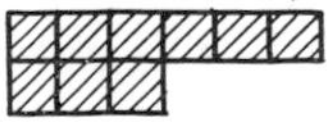

TABLE 1.3 (Continued)

Rank	Irreducible representation		Mixed tensor	Young diagram
7	$D(5, 2)$	81	ξ^{rs}_{jklmn},	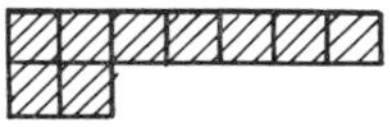
	$D(2, 5)$	$\overline{81}$	ξ^{lmnrs}_{jk},	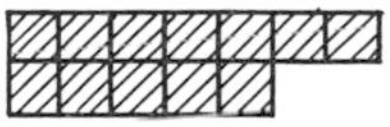
8	$D(7, 1)$	80	$\xi^{t}_{jklmnrs}$,	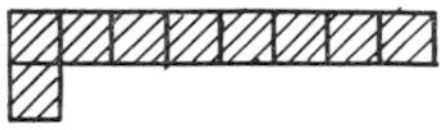
	$D(1, 7)$	$\overline{80}$	$\xi^{klmnrst}_{j}$,	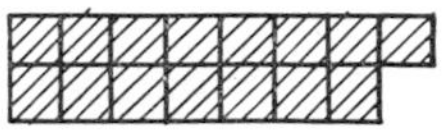
	$D(4, 4)$	125	ξ^{nrst}_{jklm},	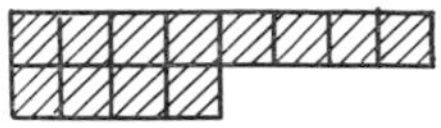

5. The reduction in its irreducible parts of a product of representations can be obtained by an algebraic analysis with the tensors or by using the Littlewood method with the Young diagrams. We give some useful results in the tables 1.4 and 1.5, the last ones being devoted to the factor group $SU(3)/Z_3$ only.

TABLE 1.4

	$3\otimes 3$	$3\otimes\bar{3}$	$6\otimes 3$	$6\otimes\bar{3}$	$6\otimes 6$	$6\otimes\bar{6}$	$8\otimes 3$	$8\otimes 6$	$3\otimes 3\otimes 3$	$3\otimes 3\otimes\bar{3}$
$D^{(1)}(0, 0)$		1				1			1	
$D^{(8)}(1, 1)$		1	1			1			2	
$D^{(10)}(3, 0)$			1						1	
$D^{(27)}(2, 2)$						1				
$D^{(3)}(1, 0)$				1			1			2
$D^{(6)}(0, 2)$					1		1			1
$D^{(15)}(2, 1)$				1	1		1			1
$D^{(15)}(4, 0)$					1					
$D^{(3)}(0, 1)$	1							1		
$D^{(6)}(2, 0)$	1							1		
$D^{(15)}(1, 2)$								1		
$D^{(24)}(3, 1)$								1		

TABLE 1.5

	$8\otimes 8$	$10\otimes 8$	$10\otimes 10$	$10\otimes \overline{10}$	$27\otimes 8$	$27\otimes 10$	$27\otimes 27$	$8\otimes 8\otimes 8$	$8\otimes 8\otimes 8\otimes 8$
$D^{(1)}(0, 0)$	1						1	2	8
$D^{(8)}(1, 1)$	2	1		1	1	1	2	8	32
$D^{(10)}(3, 0)$	1	1			1	1	1	4	20
$D^{(10)}(0, 3)$	1		1		1	1	1	4	20
$D^{(27)}(2, 2)$	1	1	1	1	2	1	3	6	33
$D^{(28)}(6, 0)$			1				1		2
$D^{(28)}(0, 6)$							1		2
$D^{(35)}(4, 1)$		1	1		1	1	2	2	15
$D^{(35)}(1, 4)$					1	1	2	2	15
$D^{(64)}(3, 3)$				1	1	1	2	1	12
$D^{(81)}(5, 2)$						1	1		3
$D^{(81)}(2, 5)$							1		3
$D^{(25)}(4, 4)$							1		1

6. The product of two irreducible representations D_1 and D_2 is expanded on the complete basis of the irreducible representations,

$$D_1 \otimes D_2 = \sum_{\sigma} v_{\sigma} D_{\sigma},$$

where the non negative integer v_σ indicates the number of irreducible representations D_σ appearing in the previous product. These representations are then differentiated by an index χ.

Let us now consider two fields ψ_1 and ψ_2 respectively associated to the irreducible representations D_1 and D_2. In order to construct covariant quantities from ψ_1 and ψ_2, we call isometry an operator $\Omega^{(\sigma, \chi)}$ such that the quantity:

$$[\Omega_{\rho}^{(\sigma, \chi)}]^{j_1 j_2} \psi_{1 j_1} \psi_{2 j_2}$$

is transformed like the ρ component of the irreducible representation (σ, χ) of the product $D_1 \otimes D_2$. These isometries can be normalized but it is more simple to choose a convenient scalar coefficient in front from a criterium of simplicity.

The knowledge of the isometrics is strongly connected with the determination of the Clebsch-Gordan coefficients. We do not study this question in details here and we refer to the various tables published in EDMONDS [1962], RASHID [1962], TARJANNE [1963a], DE SWART [1963] and MCNAMEE and CHILTON [1964].

1.6. Weight diagrams

1. The two fundamental weight diagrams are two regular triangles, symmetric to each other with respect to the origin. In both cases we have three simple equivalent weights.

The weight diagram of an irreducible representation $D^N(\lambda_1, \lambda_2)$ is constructed by tensor product from the two fundamental weight diagrams. It follows that in the weight space the possible weights are distributed on a lattice as shown in fig. 1.5.

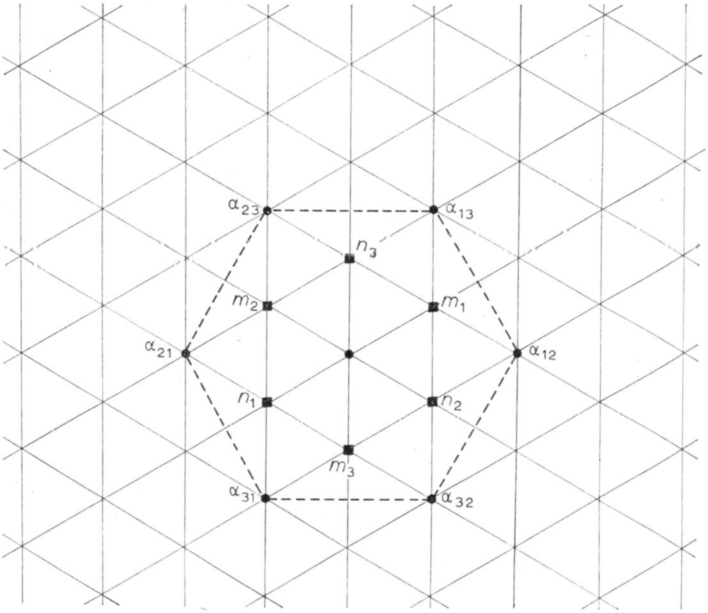

Fig. 1.5. Fundamental weights, roots and weight lattice.

2. The irreducible representations are finite dimensional and all the possible sites are not occupied. Moreover we know that the application of a generator E_α to a weight m gives either a new weight of the same representation or zero. It follows that for a given representation, the possible weights are distributed at the interaction of the full lattice with the lattice defined by the root diagram. We then have three new sub-lattices associated to each class of representation C_0, C_1, C_{-1} as shown in figs. 1.6, 1.7 and 1.8.

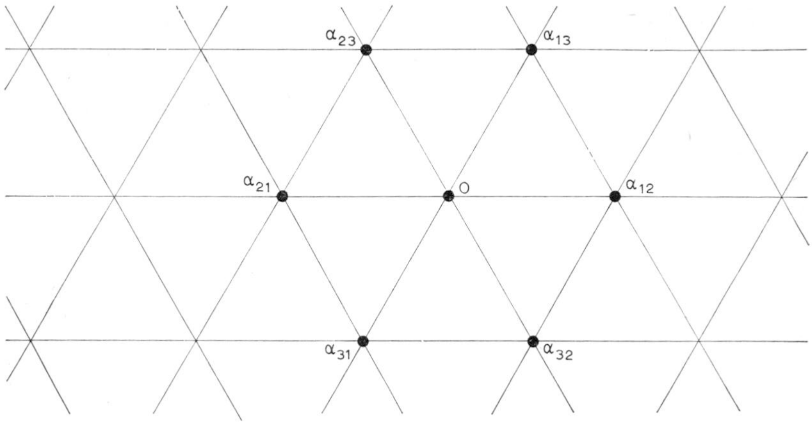

Fig. 1.6. Weight lattice for the irreducible representations of $SU(3)/Z_3$.

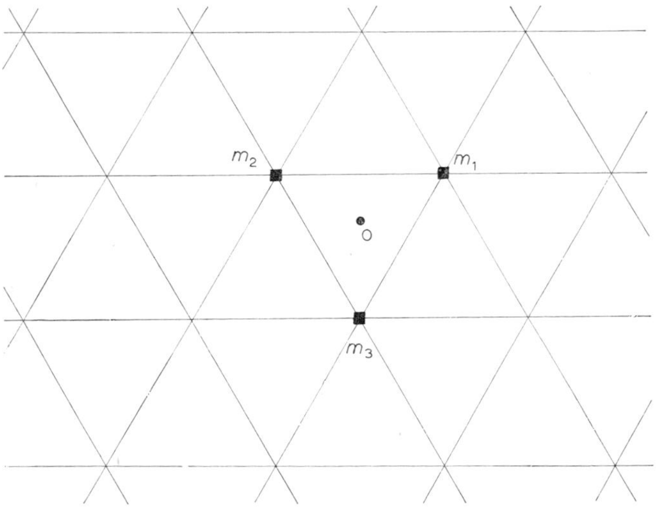

Fig. 1.7. Weight lattice for the representations of triality +1.

3. The Weyl group has six independent elements:
a) the identity;
b) the 3 symmetries with respect to the axis OX_1, OX_2, OX_3;
c) the 2 rotations of angle $\frac{2}{3}\pi$ and $-\frac{2}{3}\pi$.

In general, in a set of equivalent weights, we find six weights. This number can reduce to three if the weights are located on the axis and to one for the weight zero itself.

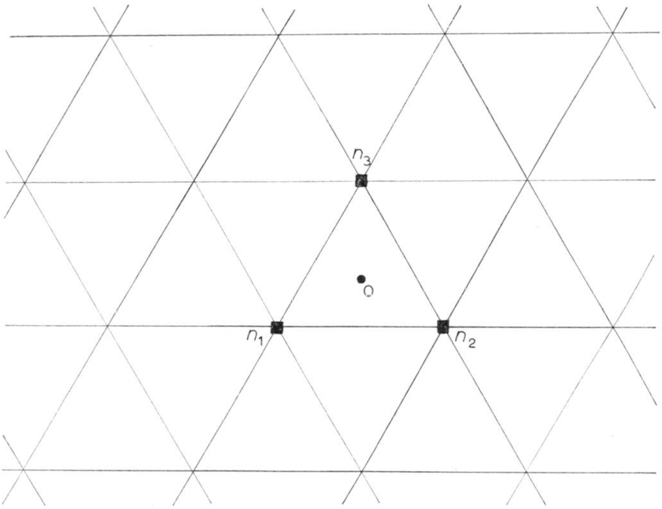

Fig. 1.8. Weight lattices for the representations of triality -1.

4. The boundary of the set of weights of an irreducible representation cannot be concave. This important result is a simple consequence of the following lemma:

LEMMA: If m, $m+\alpha_{ij}$, $m+\alpha_{jk}$ are three weights of an irreducible representation, then $m+\alpha_{ik}$ is also a weight of the representation.

Proof: By hypothesis, the eigenvectors $|m\rangle$, $|m+\alpha_{ij}\rangle$, $|m+\alpha_{jk}\rangle$ are connected by an operation of the group:

$$|m+\alpha_{jk}\rangle = \lambda E_{jk}|m\rangle$$
$$|m\rangle = \mu E_{ji}|m+\alpha_{ij}\rangle$$

where λ and μ are two non zero normalization constants.

We have also

$$|m+\alpha_{jk}\rangle = \lambda\mu E_{jk}E_{ji}|m+\alpha_{ij}\rangle.$$

Taking into account the commutation relation

$$[E_{jk}, E_{ji}] = 0$$

we deduce:

$$|m+\alpha_{jk}\rangle = \lambda\mu E_{ji}E_{jk}|m+\alpha_{ji}\rangle.$$

It follows immediately that $E_{jk}|m+\alpha_{ij}\rangle$ cannot be zero and the vector $m+\alpha_{ij}+\alpha_{jk} = m+\alpha_{ik}$ is also a weight of the same representation.

5. We now consider the highest weight M of an irreducible representation and we define as P_M a polygone such that its tops are the weights equivalent to M. The possible forms of P_M are drawn in the figs. 1.9 and 1.10. The equilateral triangles 10(a) and 10(b) correspond respectively to the representations $D(\lambda_1, 0)$ and $D(0, \lambda_2)$. In the case $\lambda_1 \lambda_2 \neq 0$, we have a hexagon which is regular for the symmetric representations $\lambda_1 = \lambda_2$.

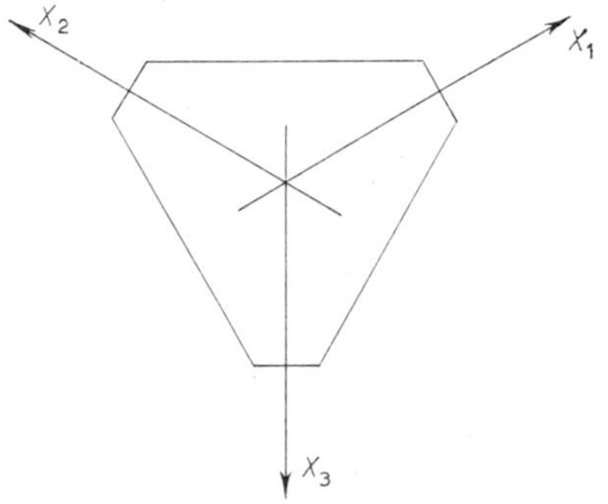

Fig. 1.9.

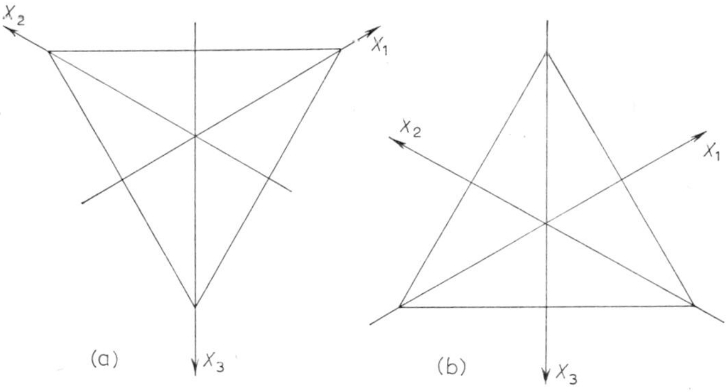

Fig. 1.10.

All the sites of the lattice associated to M and located on P_M or in the interior of P_M are weights of the irreducible representation. This property is only a consequence of a more general one: if m and $m+p\alpha$ are two weights of an irreducible representation where α is a root and p an algebraic integer number, then all the vectors $m+k\alpha$ are also weights of the same representation for all the algebraic integer values of k between 0 and p.

Due to the convexity character of the boundary and to the property of M

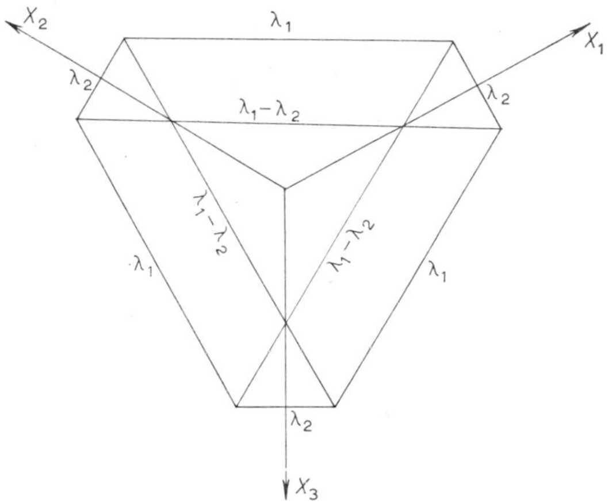

Fig. 1.11.

to be the highest weight, the polygone P_M is the boundary of the weight diagram of an irreducible representation of highest weight M.

6. We consider the subset of all the weights excepted those located on P_M and we will call as P_2 the boundary of this subset. More generally, we define as P_j the boundary of the subset of all the weights excepted $P_M, P_2, \ldots P_{j-1}$. We define in this way a finite number of polygones.

The highest weight M is a simple weight.

All the weights of an irreducible representation can be reached from M by successive application of the operators E_α to M:

$$|m_{\alpha_1\alpha_2\ldots\alpha_k}\rangle = E_{\alpha_1} E_{\alpha_2} \ldots E_{\alpha_k}|M\rangle.$$

The multiplicity of the weight m is the number of linearly independent paths to go from M to m.

It is then easy to prove the following results:

a) all the weights located on the boundary P_M are simple;

b) if $\lambda_1 \lambda_2 = 0$ the boundary P_M and all the polygones P_j are equilateral triangles. All the weights of the representations $D(\lambda_1, 0)$ and $D(0, \lambda_2)$ are simple;

c) if $\lambda_1 \lambda_2 \neq 0$, the boundary P_M is a hexagon. All the weights located on P_2 have the multiplicity 2;

d) if P_2 is a triangle, all the other weights on $P_3, \ldots, P_j, \ldots$ have the multiplicity 2;

e) if P_2 is an hexagon, all the weights located on P_3 have the multiplicity 3. The multiplicity increases at each step of one unity until the polygone P_k

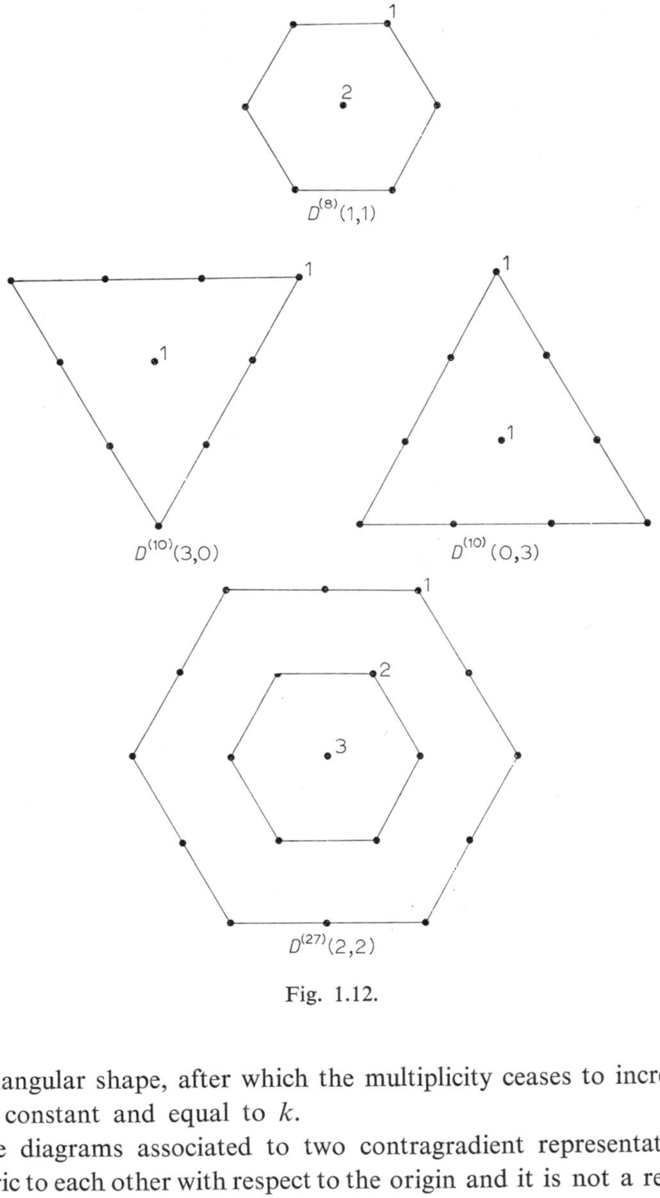

Fig. 1.12.

has a triangular shape, after which the multiplicity ceases to increase and remains constant and equal to k.

7. The diagrams associated to two contragradient representations are symmetric to each other with respect to the origin and it is not a restriction to discuss only the case $\lambda_1 \geqq \lambda_2$.

In units where the roots are normalized to the unity, the sides of the polygones P_M are measured by λ_1 and λ_2. It follows that P_M contains $3(\lambda_1+\lambda_2)$ simple weights.

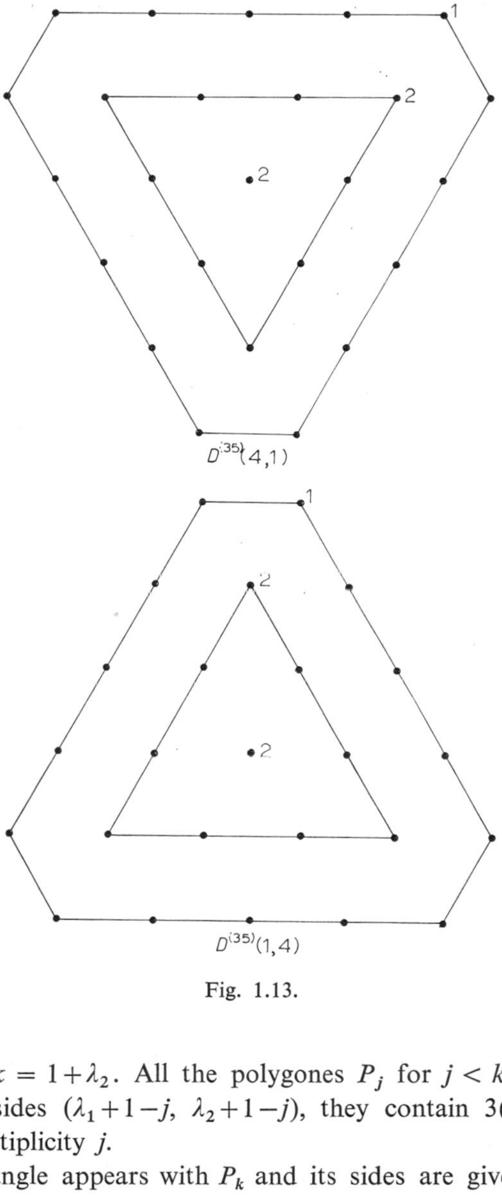

Fig. 1.13.

Let us put $k = 1+\lambda_2$. All the polygones P_j for $j < k(P_1 \equiv P_M)$ are hexagones of sides $(\lambda_1+1-j,\ \lambda_2+1-j)$, they contain $3(\lambda_1+\lambda_2+2-2j)$ weights of multiplicity j.

The first triangle appears with P_k and its sides are given precisely by $\lambda_1-\lambda_2$; we have $3(\lambda_1-\lambda_2)$ weights of multiplicity $k = 1+\lambda_2$.

All the polygones P_j for $j \geqq k$ are equilateral triangles of sides $(\lambda_1+2\lambda_2+3-3j)$ and they contain $3(\lambda_1+2\lambda_2+3-3j)$ weights of multiplicity $k = 1+\lambda_2$. The maximum value of j is then given by:

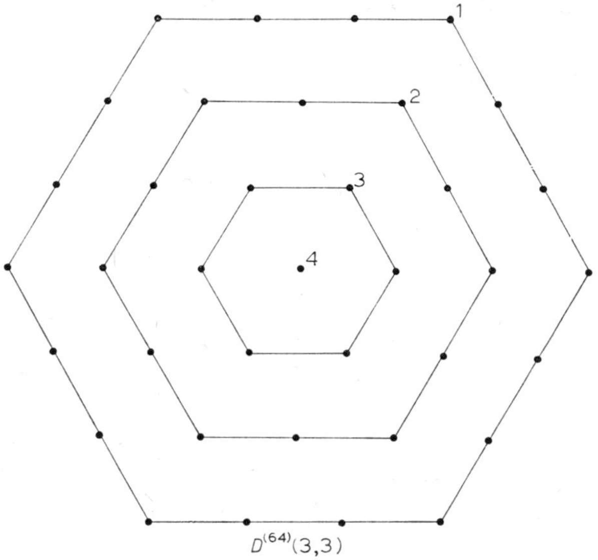

Fig. 1.14.

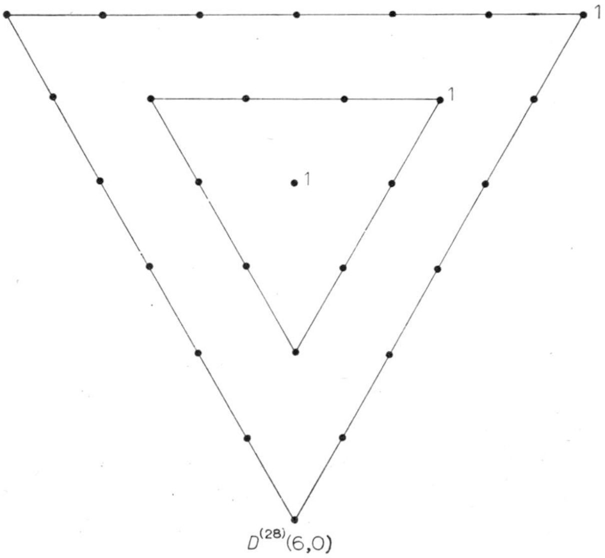

Fig. 1.15.

$$j_{max} = (1+\lambda_2)+[\tfrac{1}{3}(\lambda_1-\lambda_2)].$$

At the last step, for $j = j_{max}$, we obtain the weight zero with the multiplicity $1+\lambda_2$ for the representations of the class C_0 and the triangles of the fundamental representations $D^{(3)}(1,0)$ and $D^{(3)}(0,1)$ respectively for the representations of the classes C_1 and C_{-1}.

The total number of weights, taking into account their multiplicity, is the dimension of the representation. It is tedious but straightforward to check directly the formula:

$$N(\lambda_1, \lambda_2) = (1+\lambda_1)(1+\lambda_2)\big(1+\tfrac{1}{2}(\lambda_1+\lambda_2)\big).$$

1.7. Unitary group U(3)

The Lie algebra u(3) can be decomposed in the direct sum:

$$u(3) \simeq su(3) \oplus A.$$

The universal covering group is the direct product of the universal covering groups:

$$G_3^* \simeq SU(3) \otimes R.$$

The unitary group U(3) can be obtained from G_3^* by a covering homomorphism. The elements of G_3^* have the form $[\Sigma_3, \alpha]$ where Σ_3 is an unimodular 3×3 unitary matrix and α a real number. The homomorphism to go from G_3^* to U(3)

$$\{\Sigma_3, \alpha\} \Rightarrow e^{i\alpha}\Sigma_3$$

has a kernel Δ_3 generated by the element $[jI_3, -\tfrac{2}{3}\pi]$ of G_3^*. We then have

$$U(3) \simeq \frac{SU(3)\otimes R}{\Delta_3} \simeq \frac{SU(3)\otimes T}{\Delta_3}.$$

The center of U(3) is obviously the one parameter group T and we have:

$$U(3)/T \simeq SU(3)/Z_3.$$

The irreducible representations of SU(3) are characterized by two non negative integers λ_1 and λ_2. The irreducible representations of R are characterized by a real number r which is an integer for the representations of T.

In the representations $(\lambda_1, \lambda_2, r)$ of G_3^* of dimension $N(\lambda_1, \lambda_2)$, the element $[jI_3, -\tfrac{2}{3}\pi]$ which generates in the kernel Δ_3 is represented by:

$$I_N \exp \tfrac{2}{3}i\pi(\lambda_1 - \lambda_2 - r)$$

where I_N is the $N \times N$ unit matrix. Such a representation of G_3^* is also a representation of U(3) if and only if:

$$r \equiv (\lambda_1 - \lambda_2) \qquad (3).$$

It is convenient to define three algebraic integers f_1, f_2, f_3 to characterize the irreducible representations $[f_1, f_2, f_3]$ of the unitary group U(3):

$$f_1 = \lambda_1 + s \qquad f_2 = s \qquad f_3 = -\lambda_2 + s$$

and we have the two properties:

$$f_1 \geqq f_2 \geqq f_3$$
$$r = f_1 + f_2 + f_3 .$$

2. The maximal commutative subalgebra of u(3) is now three dimensional and we can define three generators $\mathscr{H}_1, \mathscr{H}_2, \mathscr{H}_3$ such that the sum $\mathscr{H} = \mathscr{H}_1 + \mathscr{H}_2 + \mathscr{H}_3$ is associated to the part A_0 of the Lie algebra u(3).

The relation between the $\mathscr{H}_j$'s and the infinitesimal generators H_j of su(3) is simply given by:

$$H_j = \mathscr{H}_j - \tfrac{1}{3}\mathscr{H}.$$

The generator $\mathscr{H}$ is represented, in all the representations, by the unit matrix up to a constant factor proportional to r:

$$\sqrt{6}\mathscr{H} = rI_N .$$

To the fundamental representation $D^{(3)}(1, 0)$ of SU(3) corresponds an infinity of three dimensional representations $[1+s, s, s]$ of U(3). Let us consider the case $s = 0$: the commutative subalgebra can then be represented following:

$$\sqrt{6}\mathscr{H}_1 = \begin{vmatrix} 1 & 0 & 0 \\ 0 & 0 & 0 \\ 0 & 0 & 0 \end{vmatrix}, \qquad \sqrt{6}\mathscr{H}_2 = \begin{vmatrix} 0 & 0 & 0 \\ 0 & 1 & 0 \\ 0 & 0 & 0 \end{vmatrix}, \qquad \sqrt{6}\mathscr{H}_3 = \begin{vmatrix} 0 & 0 & 0 \\ 0 & 0 & 0 \\ 0 & 0 & 1 \end{vmatrix}$$

and $\sqrt{6}\mathscr{H}$ is simply the unit 3×3 matrix. In a more general way:

$$\sqrt{6}\mathscr{H}_1 = \begin{vmatrix} 1+s & 0 & 0 \\ 0 & s & 0 \\ 0 & 0 & s \end{vmatrix}, \quad \sqrt{6}\mathscr{H}_2 = \begin{vmatrix} s & 0 & 0 \\ 0 & 1+s & 0 \\ 0 & 0 & s \end{vmatrix}, \quad \sqrt{6}\mathscr{H}_3 = \begin{vmatrix} s & 0 & 0 \\ 0 & s & 0 \\ 0 & 0 & 1+s \end{vmatrix}$$

and, of course:

$$\sqrt{6}\mathscr{H} = \begin{vmatrix} 1+s & 0 & 0 \\ 0 & 1+s & 0 \\ 0 & 0 & 1+s \end{vmatrix}.$$

CHAPTER II

PHYSICAL INTERPRETATION OF THE UNITARY SYMMETRY

2.1. Baryon classification

1. We know experimentally 8 baryons of spin $J = \frac{1}{2}$ which are classified, with respect to isotopic spin and hypercharge in the following way:

TABLE 2.1

Y	I	Multiplet
1	$\frac{1}{2}$	[p, n]
0	1	$[\Sigma^+, \Sigma^0, \Sigma^-]$
0	0	Λ^0
-1	$\frac{1}{2}$	$[\Xi^0, \Xi^-]$

2. It is interesting to draw a two dimensional diagram with one vertical axis for the hypercharge and one horizontal axis for the third component of the isotopic spin, as shown in fig. 2.1.

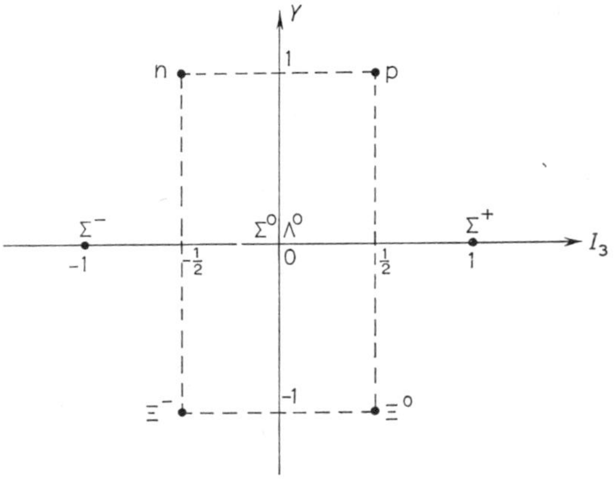

Fig. 2.1.

If the hexagon is regular, roughly speaking, we assume the unitary symmetry in the octuplet version, the so-called eightfold way.

3. The baryon diagram of fig. 2.1. is now identified with the root diagram of the algebra A_2. It follows immediately that the isotopic spin, hypercharge and charge operators are defined by:

$$I^+ = \sqrt{6}E_{12}, \quad I^- = \sqrt{6}E_{21}, \quad I_3 = \tfrac{1}{2}\sqrt{6}(H_1 - H_2),$$
$$Y = -\sqrt{6}H_3, \quad Q = \sqrt{6}H_1.$$

2.2. Charge operator

1. The charge operator Q has been identified with the infinitesimal generator $\sqrt{6}H_1$ of the Cartan subalgebra. It follows that the electric charge of a weight of triangular coordinates X_1, X_2, X_3 of sum zero, is simply given, in units e, by:

$$Q = X_1.$$

From the previous results, all the weights of the irreducible representations of the factor group $SU(3)/Z_3$ are integer numbers. Of course such a result cannot be extended to all the representations of the universal covering group SU(3).

2. The connected Lie groups associated to the Lie algebra:

$$u(3) \simeq su(3) \oplus A_0,$$

where A_0 is always the one dimensional Lie algebra representing the baryonic number gauge transformations, are easily determined from the general theorems and we have only five possibilities:

a) $SU(3) \otimes R$
b) $(SU(3)/Z_3) \otimes R$
c) $SU(3) \otimes T$
d) $(SU(3)/Z_3) \otimes T$
e) $U(3)$.

If we require the baryonic number and the electric charge to be integer numbers for all the irreducible representations, the first three possibilities are excluded and the groups $(SU(3)/Z_3) \otimes T$ and $U(3)$ can only be used in physical models.

The first group which is a direct product, is associated to the octuplet version of the unitary symmetry, the so-called eightfold way first studied by NE'EMAN [1961] and GELL-MANN [1961, 1962].

The unitary group U(3) is the mathematical basis of some triplet models as, for instance, the Sakata model (SAKATA [1956]).

The physical interpretation of the Lie algebra is different in both cases and we have the following relations:

$$\begin{aligned}(I_3)_3 &= (I_3)_8\\ (B)_3 &= (B)_8\\ (Y)_3 &= (Y)_8+\tfrac{2}{3}B\\ (Q)_3 &= (Q)_8+\tfrac{1}{3}B.\end{aligned}$$

Of course, the physical implications are extremely different in the two models. The simplicity of the Sakata model is extremely attractive but the agreement with experiment is better in the eightfold way.

3. Recently, GELL-MANN [1964a] and independently ZWEIG [1964], have suggested to construct a composite model for the eightfold way, using, as fundamental particles, three quarks of spin $\frac{1}{2}$.

The baryons of the adjoint representation are constructed from the product of three quarks following:

$$3 \otimes 3 \otimes 3 = 1 \oplus 8 \oplus 8 \oplus 10.$$

The quarks must then have a baryonic number $B = \frac{1}{3}$ and a fractional charge as indicated in fig. 2.2.

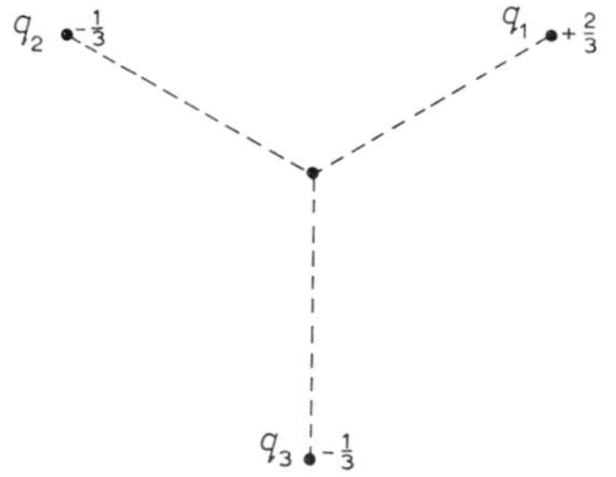

Fig. 2.2. Electric charge of quarks.

The simplest realization of mesons is a quark-antiquark system:

$$3 \otimes \bar{3} = 1 \oplus 8.$$

Such particles have not yet been experimentally discovered up to a mass of 2 GeV. If the quarks exist, they must have a very large mass of the order of a few GeV.The ordinary observed particles are considered, in the quark model, as bound states of systems of quarks and antiquarks with a large binding energy of the order of few GeV. The definition of the isotopic spin, hypercharge and charge operators in the Lie algebra is the same as for the eightfoldway model and the experimental consequences will be identical as far as the ordinary particles only are concerned. But the group now associated to the quark model is the unitary group U(3) and for instance the quarks, the antiquarks, the baryons and the antibaryons belong to the following irreducible representations of U(3):

$$q : [1, 0, 0] \qquad \bar{q} : [0, 0, -1]$$
$$B : [2, 1, 0] \qquad \bar{B} : [0, -1, -2]$$

and the classification of the particles is that of the eightfoldway.

The simplest $B = 1$ system is obtained with 3 quarks and corresponds to the 1, 8, 10 dimensional representations of $SU(3)/Z_3$. Other representations can be constructed using more complicated composite systems such as $qqqq\bar{q}$ or $qqqqq\bar{q}\bar{q}$. It is remarkable that the qqq system is actually sufficient for the classification of the observed particles as it will be seen later.

For the mesons $B = 0$, the simplest bound state $q\bar{q}$ generates the singulet and the octuplet representations only. In this case also, the quasi totality of the observed particles can be distributed into singulet and octuplet multiplets and the quark model can give an explanation of this empirical fact.

2.3. Mass formula

1. The existance of large mass differences between baryons or between mesons belonging to an irreducible representation is the simplest manifestation of the breakdown of unitary symmetry. Such a phenomenon is present, but with a much smaller magnitude, in the isotopic spin multiplet and these effects are then attributed to the existence of electromagnetic interactions which violate the charge independence of strong interactions.

We shall now make a similar hypothesis and we shall define two types of strong interactions:

a) The very strong interactions, invariant with respect to unitary symmetry. The supermultiplets are defined in this scheme and all the particles associated with the same irreducible representation have in particular the same mass.

b) The medium strong interactions which are only invariant under isotopic spin rotations and hypercharge gauge transformations. These interactions are responsible for the separation inside a supermultiplet into isotopic spin multiplets.

2. We will use a hamiltonian formalism and we assume that the physical quantities, in which we are interested, can be calculated in a perturbative way. Of course, we shall not do such a calculation which requires the use of some dynamics. It is nevertheless possible to obtain some important results uniquely due to the covariance properties of the medium strong interaction hamiltonian.

3. From the mathematical point of view, we shall make a hypothesis which has its best justification, a posteriori, by its consequences. We assume the medium strong interaction hamiltonian H_Y to transform like the Y component of an octuplet. Of course, H_Y commutes with the three isotopic spin generators and the hypercharge operator as expected. But the choice of the adjoint representation is a pure assumption.

4. It is interesting to remark that, in a quark model, if the mass difference of the composite particles are basically due to a fundamental mass difference between the isotopic spin doublet and the isotopic spin singulet of the triplet of quarks, the previous assumption is quite natural.

5. The problem of the mass differences between the isotopic spin multiplets belonging to the same irreducible representation can be easily formulated in terms of isometries.

Let M_ρ be an operator which transforms like the ρ component of the adjoint representation. We use the generalized Wigner Eckart theorem to write the matrix elements of M_ρ between two states ψ_1 and ψ_2 associated with the irreducible representations D_1 and D_2 in the form

$$\langle\psi_1|M_\rho|\psi_2\rangle = \sum_\chi F_\chi \Omega_\rho^{(8\chi)jk}\psi_{1j}\psi_{2k}.$$

The sum over χ is extended to the different adjoint representations appearing in the product $D_1 \otimes D_2$. For a semi simple rank l group, the number of terms χ is equal to the number of non zero λ_j for the irreducible representation $D(\lambda_1 \lambda_2 \ldots \lambda_l)$.

We go back to the case of the unitary symmetry and we restrict ψ_1 and ψ_2 to two contragradient representations. There exist at most two isometries which allow us to obtain the adjoint representation. The first one is given by the infinitesimal generators themselves. The second one exists if and only if $\lambda_1\lambda_2 \neq 0$ (GINIBRE [1963a, b]) and belongs to the covering algebra and is built from the symmetrized products of the infinitesimal generators.

The mass operator can then be written in the following way:

$$m = m_0 + m_1 \Omega_Y^{(8a)} + m_2 \Omega_Y^{(8s)}.$$

6. The antisymmetric isometries $\Omega^{(8a)}$ can be considered as antisymmetric products of the generators and because of the commutation relations, they are generators of the Lie algebra. For instance:

$$\Omega_Y^{(8a)} = Y \qquad \Omega_Q^{(8a)} = Q.$$

The symmetric isometries $\Omega^{(8s)}$ are symmetric products of generators and we must introduce the covering algebra of su(3). The operator $\Omega_Y^{(8s)}$ must commute with the three isotopic spin and the hypercharge generators. It follows that the symmetric isometrie $\Omega_Y^{(8s)}$ can be written as a linear combination of Y^2, I^2 and x, the first Casimir operator of SU(3). Some algebraic manipulations are needed to obtain explicit expressions of x and $\Omega_Y^{(8s)}$.

We first consider the Casimir operator x defined by:

$$x = \operatorname{Tr} X^2 = X_{mn} X_{nm}$$

where $X_{ij} = \sqrt{6}E_{ij}$ and $X_{ii} = \sqrt{6}H_i$. The weights of all the representations are eigenstates of the I spin, the U spin, the V spin and it is convenient to introduce the expressions:

$$X_{12}X_{21}+X_{21}X_{12} = 2I(I+1)-\tfrac{1}{2}(X_{11}-X_{22})^2$$
$$X_{23}X_{32}+X_{32}X_{23} = 2U(U+1)-\tfrac{1}{2}(X_{22}-X_{33})^2$$
$$X_{31}X_{13}+X_{13}X_{31} = 2V(V+1)-\tfrac{1}{2}(X_{33}-X_{11})^2.$$

Taking into account the zero trace condition:

$$X_{11}+X_{22}+X_{33} = 0$$

the Casimir operator x can be written as:

$$x = 2[I(I+1)+U(U+1)+V(V+1)]-\tfrac{1}{2}(X_{11}^2+X_{22}^2+X_{33}^2).$$

We now calculate the value of x for the highest weight $M(\lambda_1, \lambda_2)$ of the irreducible representation $D(\lambda_1, \lambda_2)$. For such a weight we have:

$$I = \tfrac{1}{2}\lambda_1 \qquad U = \tfrac{1}{2}\lambda_2 \qquad V = \tfrac{1}{2}(\lambda_1+\lambda_2)$$
$$X_{11} = \tfrac{1}{3}(2\lambda_1+\lambda_2) \qquad X_{22} = \tfrac{1}{3}(\lambda_2-\lambda_1) \qquad X_{33} = \tfrac{1}{3}(2\lambda_2+\lambda_1)$$

and it follows immediately the well known expression:

$$x = \tfrac{2}{3}(\lambda_1^2+\lambda_2^2+\lambda_1\lambda_2)+2(\lambda_1+\lambda_2).$$

The component Y of the symmetric isometry $\Omega^{(8s)}$ is now defined by:

$$\Omega_Y^{(8s)} = X_{3j}X_{j3}+X_{j3}X_{3j}-\tfrac{2}{3}x.$$

Using the expression previously given for isotopic spin, it is straightforward to relate the isometry to the Casimir operator following:

$$\Omega_Y^{(8s)} = \tfrac{1}{3}x - 2I(I+1) + \tfrac{1}{2}Y^2.$$

The component Q of the same isometry is then immediately given by:

$$\Omega_Q^{(8s)} = \tfrac{1}{3}x - 2U(U+1) + \tfrac{1}{2}Q^2.$$

7. Finally, we consider the particular case of the baryon octuplet representation. In this case, the mass operator is written as:

$$m = m_0 + m_1 Y + m_2[2 - 2I(I+1) + \tfrac{1}{2}Y^2].$$

The three reduced matrix elements m_0, m_1, m_2 can be eliminated between the four isotopic spin multiplet masses and we obtain the Gell-Mann-Okubo mass formula for the baryons (GELL-MANN [1962] and OKUBO [1962]):

$$2(m_{\mathrm{N}} + m_{\Xi}) = 3m_{\Lambda} + m_{\Sigma}.$$

This relation is experimentally satisfied with an accuracy better than $\frac{1}{2}\%$.

The coefficients m_1 and m_2 due to the perturbation are relatively large and the importance of the perturbation can be roughly evaluated to 16 %.

We obtain for a best fit:

$$m_0 = 1150 \text{ MeV} \qquad m_1 = -189 \text{ MeV} \qquad m_2 = -20 \text{ MeV}$$

and the calculated masses are then given by:

$$m_{\mathrm{N}} = 941 \text{ MeV} \qquad m_{\Xi} = 1319 \text{ MeV}$$
$$m_{\Sigma} = 1190 \text{ MeV} \qquad m_{\Lambda} = 1110 \text{ MeV}.$$

CHAPTER III

PARTICLE CLASSIFICATION

3.1. Generalities

1. Even in the presence of a breakdown of the symmetry the notion of classification of the particles, bound states and resonances in the irreducible representations of $SU(3)/Z_3$ is an extremely useful concept.

2. The breakdown of the unitary symmetry will produce mass differences inside a given multiplet and also some mixing of different multiplets between weights of same isotopic spin and same hypercharge.

3. The unitary symmetry group commutes with the Lorentz group and the spin and the parity are the same for all the partners in a given multiplet.

The complete group being:

$$(SU(3)/Z_3) \otimes T$$

particles and antiparticles of baryonic number different from zero belong to distinct contragradient representations.

The situation is quite different for the mesons of baryonic number zero. The simplest solution for $SU(3)/Z_3$ self contragradient representations, as for instance the octuplet representation, is to put particles and antiparticles in the same representation. For non self-contragradient representations as the decuplet we must consider simultaneously the representation and its contragradient representation.

4. The notion of Regge trajectories has been useful to classify the particles in families and in the actual problem we will use some of the results as a guide for the unitary symmetry classification extending the concept of trajectory to an irreducible representation itself.

5. The Gell-Mann-Okubo mass formula describing a first order breakdown of the unitary symmetry will be used to relate the masses of the isotopic members of a multiplet.

A mass squared formula is generally used for the boson states on the basis of the structure of the free lagrangian.

3.2. Pseudoscalar mesons

1. The existence of a Yukawa type coupling between the baryons and the pseudoscalar mesons, assumed to satisfy unitary symmetry, allows us to consider, at least in a formal way, the mesons as bound states of the baryon antibaryon system. We then must choose one of the representations of the product of two octuplets:

$$8 \otimes 8 = 1 \oplus 8_s \oplus 27 \oplus 8_a \oplus 10 \oplus \overline{10}.$$

2. We first consider the three π mesons and the four K mesons. It is rather natural to use the adjoint representation for the pseudoscalar mesons. The unitary symmetry predicts the existence of a $I = Y = 0$ pseudoscalar meson of positive charge parity, as the π^0 meson. Let us call as η^0 such a particle. The Gell-Mann-Okubo formula, in this case, reduces to:

$$3m_{\eta^0}^2 + m_\pi^2 = 4m_K^2$$

and predicts the η^0 mass to be:

$$m_{\eta^0} \simeq 566 \text{ MeV}.$$

Experimentally, a 3π resonance, called η, has been found at $m_\eta = 548$ MeV, with the correct quantum numbers.

If the η resonance belongs to the octuplet, despite the very large mass differences between the π, K and η mesons, the Gell-Mann-Okubo equality is satisfied to 6 % which is remarkable and unexpected.

3. Due to *PCT* invariance, the mass formula depends only of two parameters:

$$m^2 = m_0^2 + m_2^2[2 - 2I(I+1) + \tfrac{1}{2}Y^2]$$

related to the K meson and π meson masses by:

$$m_0^2 = \tfrac{1}{3}(2m_K^2 + m_\pi^2) \qquad m_2^2 = \tfrac{1}{3}(m_K^2 - m_\pi^2).$$

The experimental ratio m_2^2/m_0^2 is easily computed:

$$m_2^2/m_0^2 \simeq 0.44$$

and found to be considerably larger than the corresponding ones for the octuplet of baryons:

$$(m_2/m_0)_{\text{baryon}} \simeq 0.0174.$$

In the actual interpretation the perturbation turns out to be extremely important as expected due to the large K–π mass difference.

A very nice explanation of such a situation has been proposed by GÜRSEY, LEE and NAUENBERG [1964]. In absence of breakdown of the unitary symmetry, the bare mass of the pseudoscalar mesons is assumed to be zero and this property defines unambiguously the primary interaction H_0. Now the perturbation h is written as the sum of two terms:

$$h = h_0 + h_1$$

where h_0 is a scalar and h_1 the Y component of an octuplet as previously. It follows that m_0^2 and m_2^2 are both due to the perturbation and the ratio do not measure the perturbation. It must be noted that the use of a mass squared formula for the pseudoscalar mesons appears rather naturally in this scheme.

4. Recently a new pseudoscalar meson, X^0, has been discovered at $m_{X^0} = 959$ MeV, with the same quantum numbers as the η meson. It is then natural to associate the X^0 meson to a singulet representation but, in the presence of the medium strong interactions we can expect some mixing between the two states. We call as previously η^0 the $I = Y = 0$ member of the octuplet and X_1^0 the singulet state. The two observed physical states are assumed to be a linear superposition of the octuplet and singulet states. Let us define an α mixing angle in the following way:

$$X^0 = X_1^0 \cos\alpha + \eta^0 \sin\alpha$$
$$\eta = \eta^0 \cos\alpha - X_1^0 \sin\alpha.$$

The rotation matrix $R(\alpha)$

$$R(\alpha) = \begin{vmatrix} \cos\alpha & \sin\alpha \\ -\sin\alpha & \cos\alpha \end{vmatrix}$$

can be used to diagonalize the mass matrix:

$$M = R(\alpha) M_0 R^{-1}(\alpha)$$

where:

$$M = \begin{vmatrix} m_{X^0}^2 & 0 \\ 0 & m_\eta^2 \end{vmatrix}, \quad M_0 = \begin{vmatrix} m_{X_1^0}^2 & \delta m_{X_1^0\eta^0}^2 \\ \delta m_{X_1^0\eta^0}^2 & m_{\eta^0}^2 \end{vmatrix}.$$

We then deduce, from the previous equality three relations:

$$m_{X_1^0}^2 + m_{\eta^0}^2 = m_{X^0}^2 + m_\eta^2,$$

$$\delta m_{X_1^0\eta^0}^2 = \{(m_{X^0}^2 - m_{\eta^0}^2)(m_{\eta^0}^2 - m_\eta^2)\}^{\frac{1}{2}}$$

$$\mathrm{tg}\, 2\alpha = \frac{2\delta m_{X_1^0\eta^0}^2}{m_{X_1^0}^2 - m_{\eta^0}^2}.$$

The two physical masses m_η and m_{X^0} are known from experiment:

$$m_\eta = 548.7 \text{ MeV} \qquad m_{X^0} = 959 \text{ MeV}.$$

The octuplet mass m_{η^0} is calculated using the Gell-Mann-Okubo mass formula and the trace condition gives the singulet mass $m_{X_1{}^0}$

$$m_{\eta^0} = 566.5 \text{ MeV} \qquad m_{X_1{}^0} = 948.6 \text{ MeV}.$$

The non diagonal matrix element $\delta m^2_{X_1{}^0\eta^0}$ turns out to be relatively small and the mixing angle α is given by:

$$\text{tg } 2\alpha = 0.37$$

or, equivalently:

$$\cos\alpha = 0.984 \qquad \sin\alpha = 0.179.$$

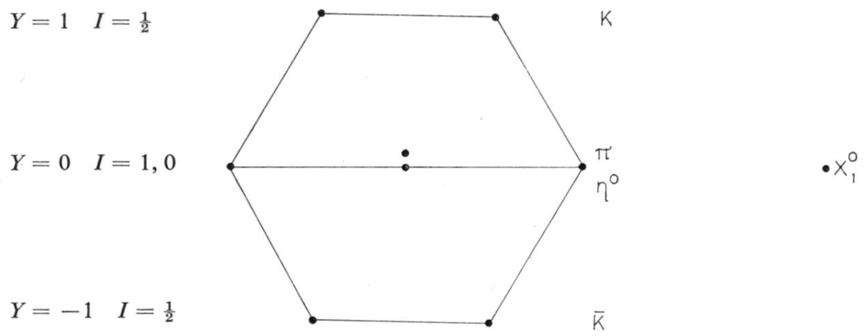

Fig. 3.1. Pseudoscalar mesons.

3.3. Meson-baryon $J = \frac{3}{2}^+$ resonances

1. The π meson-nucleon resonance, $N^*_{\frac{3}{2}}$, observed in a $P_{\frac{3}{2}}$ state at the total energy $m_{N^*_{\frac{3}{2}}} = 1238$ MeV has an isotopic spin $I = \frac{3}{2}$ and can therefore be only classified in a 10 or a 27 representation.

The choice of a decuplet has been determined on the basis of other observed meson-hyperon resonances, namely

$$Y^*_1 \text{ a } \pi\text{-}\Lambda \text{ resonance at } m_{Y^*_1} = 1385 \text{ MeV of isotopic spin } I = 1$$

$$\Xi^*_{\frac{1}{2}} \text{ a } \pi\text{-}\Xi \text{ resonance at } m_{\Xi^*_{\frac{1}{2}}} = 1530 \text{ MeV of isotopic spin } I = \tfrac{1}{2}.$$

2. The Gell-Mann-Okubo mass formula, in the case of triangular representations reduces to a linear function of the hypercharge Y at first order:

$$m = m_0 + m_1 Y$$

and predicts then an equal spacing rule between the isotopic spin multiplet which is satisfied for the three previous resonances with a great accuracy:

$$m_{Y_1^*} - m_{N_{\frac{3}{2}}^*} \simeq 147 \text{ MeV} \qquad m_{\Xi_{\frac{1}{2}}^*} - m_{Y_1^*} \simeq 145 \text{ MeV}.$$

3. The unitary symmetry predicts then the existence of a strangeness $S = -3$ particle, of negative charge and isotopic spin $I = 0$, called Ω^- by Gell-Mann. On the basis of the equal spacing rule, the predicted mass is:

$$(m_{\Omega^-})_{\text{th}} = 1673\text{–}1679 \text{ MeV}.$$

Such a particle has been experimentally observed and the measured mass is very close to the theoretical value:

$$m_{\Omega^-} = 1674 \pm 3 \text{ MeV}.$$

Therefore, the Ω^- particle is not a meson-baryon resonance – the threshold of the $\overline{\text{K}}$ system is 1820 MeV – but can be interpreted as a $\overline{\text{K}}\Xi$ bound state. As for the case of ordinary baryons the Ω^- is stable with respect to strong interactions and the only allowed disintegration processes will be weak decays.

4. The decuplet containing the $N_{\frac{3}{2}}^*$ resonance is characterized by $J = \frac{3}{2}^+$. Such an assignment has been checked for the Y_1^* resonance and the most recent measurements of the spin and the parity of the $\Xi_{\frac{1}{2}}^*$ resonance indicate that the value $J = \frac{3}{2}^+$ is favoured. Of course, we have no data for the Ω^- particle but the unitary symmetry predicts its spin and its parity.

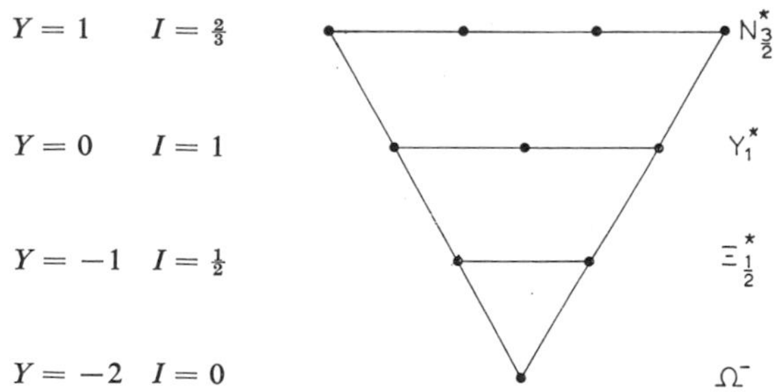

Fig. 3.2. Decuplet representation.

5. The Gell-Mann-Okubo mass formula gives two relations between the decuplet masses in excellent agreement with experiment, despite the different analytic structure – resonance or bound state – of the particles belonging to the decuplet representation.

The magnitude of the first order perturbation, estimated from the ratio of the two parameters of the mass formula is of the order of 11 %. It is amusing to compare the parameters of the perturbation for the baryon octuplet and the decuplet. The octuplet type formula:

$$m = m_0 + m_1 Y + m_2[2 - 2I(I+1) + \tfrac{1}{2}Y^2]$$

reduces, in the decuplet case where $I = \frac{1}{2}Y + 1$, to a linear function of the hypercharge:

$$m = (m_0 - 2m_2) + (m_1 - 3m_2)Y.$$

If now we use the parameters m_1 and m_2 as determined in the mass formula for the baryon octuplet:

$$m_1 = -189 \text{ MeV} \qquad m_2 = -20 \text{ MeV}$$

we obtain:

$$m_1 - 6m_2 \simeq -129 \text{ MeV}.$$

This value is very close to the experimental spacing of -145 MeV observed in the $J = \frac{3}{2}^+$ decuplet.

Perhaps, a larger symmetry will explain latter this empirical result relating the perturbation parameters for the $J = \frac{1}{2}^+$ and $J = \frac{3}{2}^+$ baryon multiplets.

3.4. Vector mesons

1. Nine vector mesons have been experimentally observed:

$$\rho(763 \text{ MeV}), \quad \text{K}^*(891 \text{ MeV}), \quad \omega(782.8 \text{ MeV}), \quad \varphi(1019.5 \text{ MeV})$$

and the most reasonable assignment in the unitary scheme is an octuplet and a singulet.

Of course, the ρ and K^* mesons belong to an octuplet but the φ and ω mesons have the same quantum numbers $J = 1$, $I = 0$, $C = -1$ and it is impossible to choose unambiguously the correct attribution.

Let us consider the Gell-Mann-Okubo mass formula:

$$m_\rho^2 + 3m_{\varphi^0}^2 = 4m_{\text{K}^*}^2$$

where φ^0 is the $I = Y = 0$ member of the octuplet, with ρ and K^*. The predicted mass for φ^0 lies between the φ and ω physical masses:

$$m_{\varphi^0} \simeq 929.8 \text{ MeV}$$

and we can expect, on this basis, a large ω-φ mixing.

2. Let us call as ω^0 the singulet weight. The observed φ and ω states are assumed to be linear superpositions of the pure unitary symmetry eigen states following SAKURAI [1962]:

$$\varphi = \varphi^0 \cos\lambda - \omega^0 \sin\lambda$$
$$\omega = \omega^0 \cos\lambda + \varphi^0 \sin\lambda.$$

The rotation matrix $R(\lambda)$:

$$R(\lambda) = \begin{vmatrix} \cos\lambda & -\sin\lambda \\ \sin\lambda & \cos\lambda \end{vmatrix}$$

is used in order to diagonalize the mass matrix:

$$M = R(\lambda) M_0 R^{-1}(\lambda)$$

with:

$$M = \begin{vmatrix} m_\varphi^2 & 0 \\ 0 & m_\omega^2 \end{vmatrix} \qquad M_0 = \begin{vmatrix} m_{\varphi^0}^2 & -\delta m_{\varphi^0\omega^0}^2 \\ -\delta m_{\varphi^0\omega^0}^2 & m_{\omega^0}^2 \end{vmatrix}$$

and we obtain three relations:

$$m_{\varphi^0}^2 + m_{\omega^0}^2 = m_\varphi^2 + m_\omega^2$$
$$\delta m_{\varphi^0\omega^0}^2 = \{(m_{\varphi^0}^2 - m_\omega^2)(m_\varphi^2 - m_{\varphi^0}^2)\}^{\frac{1}{2}}$$
$$\operatorname{tg} 2\lambda = \frac{2\delta m_{\varphi^0\omega^0}^2}{m_{\varphi^0}^2 - m_{\omega^0}^2}.$$

The singulet ω^0 mass is calculated using the trace conservation:

$$m_{\omega^0} \simeq 887.5 \text{ MeV}.$$

The non diagonal element terms out to be rather large and the ω-φ mixing is extremely important:

$$\operatorname{tg} 2\lambda \simeq 5.468$$

or equivalently:

$$\cos\lambda = 0.768 \qquad \sin\lambda = 0.640 \qquad \operatorname{tg}\lambda \simeq 0.833.$$

Let us finally remark that the Gell-Mann-Okubo relation can be written in terms of physical masses using the mixing angle λ:

$$4m_{K^*}^2 = m_\rho^2 + 3\, m_\varphi^2 \cos^2\lambda + 3\, m_\omega^2 \sin^2\lambda.$$

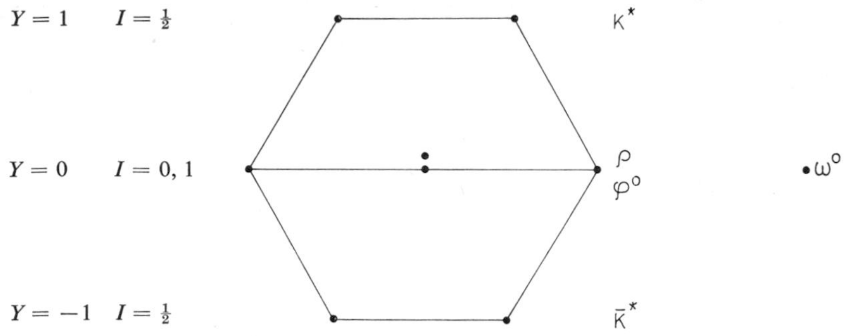

Fig. 3.3. Vector mesons.

3. The ω-φ mixing can appear in a rather natural way in some composite models. For instance, in a quark model, the nine vector mesons are assumed to be eigenstates of a $q\bar{q}$ system. The three weights of hypercharge $Y = 0$ are defined by:

$$\rho^0 = \frac{1}{\sqrt{2}}(q_1\bar{q}_1 - q_2\bar{q}_2),$$

$$\omega = \frac{1}{\sqrt{2}}(q_1\bar{q}_1 + q_2\bar{q}_2),$$

$$\varphi = -q_3\bar{q}_3 .$$

The ω-φ mixing angle λ is then predicted to be (OKUBO [1963b]):

$$\cos\lambda = \sqrt{\tfrac{2}{3}} \qquad \sin\lambda = \sqrt{\tfrac{1}{3}}$$

in qualitative agreement with experiment.

The nine vector meson states are assumed to be degenerate in an exact unitary symmetry. The degeneracy is partially removed by a first order perturbation and we then obtain two mass formulae:

$$m_\omega = m_\rho$$

$$4m_{K^*}^2 = 2m_\varphi^2 + m_\omega^2 + m_\rho^2 .$$

The agreement with experiment is good up to few percent.

4. The mass formula for the octuplet part depends of two parameters m_0^2 and m_2^2 related to the K* meson and ρ meson masses by:

$$m_0^2 = \tfrac{1}{3}(2m_{K^*}^2 + m_\rho^2) \qquad m_2^2 = \tfrac{1}{3}(m_{K^*}^2 - m_\rho^2).$$

The mass shift m_2 due to the perturbation is remarkably close to the value obtained for the pseudoscalar meson octuplet and we observe an emperical mass relation between pseudoscalar and vector mesons:

$$m_{K^*}^2 - m_\rho^2 = m_K^2 - m_\pi^2$$

in extremely good agreement with experiment.

In other term, the coefficient m_2 appears to be spin independent in a more general expression giving the pseudoscalar ($J = 0^-$) and the vector ($J = 1^-$) meson masses.

3.5. Meson-baryon resonances

1. A large number of bumps in meson-baryon scattering has been observed but the existence of some of them as resonances has not yet been definitely established.

Moreover the determination of the spin and the parity turns out to be extremely hard in many cases and therefore a tentative classification in SU(3) multiplets becomes highly speculative.

2. The best studied system, both from experimental and from theoretical point of view is the π meson nucleon system. We have a considerable amount of experimental data for angular distributions and polarizations and the use of a phase shift analysis combined with the dispersion relation has thrown some light on the structure of pion-nucleon scattering.

TABLE 3.1

$L_{2I,2J}$	J^P	T_π (MeV)	Mass (MeV)	Width (MeV)
P_{33}	$\frac{3}{2}^+$	196	1236	120
S_{31}	$\frac{1}{2}^-$	906	1692	$\simeq$ 230
F_{37}	$\frac{7}{2}^+$	1354	1924	$\simeq$ 200
(G_{39})	$(\frac{9}{2}^-)$	2349	2360	$\simeq$ 200
$(H_{3\,11})$	$(\frac{11}{2}^+)$	3633	2825	$\simeq$ 260
P_{11}	$\frac{1}{2}^+$	$\simeq$ 550	$\simeq$ 1480	$\simeq$ 200
D_{13}	$\frac{3}{2}^-$	610	1518	120
D_{15}	$\frac{5}{2}^-$	880	1674	$\simeq$ 100
F_{15}	$\frac{5}{2}^+$	900	1688	$\simeq$ 100
S_{11}	$\frac{1}{2}^-$	920	1700	
(G_{17})	$(\frac{7}{2}^-)$	1935	2190	$\simeq$ 200
(H_{19})	$(\frac{9}{2}^+)$	3113	2645	$\simeq$ 200

We give, in table 3.1, the situation in october 1965. The first column indicates the pion-nucleon partial wave where the resonance has been found: $L_{2I,2J}$. The second column gives the corresponding value of the spin and of the parity J^P. In the third column we report the kinetic energy of the incident pion in the laboratory system, T_π, where the peak occurs. Finally, columns 4 and 5 give the mass and the width of the resonance.

Parenthesis have been used when the spin and the parity are speculations and not experimentally measured quantities.

3. The experimental situation is some what more unstable concerning the hypercharge $Y = 0$ meson-baryon resonances. Let us first give in table 3.2 a list of experimental data:

TABLE 3.2

Isotopic spin Y_I^*	Spin parity J^P	Mass (MeV)	Width (MeV)
Y_0^*	$\frac{1}{2}^-$	1405	35
Y_0^*	$\frac{3}{2}^-$	1520	16
Y_0^*	$\frac{5}{2}^+$	1815	50
Y_0^*	(?)	2299	150
Y_1^*	$\frac{3}{2}^+$	1385	$\simeq$ 35
Y_1^*	$\frac{3}{2}^{(?)}$	1660	44
Y_1^*	$\frac{5}{2}^-$	1765	75
Y_1^*	(?)	1942	36
Y_1^*	$\frac{7}{2}^+$	2065	$\simeq$ 160

4. It has also been observed π-Ξ resonances with probable isotopic spin $I = \frac{1}{2}$. The experimental results are listed in table 3.3:

TABLE 3.3

Isotopic spin Ξ_I^*	Spin parity J^P	Mass (MeV)	Width (MeV)
$\Xi_{\frac{1}{2}}^*$	$\frac{3}{2}^+$	1530	7.5
$\Xi_{\frac{1}{2}}^*$	( )	1705	$\simeq$ 20
$\Xi_{\frac{1}{2}}^*$	$(\frac{3}{2}^-)$	1816	16
$\Xi_{( )}^*$	$(\frac{5}{2}^+)$	1933	140

General tables for mass widths, branching ratios can be found in ROSENFELD et al. [1965].

5. Only one $Y = -2$ particle has been experimentally observed the Ω^- at 1674 MeV discussed in a previous section.

6. We now try to clarify something about a possible SU(3) classification of some of their resonant states. We first start, of course, with the pion-nucleon systems and depending of the isotopic spin I, we have the following restrictions:

$$I = \tfrac{3}{2} \qquad D^{(10)}(3,0),\ D^{(27)}(2,2)$$

$$I = \tfrac{1}{2} \qquad D^{(8)}\ (1,1),\ D^{(10)}(0,3),\ D^{(27)}(2,2).$$

The absence of experimental evidence in strange particle resonances for

a) a π-Ξ resonance with isotopic spin $I = \frac{3}{2} : \Xi^*_{\frac{3}{2}}$
b) a π-Σ resonance with isotopic spin $I = 2 : \mathrm{Y}^*_2$

suggests strongly to retain only the first representation of each sequence as the more simple and the more attractive one and to disregard at present at least $\overline{10}$-plet and 27-plet.

We are then working only with singulet, octuplet, decuplet representation as produced in a 3 quark model.

On the basis of Regge trajectories arguments it is possible to postulate the existence of two octuplets and two decuplets

a) *octuplet* $J = \frac{5}{2}^+$ with $\mathrm{N}^*_{\frac{1}{2}}(1688)$; $\mathrm{Y}^*_0(1815)$ and perhaps $\Xi^*_{\frac{1}{2}}$ (1933);
b) *octuplet* $J = \frac{9}{2}^+$ with $\mathrm{N}^*_{\frac{1}{2}}(2645)$ only discovered;
c) *decuplet* $J = \frac{7}{2}^+$ with $\mathrm{N}^*_{\frac{3}{2}}(1924)$; $\mathrm{Y}^*_1(2065)$, the mass spacing being $\Delta M \simeq 140$ MeV;
d) *decuplet* $J = \frac{11}{2}^+$ with $\mathrm{N}^*_{\frac{3}{2}}(2825)$.

We can also try to classify the negative parity resonances in multiplets as for instance:

e) *singulet* $J = \frac{1}{2}^-$ with $\mathrm{Y}^*_0(1405)$;
f) *octuplet* $J = \frac{1}{2}^-$ with $\mathrm{N}^*_{\frac{1}{2}}(1700)$;
g) *decuplet* $J = \frac{1}{2}^-$ with $\mathrm{N}^*_{\frac{3}{2}}(1692)$;
h) *octuplet* $J = \frac{3}{2}^-$ with $\mathrm{N}^*_{\frac{1}{2}}(1518)$, $\mathrm{Y}^*_0(1520)$ and eventually the $\Xi^*_{\frac{1}{2}}(1816)$.

We must consider all these proposals as highly speculative, the experimental situation being not clear enough to allow definite conclusions.

3.6. Mesonic resonances

1. The meson spectrum has been systematically studied in a large number of reactions for instance in π meson and K meson proton scattering and in

antiproton-proton annihilation. Many peaks and bumps in the various cross sections and mass distributions have been observed but it is always very difficult to determine if the various anomalies can and must be interpreted as resonances.

The experimental situation is so fluctuating that it is practically impossible to write a complete list of mesonic resonances and we apologize for such a lack of completeness.

Nevertheless we will try to clarify, so as possible, the actual aspect of the problem.

2. Besides the two nonets of pseudoscalar mesons and of vector mesons previously studied, it seems that a nonet of tensor mesons $J = 2^+$ can be constructed and the data are given in table 3.4.

TABLE 3.4

Hypercharge	Isospin	Symbol	Mass decay mode	Mass (MeV)	Width (MeV)
± 1	$\frac{1}{2}$	K*	$K\pi$	1405 ± 8	95 ± 11
0	1	A_2	$\pi\rho$	1300 ± 6	90 ± 10
0	0	f^0	$\pi\pi$	1253 ± 20	118 ± 16
0	0	f^1	$K_1^0 K_1^0$	1500 ± 20	80 ± 10

Using the Gell-Mann-Okubo mass formua we find a f^0-f′ mixing angle (GLASHOW and SOCOLOW [1965]) of the order of 20° and the f^0 resonance turns out to be mainly in an unitary singulet state.

3. The existence of an octuplet or perhaps a nonet of scalar mesons $J=0^+$ is suggested by the $\kappa(725)$ particle. There exist some candidates for the $Y = 0$ weights such as the $S^0(710)$ but the problem of attributions is not resolved.

4. For pseudovector mesons $J = 1^+$, one octuplet and one nonet (with opposite values of C for the neutral members of hypercharge zero) are perhaps necessary to accomodate the B(1220) and the $A_1(1072)$ particles together with some K resonances. Measurements of spins and parities are necessary to firmly establish the existence of pseudovector multiplets.

5. The existence of K^+K^+ resonances (1055 and 1280 MeV) and of a $K\pi\pi$ resonance (1160 MeV) of isotopic spin $I = \frac{3}{2}$, if it is confirmed, necessitates the introduction of a 27-plet and perhaps of decuplets.

CHAPTER IV

STRONG INTERACTIONS

4.1. Introduction

We now present some consequences of the unitary symmetry for the strong interactions. In a general way we assume the S matrix operator to commute with the infinitesimal generators of the Lie algebra and we consider the T matrix elements as Lorentz invariant and SU(3) invariant quantities. Our study is divided into two parts: the three body vertices and the four body reactions.

The three body vertex is one of the most useful instruments of theoretical physics. We first consider the Yukawa type coupling between three fields and the section 4.2.1 is devoted to the particular useful case of three octuplets. Another interesting example of three body vertices is given by the two body decays and in sections 4.2.2 and 4.2.3, we study two examples of such decays for the $J = \frac{3}{2}^+$ excited baryons and for the vector mesons.

The violation of the unitary symmetry is introduced, phenomenologically in the phase space where the masses of the involved particles are taken to their experimental values. Of course, such a treatment can appear as inconsistent because, for instance some decay modes are forbidden by phase space considerations only and not by Clebsch-Gordan coefficients. In the three sections of 4.2, we consider also the case of the broken symmetry where, at first order, the T matrix element is the sum of a scalar associated with the exact symmetry and of the Y component of an octuplet, following the same assumption as for the mass problem. The comparison with experiment is studied for the two body decays.

The sections of 4.3 are devoted to a study of elastic and inelastic scattering. As in the previous case, the breakdown of the unitary symmetry is introduced in the phase space. The predictions are not so strong as for the case of three body vertices, nevertheless it seems that the agreement with experiment cannot be made quantitative and, perhaps, a first order broken symmetry only can explain the experimental results. Unfortunately, the predictions of a first order broken symmetry are in general only relations involving a large number of amplitudes and the comparison with experiment is not possible in the actual experimental situation.

4.2. Three body vertices

4.2.1. Yukawa type couplings of three octuplets

1. We forget, for the moment, the space time properties of the particles and we consider only their group properties.

The scalar representation can be obtained in two independent ways from the product of three octuplets and we can write, in general, two different Yukawa type couplings.

2. It is convenient to use a matrix representation for the weights of the adjoint representation. According to the relation:

$$3 \otimes \bar{3} = 8 \oplus 1$$

the 3×3 matrix, T_i^j, of trace zero, can be associated with an octuplet.

We give the explicit form of T_i^j for the baryons, the antibaryons, the pseudoscalar mesons and the vector mesons of the octuplet:

$$B = \begin{vmatrix} \frac{1}{\sqrt{6}}\Lambda^0 + \frac{1}{\sqrt{2}}\Sigma^0 & \Sigma^+ & p \\ \Sigma^- & \frac{1}{\sqrt{6}}\Lambda^0 - \frac{1}{\sqrt{2}}\Sigma^0 & n \\ \Xi^- & \Xi^0 & -\sqrt{\frac{2}{3}}\Lambda^0 \end{vmatrix}$$

$$\overline{B} = \begin{vmatrix} \frac{1}{\sqrt{6}}\overline{\Lambda^0} + \frac{1}{\sqrt{2}}\overline{\Sigma^0} & \overline{\Sigma^-} & \overline{\Xi^-} \\ \overline{\Sigma^+} & \frac{1}{\sqrt{6}}\overline{\Lambda^0} - \frac{1}{\sqrt{2}}\overline{\Sigma^0} & \overline{\Xi^0} \\ \overline{p} & \overline{n} & -\sqrt{\frac{2}{3}}\overline{\Lambda^0} \end{vmatrix}$$

$$M = \begin{vmatrix} \frac{1}{\sqrt{6}}\eta^0 + \frac{1}{\sqrt{2}}\pi^0 & \pi^+ & K^+ \\ \pi^- & \frac{1}{\sqrt{6}}\eta^0 - \frac{1}{\sqrt{2}}\pi^0 & K^0 \\ K^- & \overline{K^0} & -\sqrt{\frac{2}{3}}\eta^0 \end{vmatrix}$$

$$V_8 = \begin{vmatrix} \frac{1}{\sqrt{6}}\varphi^0 + \frac{1}{\sqrt{2}}\rho^0 & \rho^+ & K^{*+} \\ \rho^- & \frac{1}{\sqrt{6}}\varphi^0 + \frac{1}{\sqrt{2}}\rho^0 & K^{*0} \\ K^{*-} & \overline{K^{*0}} & -\sqrt{\tfrac{2}{3}}\varphi^0 \end{vmatrix}.$$

3. We associate with each octuplet a 3×3 matrix and the scalar representation of the product of three octuplets corresponds to the trace of the product of the three matrices. It is possible to write two linearly independent traces:

$$\mathrm{Tr}\,(T_1 T_2 T_3) \quad \text{and} \quad \mathrm{Tr}\,(T_2 T_1 T_3)$$

related to the two different isometries.

We will write explicitly the pseudoscalar meson-baryon Yukawa coupling as an example. The symmetric (D type) and the antisymmetric (F type) couplings will be defined in the following way:

$$H_A = \sqrt{2}\,g_a[\mathrm{Tr}\,(\bar{B}MB) - \mathrm{Tr}\,(\bar{B}BM)]$$

$$H_S = \sqrt{2}\,g_s[\mathrm{Tr}\,(\bar{B}MB) + \mathrm{Tr}\,(\bar{B}BM)].$$

The π meson-nucleon coupling constant is simply:

$$g = g_a + g_s$$

where $g^2/4\pi = 14.6$ and the D/F ratio is defined by:

$$\rho = g_s/g_a\,.$$

But it is more convenient to use a mixing parameter α defined by:

$$\alpha = g_a/g \qquad 1-\alpha = g_s/g.$$

A pure D type coupling corresponds to $\alpha = 0$ and a pure F type coupling to $\alpha = 1$.

The computation of the two traces is given in table 4.1 where the hamiltonians have been expanded on the basis of the 12 charge independent forms one can construct from the 8 mesons and the 8 baryons (Martin and Wali [1963] and De Swart [1963]).

The column H_S can be used for the pure D type coupling between two vector mesons and one pseudoscalar meson and the column H_A for the pure F type coupling between two pseudoscalar mesons and one vector meson.

TABLE 4.1

Charge independent form	$\mathrm{Tr}(\overline{\mathrm{B}}\mathrm{MB})$	$\mathrm{Tr}(\overline{\mathrm{B}}\mathrm{BM})$	H_{S}	H_{A}	H
$\overline{\mathrm{N}}\boldsymbol{\tau}\cdot\mathrm{N}\boldsymbol{\pi}$	$\frac{1}{\sqrt{2}}$	0	g_{s}	g_{a}	g
$\overline{\Sigma}\cdot\Xi\boldsymbol{\tau}\mathrm{K}+\overline{\Xi}\boldsymbol{\tau}\cdot\Sigma\mathrm{K}$	$\frac{1}{\sqrt{2}}$	0	g_{s}	g_{a}	g
$\mathrm{i}\overline{\Sigma}\times\Sigma\cdot\boldsymbol{\pi}$	$-\frac{1}{\sqrt{2}}$	$\frac{1}{\sqrt{2}}$	0	$-2g_{\mathrm{a}}$	$-2\alpha g$
$\overline{\Lambda}\Sigma\cdot\boldsymbol{\pi}+\overline{\Sigma}\cdot\Lambda\boldsymbol{\pi}$	$\frac{1}{\sqrt{6}}$	$\frac{1}{\sqrt{6}}$	$\frac{2}{\sqrt{3}}g_{\mathrm{s}}$	0	$\frac{2}{3}(1-\alpha)g$
$\overline{\Lambda}\Lambda\eta^0$	$-\frac{1}{\sqrt{6}}$	$-\frac{1}{\sqrt{6}}$	$-\frac{2}{\sqrt{3}}g_{\mathrm{s}}$	0	$-\frac{2}{\sqrt{3}}(1-\alpha)g$
$\overline{\Sigma}\cdot\Sigma\eta^0$	$\frac{1}{\sqrt{6}}$	$\frac{1}{\sqrt{6}}$	$\frac{2}{\sqrt{3}}g_{\mathrm{s}}$	0	$\frac{2}{\sqrt{3}}(1-\alpha)g$
$\overline{\Xi}\boldsymbol{\tau}\Xi\boldsymbol{\pi}$	0	$\frac{1}{\sqrt{2}}$	g_{s}	$-g_{\mathrm{a}}$	$(1-2\alpha)g$
$\overline{\Sigma}\mathrm{N}\boldsymbol{\tau}\overline{\mathrm{K}}+\overline{\mathrm{N}}\boldsymbol{\tau}\cdot\Sigma\mathrm{K}$	0	$\frac{1}{\sqrt{2}}$	g_{s}	$-g_{\mathrm{a}}$	$(1-2\alpha)g$
$\overline{\mathrm{N}}\mathrm{N}\eta^0$	$\frac{1}{\sqrt{6}}$	$-\frac{2}{\sqrt{6}}$	$-\frac{1}{\sqrt{3}}g_{\mathrm{s}}$	$\sqrt{3}g_{\mathrm{a}}$	$-\frac{1}{\sqrt{3}}(1-4\alpha)g$
$\overline{\Sigma}\mathrm{N}\boldsymbol{\tau}\overline{\mathrm{K}}+\overline{\mathrm{N}}\boldsymbol{\tau}\cdot\Sigma\mathrm{K}$	$\frac{1}{\sqrt{6}}$	$-\frac{2}{\sqrt{6}}$	$-\frac{1}{\sqrt{3}}g_{\mathrm{s}}$	$\sqrt{3}g_{\mathrm{a}}$	$-\frac{1}{\sqrt{3}}(1-4\alpha)g$
$\overline{\Xi}\Xi\eta$	$-\frac{2}{\sqrt{6}}$	$\frac{1}{\sqrt{6}}$	$-\frac{1}{\sqrt{3}}g_{\mathrm{s}}$	$-\sqrt{3}g_{\mathrm{a}}$	$-\frac{1}{\sqrt{3}}(1+2\alpha)g$
$\overline{\Lambda}\mathrm{N}\overline{\mathrm{K}}+\overline{\mathrm{N}}\Lambda\mathrm{K}$	$-\frac{2}{\sqrt{6}}$	$\frac{1}{\sqrt{6}}$	$-\frac{1}{\sqrt{3}}g_{\mathrm{s}}$	$-\sqrt{3}g_{\mathrm{a}}$	$-\frac{1}{\sqrt{3}}(1+2\alpha)g$

To be exhaustive, we give in table 4.2 the explicit expression of the charge independent forms corresponding to our particular choice of phases as included in the T_i^j matrices.

TABLE 4.2

$\overline{\mathrm{N}}\boldsymbol{\tau}\mathrm{N}\boldsymbol{\pi}$	$(\bar{\mathrm{p}}\mathrm{p}-\bar{\mathrm{n}}\mathrm{n})\pi^0+\sqrt{2}(\bar{\mathrm{n}}\mathrm{p}\pi^-+\bar{\mathrm{p}}\mathrm{n}\pi^+)$
$\overline{\Sigma}\Xi\boldsymbol{\tau}\mathrm{K}$	$\overline{\Sigma^0}(\Xi^-\mathrm{K}^+-\Xi^0\mathrm{K}^0)+\sqrt{2}(\overline{\Sigma^-}\Xi^-\mathrm{K}^0+\overline{\Sigma^+}\Xi^0\mathrm{K}^+)$
$\Xi\boldsymbol{\tau}\cdot\Sigma\overline{\mathrm{K}}$	$(\overline{\Xi^-}\mathrm{K}^--\overline{\Xi^0}\overline{\mathrm{K}^0})\Sigma^0+\sqrt{2}(\overline{\Xi^-}\overline{\mathrm{K}^0}\Sigma^-+\overline{\Xi^0}\mathrm{K}^-\Sigma^+)$
$\mathrm{i}\overline{\Sigma}\times\Sigma\cdot\boldsymbol{\pi}$	$(\overline{\Sigma^-}\Sigma^--\overline{\Sigma^+}\Sigma^+)\pi^0+(\overline{\Sigma^0}\Sigma^+-\overline{\Sigma^-}\Sigma^0)\pi^-+(\overline{\Sigma^+}\Sigma^0-\overline{\Sigma^0}\Sigma^-)\pi^+$
$\overline{\Lambda}\Sigma\cdot\pi+\overline{\Sigma}\Lambda\boldsymbol{\pi}$	$\overline{\Lambda}(\Sigma^+\pi^-+\Sigma^-\pi^++\Sigma^0\pi^0)+(\overline{\Sigma^+}\pi^++\overline{\Sigma^-}\pi^-+\overline{\Sigma^0}\pi^0)\Lambda$
$\overline{\Lambda}\Lambda\eta^0$	$\overline{\Lambda}\Lambda\eta^0$
$\overline{\Sigma}\cdot\Sigma\eta^0$	$(\overline{\Sigma^+}\Sigma^++\overline{\Sigma^-}\Sigma^-+\overline{\Sigma^0}\Sigma^0)\eta^0$
$\overline{\Xi}\boldsymbol{\tau}\Xi\boldsymbol{\pi}$	$(\overline{\Xi^-}\Xi^--\overline{\Xi^0}\Xi^0)\pi^0+\sqrt{2}(\overline{\Xi^-}\Xi^0\pi^-+\overline{\Xi^0}\Xi^-\pi^+)$
$\overline{\Sigma}\mathrm{N}\boldsymbol{\tau}\overline{\mathrm{K}}$	$\overline{\Sigma^0}(\mathrm{p}\mathrm{K}^--\mathrm{n}\overline{\mathrm{K}^0})+\sqrt{2}(\overline{\Sigma^-}\mathrm{n}\mathrm{K}^-+\overline{\Sigma^+}\mathrm{p}\overline{\mathrm{K}^0})$
$\overline{\mathrm{N}}\boldsymbol{\tau}\cdot\Sigma\mathrm{K}$	$(\bar{\mathrm{p}}\mathrm{K}^+-\bar{\mathrm{n}}\mathrm{K}^0)\Sigma^0+\sqrt{2}(\bar{\mathrm{n}}\mathrm{K}^-\Sigma^++\bar{\mathrm{p}}\Sigma^+\mathrm{K}^0)$
$\overline{\mathrm{N}}\mathrm{N}\eta^0$	$(\bar{\mathrm{p}}\mathrm{p}+\bar{\mathrm{n}}\mathrm{n})\eta^0$
$\overline{\Lambda}\Xi\mathrm{K}+\overline{\Xi}\Lambda\overline{\mathrm{K}}$	$\overline{\Lambda}(\Xi^-\mathrm{K}^++\Xi^0\mathrm{K}^0)+(\overline{\Xi^-}\mathrm{K}^-+\overline{\Xi^0}\overline{\mathrm{K}^0})\Lambda$
$\overline{\Xi}\Xi\eta^0$	$(\overline{\Xi^-}\Xi^-+\overline{\Xi^0}\Xi^0)\eta^0$
$\overline{\Lambda}\mathrm{N}\overline{\mathrm{K}}+\overline{\mathrm{N}}\Lambda\mathrm{K}$	$\overline{\Lambda}(\mathrm{p}\mathrm{K}^-+\mathrm{n}\overline{\mathrm{K}^0})+(\bar{\mathrm{p}}\mathrm{K}^++\mathrm{n}\mathrm{K}^0)\Lambda$

4. It can be useful to consider a first order breaking of the symmetry. The product of the three octuplets can now be written as the sum of two types of terms:

a) A scalar term corresponding to the exact symmetry with two parameters g_s and g_a.

b) A non invariant term which behaves, under unitary transformation, as the Y component of an octuplet. The requirement of charge conjugation invariance restricts the number of independent parameters, for this term, to five: λ_1, λ_{8s}, λ_{27}, λ_{8a}, $\lambda_{10+\overline{10}}$, where $\lambda_{\sigma\chi}$ corresponds to the $\overline{\mathrm{B}}\mathrm{B}$ system in the state $\sigma\chi$.

The results are given in table 4.3 and they agree with corresponding calculations performed by DIU, RUBINSTEIN and BASDEVANT [1965].

TABLE 4.3

Couplings	g_s	g_a	λ_1	λ_{8s}	λ_{8a}	$\lambda_{10+\overline{10}}$	λ_{27}
$\overline{\mathrm{N}}\mathrm{N}\pi$	1	1	0	1	1	1	1
$\overline{\Sigma}\Xi\mathrm{K}$	1	1	0	$-\frac{1}{2}$	$-\frac{1}{2}$	$-\frac{1}{2}$	$-\frac{1}{2}$
$\overline{\Sigma}\Sigma\pi$	0	-2	0	0	-2	1	0
$\overline{\Sigma}\Lambda\pi$	$\frac{2}{\sqrt{3}}$	0	0	$\frac{2}{\sqrt{3}}$	0	0	$-\sqrt{3}$
$\overline{\Lambda}\Lambda\eta^0$	$-\frac{2}{\sqrt{3}}$	0	1	$\frac{2}{\sqrt{3}}$	0	0	$-\frac{9\sqrt{3}}{4}$
$\overline{\Sigma}\Sigma\eta^0$	$\frac{2}{\sqrt{3}}$	0	1	$-\frac{2}{\sqrt{3}}$	0	0	$-\frac{\sqrt{3}}{2\sqrt{2}}$
$\overline{\Xi}\Xi\pi$	1	-1	0	1	-1	-1	1
$\overline{\Sigma}\mathrm{N}\overline{\mathrm{K}}$	1	-1	0	$-\frac{1}{2}$	$\frac{1}{2}$	$\frac{1}{2}$	$-\frac{1}{2}$
$\overline{\mathrm{N}}\mathrm{N}\eta^0$	$-\frac{1}{\sqrt{3}}$	$\sqrt{3}$	1	$\frac{1}{\sqrt{3}}$	$-\sqrt{3}$	0	$\frac{3\sqrt{3}}{4}$
$\overline{\Xi}\Lambda\overline{\mathrm{K}}$	$-\frac{1}{\sqrt{3}}$	$\sqrt{3}$	0	$\frac{1}{2\sqrt{3}}$	$-\frac{\sqrt{3}}{2}$	$\frac{1}{2\sqrt{3}}$	$-\frac{3\sqrt{3}}{2}$
$\overline{\Xi}\Xi\eta^0$	$-\frac{1}{\sqrt{3}}$	$-\sqrt{3}$	1	$\frac{1}{\sqrt{3}}$	$\sqrt{3}$	0	$\frac{3\sqrt{3}}{4}$
$\overline{\mathrm{N}}\Lambda\mathrm{K}$	$-\frac{1}{\sqrt{3}}$	$-\sqrt{3}$	0	$\frac{1}{2\sqrt{3}}$	$\frac{\sqrt{3}}{2}$	$-\frac{1}{2\sqrt{3}}$	$-\frac{3\sqrt{3}}{2}$

4.2.2. DECAY OF THE BARYON DECUPLET

1. We are interested in the decay of the spin $J = \frac{3}{2}^+$ excited baryons B^* into a pseudoscalar meson M and a spin $J = \frac{1}{2}^+$ baryon B. From Lorentz invariance and parity conservation the T matrix elements for the $\mathrm{B}^* \Rightarrow \mathrm{B} + \mathrm{M}$ decay have the general structure:

$$\langle K', \lambda', k|T|K, \lambda\rangle = \mathrm{i}\Lambda\bar{u}(K', \lambda')k^{\sigma}u_{\sigma}(K, \lambda)$$

where $u(K', \lambda')$ is the spin $\frac{1}{2}$ Dirac spinor for baryons of energy momentum K' and helicity λ'; $u_{\sigma}(K, \lambda)$ the spin $\frac{3}{2}$ Rarita-Schwinger spinor for the excited baryons of energy momentum K and helicity λ. The meson momentum is $k = K - K'$.

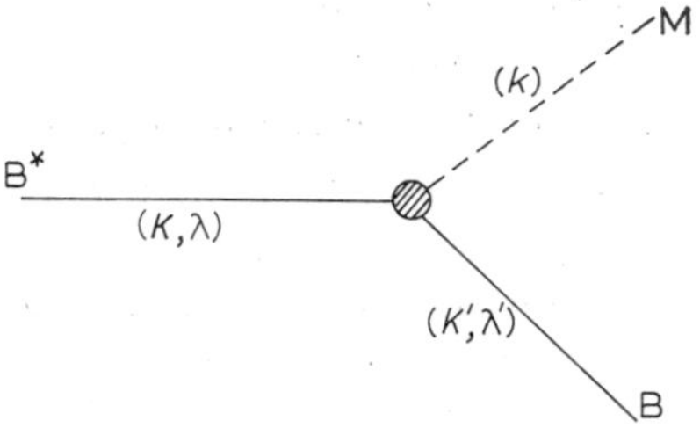

Fig. 4.1.

The decay rate $\Gamma(\mathrm{B}^* \Rightarrow \mathrm{B}+\mathrm{M})$ is computed after summation over the B and B* polarizations. The result is the following (GOURDIN and SALIN [1963a]):

$$\Gamma(\mathrm{B}^* \Rightarrow \mathrm{B}+\mathrm{M}) = \frac{\Lambda^2}{4\pi}\,\tfrac{2}{3}k_{\mathrm{CM}}^3\left(\frac{M^*+M}{2M^*}\right)^2\left[1-\frac{m^2}{(M^*+M)^2}\right].$$

In this expression, M is the baryon mass, M^* the resonance total energy and m the meson mass. The final momentum k_{CM} is defined in the B* rest system and is easily calculated for the four physical situations in table 4.4 (GLASHOW and ROSENFELD [1963a]).

TABLE 4.4

Resonance	Final state	k_{CM}(MeV/c)
$\mathrm{N}^*_{\frac{3}{2}}$	$\mathrm{N}\pi$	233
Y^*_1	$\Lambda\pi$	205
	$\Sigma\pi$	124
$\Xi^*_{\frac{1}{2}}$	$\Xi\pi$	148

The coupling constant Λ is adjusted so that it reproduces the experimental width for the $\mathrm{N}^* \Rightarrow \mathrm{N}+\pi$ decay.

Using $\Gamma(\mathrm{N}^* \Rightarrow \mathrm{N}+\pi) = 120$ MeV, we obtain:

$$\Lambda_{\mathrm{N^*N}\pi} \simeq \frac{2.13}{m_{\pi}}.$$

2. All these decays are described by one reduced matrix element only because of the classification of the B* resonance in a decuplet which appears only once in the product of two octuplets.

We now calculate the phase space factors, the Clebsch-Gordan coefficients and the widths. The results are given in the table 4.5, the $N^* \Rightarrow N\pi$ decay being taken as a reference.

TABLE 4.5

Resonance	Final state	Phase space	CG coefficient	Width
$N^*_{\frac{3}{2}}$	$N\pi$	1	1	1
Y^*_1	$\Lambda\pi$	0.718	$\frac{1}{2}$	0.359
	$\Sigma\pi$	0.169	$\frac{1}{3}$	0.056
$\Xi^*_{\frac{1}{2}}$	$\Xi\pi$	0.287	$\frac{1}{2}$	0.143

Using, as previously, $\Gamma(N^*_{\frac{3}{2}} \Rightarrow N\pi) = 120$ MeV, the widths for Y^*_1 and $\Xi^*_{\frac{1}{2}}$ are calculated from unitary symmetry to be:

$$\Gamma(Y^*_1 \Rightarrow \Lambda\pi)_{th} = 43 \text{ MeV}$$

$$\left(\frac{\Gamma(Y^*_1 \Rightarrow \Sigma\pi)}{\Gamma(Y^*_1 \Rightarrow \Lambda\pi)}\right)_{th} = 0.157$$

$$\Gamma(\Xi^*_{\frac{1}{2}} \Rightarrow \Xi\pi)_{th} = 17 \text{ MeV}.$$

These values can be compared with the experimental one (ROSENFELD et al. [1965] and ARMENTEROS et al. [1965]):

$$\Gamma(Y^*_1 \Rightarrow \Lambda\pi)_{exp} = (30 \pm 3) \text{ MeV}, \qquad \left(\frac{\Gamma(Y^*_1 \Rightarrow \Sigma\pi)}{\Gamma(Y^*_1 \Rightarrow \Lambda\pi)}\right)_{exp} \simeq 0.16 \pm 0.04$$

$$\Gamma(\Xi^*_{\frac{1}{2}} \Rightarrow \Xi\pi)_{exp} = (7.15 \pm 1.7) \text{ MeV}.$$

The predicted widths are generally too large and we must look to a first order broken symmetry to explain the disagreement between theory and experiment.

3. In a first order symmetry, the $B^* \Rightarrow B + M$ unitary symmetry violating amplitudes are given in terms of four reduced matrix elements; it is convenient to classify according to the eigenstates of the final BM system, $A_{\sigma\chi}$.

We give in table 4.6, the expression of the four physical and eight unphysical B*BM amplitudes. The first column A_0 is associated to an exact unitary symmetry (DIU et al. [1965]).

TABLE 4.6

Transition	A_0	A_{88}	A_{8a}	A_{10}	A_{27}
$N^*_{\frac{3}{2}}N\pi$	$\frac{1}{\sqrt{2}}$			$-\frac{1}{4}$	$\frac{3}{4\sqrt{2}}$
$Y^*_1\Lambda\pi$	$\frac{1}{2}$	$-\frac{1}{5}$			$\frac{3}{10}$
$Y^*_1\Sigma\pi$	$\frac{1}{\sqrt{6}}$		$\sqrt{\frac{2}{15}}$		
$\Xi^*_{\frac{1}{2}}\Xi\pi$	$\frac{1}{2}$	$-\frac{3}{10}$	$\frac{1}{2\sqrt{5}}$	$\frac{1}{4\sqrt{2}}$	$\frac{3}{40}$
$N^*_{\frac{3}{2}}\Sigma K$	$-\frac{1}{\sqrt{2}}$			$\frac{1}{4}$	$\frac{3}{4\sqrt{2}}$
$Y^*_1 N\bar{K}$	$\frac{1}{\sqrt{6}}$	$\frac{1}{5}\sqrt{\frac{3}{2}}$	$-\frac{1}{\sqrt{30}}$		$\frac{1}{5}\sqrt{\frac{3}{2}}$
$Y^*_1\Sigma\eta^0$	$-\frac{1}{2}$	$-\frac{1}{5}$			$\frac{3}{10}$
$Y^*_1\Xi K$	$-\frac{1}{\sqrt{6}}$	$\frac{1}{5}\sqrt{\frac{3}{2}}$	$\frac{1}{\sqrt{30}}$		$\frac{1}{5}\sqrt{\frac{3}{2}}$
$\Xi^*_{\frac{1}{2}}\Lambda K$	$\frac{1}{2}$	$\frac{1}{10}$	$-\frac{1}{2\sqrt{5}}$	$\frac{1}{4\sqrt{2}}$	$\frac{9}{40}$
$\Xi^*_{\frac{1}{2}}\Sigma K$	$-\frac{1}{2}$	$-\frac{3}{10}$	$-\frac{1}{2\sqrt{5}}$	$-\frac{1}{4\sqrt{2}}$	$\frac{3}{40}$
$\Xi^*_{\frac{1}{2}}\Xi\eta^0$	$-\frac{1}{2}$	$\frac{1}{10}$	$\frac{1}{2\sqrt{5}}$	$-\frac{1}{4\sqrt{2}}$	$\frac{9}{40}$
$\Omega^-\Xi\bar{K}$	1			$\frac{1}{\sqrt{2}}$	

The four physical amplitudes are related by one relation (KONUMA and TOMOZAWA [1964]):

$$2A(N^*_{\frac{3}{2}} \Rightarrow N\pi)+2\sqrt{2}A(\Xi^*_{\frac{1}{2}} \Rightarrow \Xi\pi) = \sqrt{3}A(Y^*_1 \Rightarrow \Sigma\pi)+3\sqrt{2}A(Y^*_1 \Rightarrow \Lambda\pi).$$

It is convenient to define reduced coupling constants, including the SU(3) Clebsch-Gordan coefficients:

$$\Lambda_{N_{\frac{3}{2}}{}^*N\pi} = \frac{1}{\sqrt{2}} A_0\lambda_{N^*} \qquad \Lambda_{\Xi_{\frac{1}{2}}{}^*\Xi\pi} = \tfrac{1}{2}A_0\lambda_{\Xi^*}$$

$$\Lambda_{Y_1{}^*\Lambda\pi} = \tfrac{1}{2}A_0\lambda_{Y^*\Lambda} \qquad \Lambda_{Y_1{}^*\Sigma\pi} = \frac{1}{\sqrt{6}} A_0\lambda_{Y^*\Sigma}\,.$$

In the exact unitary symmetry the four reduced quantities are equal:

$$\lambda_{N^*} = \lambda_{\Xi^*} = \lambda_{Y^*\Lambda} = \lambda_{Y^*\Sigma}$$

and in a first order broken symmetry, they are related by a Gell-Mann-Okubo relation (MURASKIN and GLASHOW [1963]):

$$2[\lambda_{N^*}+\lambda_{\Xi^*}] = \lambda_{Y^*\Sigma}+3\lambda_{Y^*\Lambda}\,.$$

From the experimental value of the $\Xi^*_{\frac{1}{2}}$ width, we deduce:

$$\lambda_{\Xi^*}/\lambda_{N^*} \simeq \tfrac{2}{3}.$$

The experimental ratio $\Gamma(Y_1^* \Rightarrow \Sigma\pi)/\Gamma(Y_1^* \Rightarrow \Lambda\pi)$ agrees quite well with the prediction of the exact symmetry, and, in a good approximation we take:

$$\lambda_{Y^*\Sigma} \simeq \lambda_{Y^*\Lambda} = \lambda_{Y^*}.$$

Using the previous first order broken symmetry relation, we obtain:

$$\lambda_{Y^*}/\lambda_{N^*} \simeq \tfrac{5}{6}$$

and we predict the Y* to be:

$$\Gamma(Y_1^* \Rightarrow \Lambda\pi) \simeq 30 \text{ MeV}$$

in good agreement with experiment.

4.2.3. Strong decay of the vector mesons

1. We are first interested in the decay of a vector meson V into two pseudoscalar mesons M_1 and M_2. From Lorentz invariance and parity conservation, the general structure of the matrix element is given by:

$$\langle k_1, k_2 | T | K, \lambda \rangle = g_{VM_1M_2}(k_1 - k_2)^\sigma \rho_\sigma(K, \lambda)$$

where $\rho_\sigma(K, \lambda)$ is the polarization for vectors of the vector meson of energy momentum K and helicity λ and k_1, k_2 the energy momentum for vectors of the final mesons.

The decay rate can be calculated after summation over the vector meson polarization states and the result is the following (Sakurai [1962]):

$$\Gamma(V \Rightarrow M_1 + M_2) = \frac{2}{3} \frac{g^2_{VM_1M_2}}{4\pi} \frac{k^3_{CM}}{m^2_V}.$$

The final meson momentum k_{CM} is calculated in the V rest system.

2. From the point of view of unitary symmetry, all the amplitudes associated with the octuplet of vector mesons are proportional, the only $VM_1 M_2$ coupling allowed by the generalized Pauli principle being antisymmetrical in the exchange of the two mesons octuplets.

It is easy to verify that the charge conjugation invariance forbids the decay of the ω^0 singulet vector meson into two pseudoscalar mesons. We then have for all the decays only one reduced amplitude.

The meson momentum k_{CM} is calculated for the four observable reactions:

TABLE 4.7

Resonance	Final state	k_{CM}(MeV/c)
ρ	$\pi\pi$	355
K^*	$K\pi$	288
φ	K^+K^-	126
	$K_1^0K_2^0$	109

We now determine the phase space factors, the Clebsch-Gordan coefficients due to unitary symmetry and the widths. The results are given in table 4.8, the $\rho \Rightarrow 2\pi$ decay being taken as a reference:

TABLE 4.8

Resonance	Final state	Phase space	C.G. coefficient	Width
ρ	$\pi\pi$	1	1	1
K^*	$K\pi$	0.388	$\frac{3}{4}$	0.291
φ	K^+K^-	0.0248	$\frac{3}{4}\cos^2\lambda$	0.0110
	$K_1^0K_2^0$	0.0161	$\frac{3}{4}\cos^2\lambda$	0.0071

The coupling constant $g_{\rho\pi\pi}$ is determined so that it reproduces the experimental $\Gamma(\rho \Rightarrow 2\pi)$ width of 124 MeV (ROSENFELD et al. [1965]). Using the previous formula we find:

$$\frac{g_{\rho\pi\pi}^2}{4\pi} \simeq 2.39.$$

The K^* and φ widths predicted by the unitary symmetry are not in perfect agreement with experiment (ROSENFELD et al. [1965]):

$$\begin{cases} \Gamma_{th}(K^* \Rightarrow K\pi) \simeq 36 \text{ MeV} \\ \Gamma_{exp}(K^* \Rightarrow K\pi) \simeq (49 \pm 2) \text{ MeV} \end{cases} \qquad \begin{cases} \Gamma_{th}(\varphi \Rightarrow \overline{K}K) \simeq 2.2 \text{ MeV} \\ \Gamma_{exp}(\varphi \Rightarrow \overline{K}K) \simeq (2.3 \pm 0.6) \text{ MeV}. \end{cases}$$

It seems necessary to take into account a first order perturbation with respect to the medium strong interactions in order to reconcile theory and experiment.

3. In a first order broken symmetry, the $V \Rightarrow M_1 M_2$ matrix elements are

known from three reduced matrix elements for the octuplet decay and one reduced matrix element for the singulet ω^0 decay now allowed in the $\overline{\mathrm{K}}\mathrm{K}$ mode.

Some VMM vertices vanish identically due to isotopic spin or charge conjugation invariance. In table 4.9 we give the expression of the 6 non vanishing coupling constants in terms of eigenamplitudes of the final two pseudoscalar meson states of C parity $C = -1$ (DIU et al. [1965]).

TABLE 4.9

Vector meson	MM state	Coupling constant
ρ	$\pi\pi$	$\sqrt{2}g_0(1+\alpha_1+\alpha_2)$
	$\overline{\mathrm{K}}\mathrm{K}$	$-\frac{1}{\sqrt{2}}g_0(1+\alpha_1-\alpha_2)$
K*	$\mathrm{K}\pi$	$-\frac{1}{2}\sqrt{3}g_0(1-\frac{1}{2}\alpha_1+\alpha_2)$
	$\mathrm{K}\eta$	$-\frac{1}{2}\sqrt{3}g_0(1-\frac{1}{2}\alpha_1-\alpha_2)$
φ	$\overline{\mathrm{K}}\mathrm{K}$	$-\sqrt{\frac{3}{2}}\cos\lambda\, g_0(1-\alpha_1+\mathrm{tg}\,\lambda\,\alpha_3)$
ω	$\overline{\mathrm{K}}\mathrm{K}$	$-\sqrt{\frac{3}{2}}\sin\lambda\, g_0(1-\alpha_1-\mathrm{cotg}\,\lambda\,\alpha_3)$

The MM states are pure isotopic spin eigenstates and this feature explains the coefficient $\sqrt{2}$ in front of the coupling constant for the $\rho \Rightarrow 2\pi$ transition. The constant g_0 is associated with the transition $\mathrm{V} \Rightarrow \mathrm{M}_1 + \mathrm{M}_2$ evaluated in an exact unitary symmetry. The three constants α_1, α_2, α_3 describe the relative corrections due to the breaking of the symmetry by a H_Y type term:

$$\alpha_1 : \mathrm{V}\ \text{octuplet} \Rightarrow \mathrm{M}_1\mathrm{M}_2\ \text{octuplet}\ C = -1\ (8a)$$
$$\alpha_2 : \mathrm{V}\ \text{octuplet} \Rightarrow \mathrm{M}_1\mathrm{M}_2\ \text{decuplet}\ C = -1\ (10-\overline{10})$$
$$\alpha_3 : \mathrm{V}\ \text{singulet} \Rightarrow \mathrm{M}_1\mathrm{M}_2\ \text{octuplet}\ C = -1\ (8a).$$

The observable decay widths are now linearly independent.

4. It can be interesting to test the hypothesis of the universal vector meson coupling as proposed by SAKURAI [1960]. In the present problem, the two parameters α_2 and α_3 vanish and the $\mathrm{VM}_1\mathrm{M}_2$ vertices are described by two parameters only (DIU et al. [1965]).

Let us define, for convenience, the reduced constants:

$$\lambda_\rho = g_0(1+\alpha_1) \qquad \lambda_{\mathrm{K}^*} = g_0(1-\tfrac{1}{2}\alpha_1) \qquad \lambda_\varphi = g_0(1-\alpha_1).$$

In the exact unitary symmetry:

$$\lambda_\rho = \lambda_{K^*} = \lambda_\varphi$$

and in the broken symmetry restricted by the universality condition we obtain a relation of the Gell-Mann-Okubo type:

$$4\lambda_{K^*} = 3\lambda_\varphi + \lambda_\rho .$$

Using $\Gamma(\rho) = 124$ MeV and $\Gamma(K^*) = (49 \pm 2)$ MeV, we obtain

$$\lambda_{K^*}/\lambda_\rho \simeq 1.16 \pm 0.05.$$

We then use the previous relation to calculate λ_φ:

$$\lambda_\varphi/\lambda_\rho = 1.22 \pm 0.07$$

and a theoretical estimate of the $\Gamma(\varphi \Rightarrow \overline{K}K)$ width is given by:

$$\Gamma(\varphi \Rightarrow \overline{K}K)_{th} \simeq (2.7 \pm 0.15) \text{ MeV}$$

in good agreement, within experimental errors, with the observed value:

$$\Gamma(\varphi \Rightarrow \overline{K}K)_{exp} \simeq (2.3 \pm 0.6) \text{ MeV}.$$

The parameter α_1, measuring the breaking of the symmetry turns out to be:

$$\alpha_1 \simeq -0.12$$

in agreement with different estimates.

4.3. Four body reactions

4.3.1. Generalities

1. Let us assume the invariance of the S matrix under the transformations of a group G. We are interested in a general scattering reaction:

$$A + B \Rightarrow C + D + \ldots + Z$$

where the particles A, B, C, . . ., Z are associated with irreducible representations of G. The transition amplitude:

$$\langle C, D, \ldots, Z|T|\, A, B\rangle$$

is an invariant quantity.

We first expand the initial state $|A, B\rangle$ on the complete basis of the irreducible representations of G:

$$|A, B\rangle = \sum_{\sigma, \chi} a(\sigma, \chi)|\sigma, \chi\rangle$$

where $a(\sigma, \chi)$ is a Clebsch-Gordan coefficient and $|\sigma, \chi\rangle$ an irreducible representation entering in the Kronecker product:

$$D_A \otimes D_B = \oplus\, \nu_\sigma D_\sigma .$$

The non negative integer ν_σ corresponds to the multiplicity of the representations $|\sigma\rangle$ differentiated by the index χ.

The same reduction in eigenstates of G is performed for the final state. We consider again a Kronecker product in G of the initial and final eigenstates in order to extract, now, the invariant part, because of the symmetry property of the T matrix. The orthogonality of the irreducible representations of G obliges us to combine only the initial and final states of same σ. For a given σ, we then expect, in general, $\nu_{\sigma_i}\nu_{\sigma_f}$ reduced amplitudes and it follows that the maximum number of linearly independent amplitudes is given by:

$$\sum_\sigma \nu_{\sigma_i}\nu_{\sigma_f} .$$

2. We now go back to the octuplet model and we first consider the very important problem of the scattering of the two octuplets into two octuplets:

$$K+L \Rightarrow M+N. \tag{I}$$

The product of two octuplet representations being decomposed into:

$$8 \otimes 8 = 1 \oplus 8_s \otimes 8_a \oplus 10 \oplus \overline{10} \oplus 27$$

there exist, in general, *eight* linearly independent reduced amplitudes it is convenient to quote as:

$$A_1, A_{8ss}, A_{8sa}, A_{8as}, A_{8aa}, A_{10}, A_{\overline{10}}, A_{27} .$$

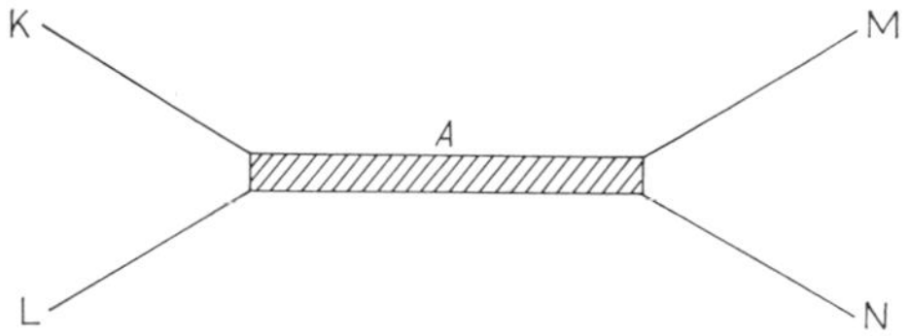

Fig. 4.2.

A particular process is determined by the weights of each of the four octuplets. For simplicity, the transition amplitude associated with the reaction $K_\alpha+L_\beta \Rightarrow M_\gamma+N_\delta$ will be written $A(\alpha+\beta \Rightarrow \gamma+\delta)$. In order, now, to expand this particular amplitude on the basis of the reduced amplitudes

$A_{\sigma\chi_i\chi_f}$ we have first to compute the Clebsch-Gordan coefficients corresponding to the projection of the initial and final states on the eigenstates $|\sigma, \chi\rangle$ associated with the product of two octuplets. We then use the isometries $\Omega^{(\sigma,\chi)}$ previously defined in chapter I and we have (BEHRENDS et al. [1962]):

$$\langle \sigma, \chi_i; \mu | 8_\alpha, 8_\beta \rangle = [\Omega^{(\sigma\chi_i)}]_{\alpha\beta},$$
$$\langle \sigma, \chi_f; \nu | 8_\gamma, 8_\delta \rangle = [\Omega_\nu^{(\sigma\chi_f)}]_{\gamma\delta}.$$

The phases of the Clebsch-Gordan coefficients are chosen as real and the normalization is given, as usual, by:

$$\sum_{\alpha\beta} [\Omega_\mu^{(\sigma\chi)}]_{\alpha\beta} [\Omega_{\mu'}^{(\sigma'\chi')}]^{\beta\alpha} = \delta_{\sigma\sigma'} \delta_{\chi\chi'} \delta_{\mu\mu'}.$$

In the present case where the reduction of the product of two octuplets is performed, the matrices $\Omega_\mu^{(\sigma\chi)}$ are either symmetric or skew symmetric:

$$\Omega^{(\sigma\chi)} = \varepsilon(\sigma, \chi) \Omega^{(\sigma\chi)\mathrm{T}}$$

following the value of $\sigma\chi$:

$$\varepsilon(\sigma, \chi) = +1 \qquad \text{for} \quad (\sigma\chi) = 1, 8_s, 27$$
$$\varepsilon(\sigma, \chi) = -1 \qquad \text{for} \quad (\sigma\chi) = 8_a, 10, \overline{10}.$$

The transition amplitude $A(\alpha+\beta \Rightarrow \gamma+\delta)$ is finally written as a linear combination of the reduced amplitudes A_{σ,χ_i,χ_f} following:

$$A(\alpha+\beta \Rightarrow \gamma+\delta) = \sum_\sigma \sum_{\chi_i\chi_f} P_{\alpha\beta;\gamma\delta}(\sigma, \chi_i, \chi_f) A_{\sigma\chi_i\chi_f}$$

where the projection operator $P(\sigma, \chi_i, \chi_f)$ is defined by:

$$P_{\alpha\beta;\gamma\delta}(\sigma, \chi_i, \chi_f) = \sum_\mu [\Omega_\mu^{(\sigma\chi_i)}]_{\alpha\beta} [\Omega^{(\sigma\chi_f)\mu}]_{\gamma\delta}$$

and it is trivial to check the idempotent character of P by using the normalization conditions fulfilled by the Ω's.

The symmetries properties of the Clebsch-Gordan coefficients Ω are reflected on the P's in the following way:

$$P_{\alpha\beta;\gamma\delta}(\sigma, \chi_i, \chi_f) = \varepsilon(\sigma, \chi_f) P_{\alpha\beta;\delta\gamma}(\sigma, \chi_i, \chi_f)$$
$$P_{\alpha\beta;\gamma\delta}(\sigma, \chi_i, \chi_f) = \varepsilon(\sigma, \chi_i) P_{\beta\alpha;\gamma\delta}(\sigma, \chi_i, \chi_f)$$
$$P_{\alpha\beta;\gamma\delta}(\sigma, \chi_i, \chi_f) = \varepsilon(\sigma, \chi_i)\varepsilon(\sigma, \chi_f) P_{\beta\alpha;\delta\gamma}(\sigma, \chi_i, \chi_f).$$

It is interesting to consider the reversed reaction operator $P_{\gamma\delta;\alpha\beta}(\sigma, \chi_i, \chi_f)$. By definition we immediately have:

$$P_{\gamma\delta;\alpha\beta}(\sigma, \chi_i, \chi_f) = P_{\alpha\beta;\gamma\delta}(\sigma, \chi_f, \chi_i).$$

In the case of elastic reactions (K ≡ M and L ≡ N), the time reversal invariance can be applied. From the previous results, the linear combination $A_{8sa} - A_{8as}$ is odd under the exchange of the initial and the final state. Such a result must be combined with the space time properties of the reduced amplitudes to obtain selection rules due to time reversal invariance.

In many applications it is interesting to consider the first crossed channel:

$$\overline{\mathrm{N}} + \mathrm{L} \Rightarrow \mathrm{M} + \overline{\mathrm{K}} \qquad \text{(II)}$$

and to expand the transition amplitude in reduced amplitudes $\mathscr{A}_{\sigma\chi_i\chi_f}$ of this channel II.

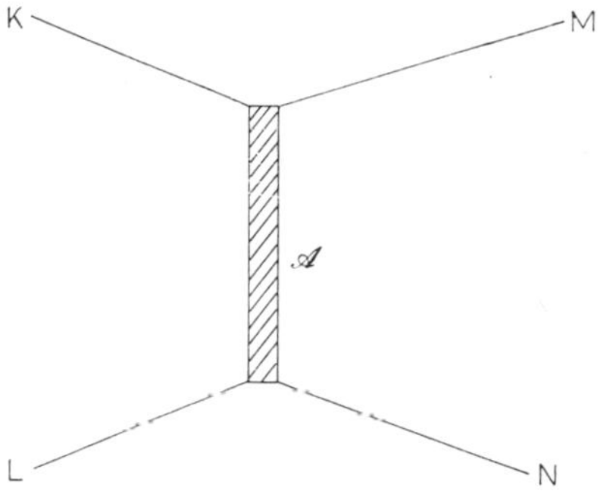

Fig. 4.3.

The relation between the A's and the $\mathscr{A}$'s amplitudes is given by a 8×8 crossing matrix; it is easy to compute resolving a simple system of eight linear equations. The result is given in the table 4.10 (DE SWART [1965]).

TABLE 4.10

	$\mathscr{A}_1$	$\mathscr{A}_{8ss}$	$\mathscr{A}_{27}$	$\mathscr{A}_{8aa}$	$\frac{1}{2}(\mathscr{A}_{10}+\mathscr{A}_{\overline{10}})$	$\frac{1}{2}(\mathscr{A}_{10}+\mathscr{A}_{\overline{10}})$	$\frac{1}{2}(\mathscr{A}_{8as}+\mathscr{A}_{8sa})$	$\frac{1}{2}(\mathscr{A}_{8as}-\mathscr{A}_{8sa})$
A_1	$\frac{1}{8}$	1	$\frac{27}{8}$	1	$\frac{5}{2}$	0	0	0
A_{8ss}	$\frac{1}{8}$	$-\frac{3}{10}$	$\frac{27}{40}$	$\frac{1}{2}$	-1	0	0	0
A_{27}	$\frac{1}{8}$	$\frac{1}{5}$	$\frac{7}{40}$	$-\frac{1}{3}$	$-\frac{1}{6}$	0	0	0
A_{8aa}	$\frac{1}{8}$	$\frac{1}{2}$	$-\frac{9}{8}$	$\frac{1}{2}$	0	0	0	0
$\frac{1}{2}(A_{10}+A_{\overline{10}})$	$\frac{1}{8}$	$-\frac{2}{5}$	$\frac{9}{40}$	0	$\frac{1}{2}$	0	0	0
$\frac{1}{2}(A_{10}-A_{\overline{10}})$	0	0	0	0	0	0	0	$-\frac{1}{15}$
$\frac{1}{2}(A_{8as}+A_{8sa})$	0	0	0	0	0	0	-1	0
$\frac{1}{2}(A_{8as}+A_{8sa})$	0	0	0	0	0	-15	0	0

The use of time reversal invariance in the channel I is strongly connected with the application of *PC* invariance in the channel II through the *PCT* theorem. From the point of view of unitary symmetry the *C* conjugation transforms a weight into its symmetric with respect to the origin in the weight space and a representation in its contragradient representation. It is easy to verify that all the eigenamplitudes of the channel II are even under such a transformation excepted the combination $\frac{1}{2}(\mathscr{A}_{10}-\mathscr{A}_{\overline{10}})$ which is odd. This result is obvious from table 4.1 where the amplitudes $\frac{1}{2}(A_{8as}-A_{8sa})$ of channel I and $\frac{1}{2}(\mathscr{A}_{10}-\mathscr{A}_{\overline{10}})$ of channel II are found to be proportional.

The second crossed channel:

$$\overline{\mathrm{M}}+\mathrm{L} \Rightarrow \overline{\mathrm{K}}+\mathrm{N} \tag{III}$$

can also be used to expand the transition amplitude in eigenamplitudes $\bar{A}_{\sigma\chi_i\chi_f}$.

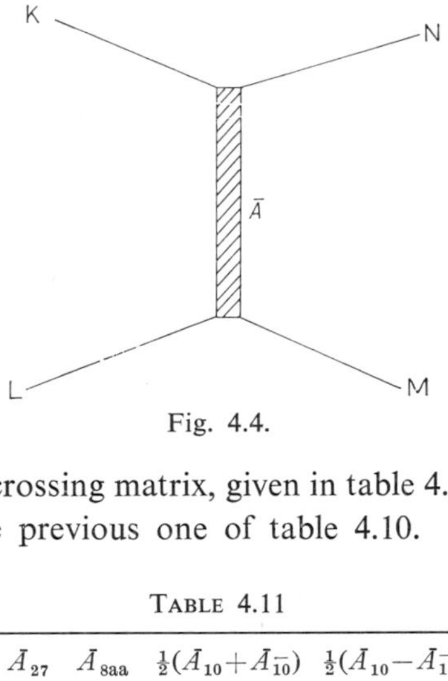

Fig. 4.4.

The corresponding crossing matrix, given in table 4.11, is connected in an obvious way with the previous one of table 4.10.

TABLE 4.11

	$\bar{A}_1$	$\bar{A}_{8ss}$	$\bar{A}_{27}$	$\bar{A}_{8aa}$	$\frac{1}{2}(\bar{A}_{10}+\bar{A}_{\overline{10}})$	$\frac{1}{2}(\bar{A}_{10}-\bar{A}_{\overline{10}})$	$\frac{1}{2}(\bar{A}_{8as}+\bar{A}_{8sa})$	$\frac{1}{2}(\bar{A}_{8as}-\bar{A}_{8sa})$
A_1	$\frac{1}{8}$	1	$\frac{27}{8}$	-1	$-\frac{5}{2}$	0	0	0
A_{8ss}	$\frac{1}{8}$	$-\frac{3}{10}$	$\frac{27}{40}$	$-\frac{1}{2}$	1	0	0	0
A_{27}	$\frac{1}{8}$	$\frac{1}{5}$	$\frac{7}{40}$	$\frac{1}{3}$	$\frac{1}{6}$	0	0	0
A_{8aa}	$-\frac{1}{8}$	$-\frac{1}{2}$	$\frac{9}{8}$	$\frac{1}{2}$	0	0	0	0
$\frac{1}{2}(A_{10}+A_{\overline{10}})$	$-\frac{1}{8}$	$\frac{2}{5}$	$\frac{9}{40}$	0	$\frac{1}{2}$	0	0	0
$\frac{1}{2}(A_{10}-A_{\overline{10}})$	0	0	0	0	0	0	$\frac{1}{15}$	0
$\frac{1}{2}(A_{8as}+A_{8sa})$	0	0	0	0	0	15	0	0
$\frac{1}{2}(A_{8as}-A_{8sa})$	0	0	0	0	0	0	0	-1

If we have an elastic reaction in channel I, K ≡ M, L ≡ N, we have also an elastic reaction in channel III, $\overline{K} \equiv \overline{M}$, L ≡ N and the amplitudes odd under the exchange of the initial and the final states are proportional as shown by the table 4.11.

The tables 4.10 and 4.11 exhibit a splitting of the eight eigenamplitudes into two sets closed by crossing:

a) $A_1, A_{8ss}, A_{27}, A_{8aa}, \frac{1}{2}(A_{10}+A_{\overline{10}})$

b) $A_{8as}, A_{8sa}, (\frac{1}{2}A_{10}-A_{\overline{10}})$.

In particular, for the second set we have the simple correspondence:

TABLE 4.12

Reaction	Amplitudes		
K+L ⇒ M+N	$15(A_{10}-A_{\overline{10}})$	$(A_{8as}+A_{8sa})$	$(A_{8as}-A_{8sa})$
$\overline{N}$+L ⇒ M+$\overline{K}$	$-(\mathscr{A}_{8as}-\mathscr{A}_{8sa})$	$-(\mathscr{A}_{8as}+\mathscr{A}_{8sa})$	$-15(\mathscr{A}_{10}-\mathscr{A}_{\overline{10}})$
$\overline{M}$+L ⇒ $\overline{K}$+N	$\bar{A}_{8as}+\bar{A}_{8sa}$	$15(\bar{A}_{10}-\bar{A}_{\overline{10}})$	$-(\bar{A}_{8as}-\bar{A}_{8sa})$

3. Another class of interesting reactions can be symbolically written as:

$$8+8 \Rightarrow 8+10.$$

The product of representations, in the final state, is given by:

$$8 \otimes 10 = 8 \oplus 10 \oplus 27 \oplus 35$$

and all the amplitudes being determined by only four reduced matrix elements it is convenient to write it as:

$$A_{8s}, A_{8a}, A_{10}, A_{27}.$$

The crossing matrix, associated with an expansion in the crossed channel is easily computed and the result is given in table 4.13 (GOURDIN [1964c]).

TABLE 4.13

	$\mathscr{A}_{27}$	$\frac{1}{\sqrt{2}}\mathscr{A}_{10}$	$\mathscr{A}_{8s}$	$\frac{1}{\sqrt{5}}\mathscr{A}_{8a}$
A_{27}	$\frac{1}{10}$	$\frac{1}{3}$	$-\frac{2}{5}$	$-\frac{2}{3}$
$\frac{1}{\sqrt{2}}A_{10}$	$\frac{9}{20}$	$-\frac{1}{2}$	$\frac{1}{5}$	-1
A_{8s}	$-\frac{27}{20}$	$\frac{1}{2}$	$\frac{2}{5}$	-1
$\frac{1}{\sqrt{5}}A_{8a}$	$-\frac{9}{20}$	$-\frac{1}{2}$	$-\frac{1}{5}$	0

4.3.2. Meson-baryon scattering

1. The pseudoscalar mesons P and the spin $J = \frac{1}{2}^+$ baryons B are classified in two octuplet representations of $SU(3)/Z_3$. The elastic meson-baryon scattering:

$$P+B \Rightarrow P+B$$

belongs to the first general class of reactions studied in 4.3.1. Seven reduced amplitudes $A_{\sigma\chi_i\chi_f}$ describe the elastic meson-baryon scattering, assuming the validity of time reversal invariance.

The general structure of the matrix element describing the elastic meson-baryon process with the notations of fig. 4.5, is given by

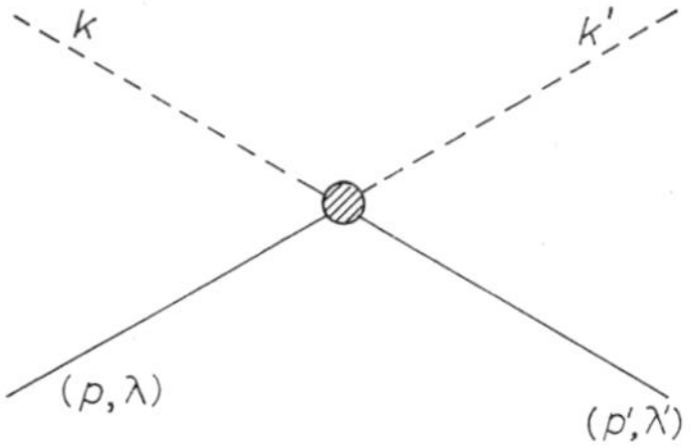

Fig. 4.5.

$$\bar{u}(p', \lambda')[-A(s, t, u)+iB(s, t, u)]\gamma^\rho \frac{k_\rho+k'_\rho}{2} u(p, \lambda)$$

where $u(p, \lambda)$ is the Dirac spinor for a baryon of energy momentum p and helicity λ. The scalar functions A and B, depend only on the Mandelstam variables and it can be easily proved that they must be even under time reversal. From the results of 4.3.1, the reduced amplitude $A_{8as}-A_{8sa}$ vanishes and we obtain only seven linearly independent eigenamplitudes (Ruegg et al. [1962] and Tarjanne [1962]).

2. We now restrict ourselves to observable reactions only where the target is a proton or a neutron (via the deuterium) and the incident particle is a charged meson $\pi^\pm$, $K^\pm$.

Using charge symmetry, it is equivalent to consider the processes with only a proton as target but with as incident particles in addition to $\pi^\pm$ and $K^\pm$ the neutral strange mesons K^0 and $\bar{K}^0$.

It is then possible to write down 6 pure elastic reactions e_k and 21 pseudo elastic reactions p_k. Application of unitary symmetry gives 19 relations and time reversal invariance only one constraint reducing the number of linearly independent amplitudes to 7 as expected.

TABLE 4.14

Meson-baryon	Process	Notation	A_1	A_{8ss}	A_{27}	A_{8aa}	A_{10}	A_{10}	A_{8sa}	A_{8as}
$\pi^- p \to \pi^- p$	$[3, 2] \to [3, 2]$	e_1		$\frac{3}{10}$	$\frac{1}{5}$	$\frac{1}{6}$	$\frac{1}{6}$	$\frac{1}{6}$	$\frac{1}{60}$	$\frac{1}{60}$
$\pi^- p \to K^+ \Sigma^-$	$[3, 2] \to [2, 3]$	p_1		$\frac{3}{10}$	$\frac{1}{5}$	$-\frac{1}{6}$	$-\frac{1}{6}$	$-\frac{1}{6}$	$-\frac{1}{60}$	$\frac{1}{60}$
$\pi^- p \to \pi^0 n$	$[3, 2] \to [r, -1]$	p_2		$-\frac{3}{10\sqrt{2}}$	$\frac{3}{10\sqrt{2}}$	$-\frac{1}{6\sqrt{2}}$	$\frac{1}{3\sqrt{2}}$	$-\frac{1}{6\sqrt{2}}$	$-\frac{1}{60\sqrt{2}}$	$-\frac{1}{60\sqrt{2}}$
$\pi^- p \to K^0 \Sigma^0$	$[3, 2] \to [-1, r]$	p_3		$-\frac{3}{10\sqrt{2}}$	$\frac{3}{10\sqrt{2}}$	$\frac{1}{6\sqrt{2}}$	$-\frac{1}{3\sqrt{2}}$	$\frac{1}{6\sqrt{2}}$	$\frac{1}{60\sqrt{2}}$	$-\frac{1}{60\sqrt{2}}$
$\pi^- p \to \eta^0 n$	$[3, 2] \to [s, -1]$	p_4		$-\frac{3}{10\sqrt{6}}$	$\frac{3}{10\sqrt{6}}$	$\frac{1}{2\sqrt{6}}$		$-\frac{1}{2\sqrt{6}}$	$\frac{1}{20\sqrt{6}}$	$-\frac{1}{60\sqrt{6}}$
$\pi^- p \to K^0 \Lambda^0$	$[3, 2] \to [-1, s]$	p_5		$-\frac{3}{10\sqrt{6}}$	$\frac{3}{10\sqrt{6}}$	$-\frac{1}{2\sqrt{6}}$		$\frac{1}{2\sqrt{6}}$	$-\frac{1}{20\sqrt{6}}$	$-\frac{1}{60\sqrt{6}}$
$\pi^+ p \to \pi^+ p$	$[-3, 2] \to [-3, 2]$	e_2			$\frac{1}{2}$		$\frac{1}{2}$			
$\pi^+ p \to K^+ \Sigma^+$	$[-3, 2] \to [2, -3]$	p_6			$\frac{1}{2}$		$-\frac{1}{2}$			
$K^- p \to K^- p$	$[-2, 2] \to [-2. 2]$	e_3	$\frac{1}{8}$	$\frac{1}{5}$	$\frac{7}{40}$	$\frac{1}{3}$	$\frac{1}{12}$	$\frac{1}{12}$		
$K^- p \to K^+ \Xi$	$[-2, 2] \to [2, -2]$	p_7	$\frac{1}{8}$	$\frac{1}{5}$	$\frac{7}{40}$	$-\frac{1}{3}$	$-\frac{1}{12}$	$-\frac{1}{12}$		
$K^- p \to K^0 \Xi^0$	$[-2, 2] \to [-1, 1]$	p_8	$\frac{1}{8}$	$-\frac{1}{10}$	$-\frac{1}{40}$	$-\frac{1}{6}$	$\frac{1}{12}$	$\frac{1}{12}$	$-\frac{1}{60}$	$\frac{1}{60}$
$K^- p \to \overline{K}^0 n$	$[-2, 2] \to [1, -1]$	p_9	$\frac{1}{8}$	$-\frac{1}{10}$	$-\frac{1}{40}$	$\frac{1}{6}$	$-\frac{1}{12}$	$-\frac{1}{12}$	$\frac{1}{60}$	$\frac{1}{60}$
$K^- p \to \pi^+ \Sigma^-$	$[-2, 2] \to [-3, 3]$	p_{10}	$\frac{1}{8}$	$-\frac{1}{10}$	$-\frac{1}{40}$	$-\frac{1}{6}$	$\frac{1}{12}$	$\frac{1}{12}$	$\frac{1}{60}$	$-\frac{1}{60}$
$K^- p \to \pi^- \Sigma^-$	$[-2, 2] \to [3, -3]$	p_{11}	$\frac{1}{8}$	$-\frac{1}{10}$	$-\frac{1}{40}$	$\frac{1}{6}$	$-\frac{1}{12}$	$-\frac{1}{12}$	$-\frac{1}{60}$	$-\frac{1}{60}$
$K^- p \to \pi^0 \Sigma^0$	$[-2, 2] \to [r, r]$	p_{12}	$\frac{1}{8}$	$-\frac{1}{10}$	$-\frac{1}{40}$					$-\frac{1}{60}$
$K^- p \to \pi^0 \Lambda^0$	$[-2, 2] \to [r, s]$	p_{13}		$\frac{1}{10}\sqrt{3}$	$-\frac{1}{10}$		$-\frac{1}{4\sqrt{3}}$	$\frac{1}{4\sqrt{3}}$		$-\frac{1}{60\sqrt{3}}$
$K^- p \to \eta^0 \Sigma^0$	$[-2, 2] \to [s, r]$	p_{14}		$\frac{1}{10}\sqrt{3}$	$-\frac{1}{10}$		$\frac{1}{4\sqrt{3}}$	$-\frac{1}{4\sqrt{3}}$		$-\frac{1}{60\sqrt{3}}$
$K^- p \to \eta^0 \Lambda^0$	$[-2, 2] \to [s, s]$	p_{15}	$\frac{1}{8}$	$\frac{1}{10}$	$-\frac{9}{40}$					$\frac{1}{60}$
$K^+ p \to K^+ p$	$[2, 2] \to [2, 2]$	e_4			1					
$\overline{K}^0 p \to \overline{K}^0 p$	$[1, 2] \to [1, 2]$	e_5		$\frac{3}{10}$	$\frac{1}{5}$	$\frac{1}{6}$	$\frac{1}{6}$	$\frac{1}{6}$	$-\frac{1}{60}$	$-\frac{1}{60}$
$\overline{K}^0 p \to K^+ \Xi^0$	$[1, 2] \to [2, 1]$	p_{16}		$\frac{3}{10}$	$\frac{1}{5}$	$-\frac{1}{6}$	$-\frac{1}{6}$	$-\frac{1}{6}$	$\frac{1}{60}$	$-\frac{1}{60}$
$\overline{K}^0 p \to \pi^0 \Sigma^+$	$[1, 2] \to [r, -3]$	p_{17}				$-\frac{1}{3\sqrt{2}}$	$\frac{1}{6\sqrt{2}}$	$\frac{1}{6\sqrt{2}}$	$\frac{1}{30\sqrt{2}}$	
$\overline{K}^0 p \to \pi^+ \Sigma^0$	$[1, 2] \to [-3, r]$	p_{18}				$\frac{1}{3\sqrt{2}}$	$-\frac{1}{6\sqrt{2}}$	$-\frac{1}{6\sqrt{2}}$	$-\frac{1}{30\sqrt{2}}$	
$\overline{K}^0 p \to \eta^0 \Sigma^+$	$[1, 2] \to [s, -3]$	p_{19}		$\frac{1}{5}\sqrt{\frac{3}{2}}$	$-\frac{1}{5}\sqrt{\frac{3}{2}}$		$\frac{1}{2\sqrt{6}}$	$-\frac{1}{2\sqrt{6}}$		$-\frac{1}{30\sqrt{6}}$
$\overline{K}^0 p \to \pi^+ \Lambda^0$	$[1, 2] \to [-3, s]$	p_{20}		$\frac{1}{5}\sqrt{\frac{3}{2}}$	$-\frac{1}{5}\sqrt{\frac{3}{2}}$		$-\frac{1}{2\sqrt{6}}$	$\frac{1}{2\sqrt{6}}$		$-\frac{1}{30\sqrt{6}}$
$\overline{K}^0 p \to K^0 p$	$[-1, 2] \to [-1, 2]$	e_6			$\frac{1}{2}$			$\frac{1}{2}$		
$K^0 p \to K^+ n$	$[-1, 2] \to [2, -1]$	p_{21}			$\frac{1}{2}$			$-\frac{1}{2}$		

TABLE 4.15

Meson-baryon	Process	Notation	$\mathscr{A}_1$	$\mathscr{A}_{8ss}$	$\mathscr{A}_{27}$	$\mathscr{A}_{8aa}$	$\mathscr{A}_{10}$	$\mathscr{A}_{\overline{10}}$	$\mathscr{A}_{8sa}$	$\mathscr{A}_{8as}$
$\pi^-p \to \pi^-p$	[3, 2] → [3, 2]	e_1	$\frac{1}{8}$	$-\frac{1}{10}$	$-\frac{1}{40}$	$\frac{1}{6}$	$-\frac{1}{12}$	$-\frac{1}{12}$	$-\frac{1}{60}$	$-\frac{1}{60}$
$\pi^-p \to K^+\Sigma^-$	[3, 2] → [2, 3]	p_1			$\frac{1}{2}$		$-\frac{1}{2}$			
$\pi^-p \to \pi^0 n$	[3, 2] → [r, 1]	p_2				$-\frac{1}{3\sqrt{2}}$	$\frac{1}{6\sqrt{2}}$	$\frac{1}{6\sqrt{2}}$	$\frac{1}{30\sqrt{2}}$	
$\pi^-p \to K^0\Sigma^0$	[3, 2] → [1, r]	p_3		$\frac{3}{10\sqrt{2}}$	$-\frac{3}{10\sqrt{2}}$	$-\frac{1}{6\sqrt{2}}$	$\frac{1}{3\sqrt{2}}$	$-\frac{1}{6\sqrt{2}}$	$-\frac{1}{60\sqrt{2}}$	$\frac{1}{60\sqrt{2}}$
$\pi^-p \to \eta^0 n$	[3, 2] → [s, −1]	p_4		$\frac{3}{5\sqrt{6}}$	$-\frac{3}{5\sqrt{6}}$		$\frac{1}{2\sqrt{6}}$	$-\frac{1}{2\sqrt{6}}$		$-\frac{1}{30\sqrt{6}}$
$\pi^-p \to K^0\Lambda^0$	[3, 2] → [−1, s]	p_5		$\frac{3}{10\sqrt{6}}$	$-\frac{3}{10\sqrt{6}}$	$-\frac{1}{6\sqrt{6}}$	$\frac{1}{3\sqrt{6}}$	$-\frac{1}{6\sqrt{6}}$	$-\frac{1}{60\sqrt{6}}$	$-\frac{1}{60\sqrt{6}}$
$\pi^+p \to \pi^+p$	[−3, 2] → [−3, 2]	e_2	$\frac{1}{8}$	$-\frac{1}{10}$	$-\frac{1}{40}$	$-\frac{1}{6}$	$\frac{1}{12}$	$\frac{1}{12}$	$\frac{1}{60}$	$-\frac{1}{60}$
$\pi^+p \to K^+\Sigma^+$	[−3, 2] → [2, −3]	p_6		$\frac{3}{10}$	$\frac{1}{5}$	$-\frac{1}{6}$	$-\frac{1}{6}$	$-\frac{1}{6}$	$-\frac{1}{60}$	$\frac{1}{60}$
$K^-p \to K^-p$	[−2, 2] → [−2, 2]	e_3	$\frac{1}{8}$	$\frac{1}{5}$	$\frac{7}{40}$	$\frac{1}{3}$	$\frac{1}{12}$	$\frac{1}{12}$		
$K^-p \to K^+\Xi^0$	[−2, 2] → [2, −2]	p_7			1					
$K^-p \to K^0\Xi^0$	[−2, 2] → [−1, 1]	p_8			$\frac{1}{2}$			$\frac{1}{2}$		
$K^-p \to \overline{K}^0 n$	[−2, 2] → [1, −1]	p_9		$\frac{3}{10}$	$\frac{1}{5}$	$\frac{1}{6}$	$\frac{1}{6}$	$\frac{1}{6}$	$-\frac{1}{60}$	$-\frac{1}{60}$
$K^-p \to \pi^+\Sigma^-$	[−2, 2] → [−3, 3]	p_{10}			$\frac{1}{2}$		$\frac{1}{2}$			
$K^-p \to \pi^-\Sigma^+$	[−2, 2] → [3, −3]	p_{11}		$\frac{3}{10}$	$\frac{1}{5}$	$\frac{1}{6}$	$\frac{1}{6}$	$\frac{1}{6}$	$\frac{1}{60}$	$\frac{1}{60}$

Table 4.15 (Continued)

Meson-baryon	Process	Notation	$\mathscr{A}_1$	$\mathscr{A}_{8ss}$	$\mathscr{A}_{27}$	$\mathscr{A}_{8aa}$	$\mathscr{A}_{10}$	$\mathscr{A}_{10}$	$\mathscr{A}_{8sa}$	$\mathscr{A}_{8as}$
$K^-p \to \pi^0\Sigma^0$	[−2, 2][r, r]	p_{12}		$\frac{3}{20}$	$\frac{7}{20}$	$\frac{1}{12}$	$\frac{1}{3}$	$\frac{1}{12}$	$\frac{1}{120}$	$\frac{1}{120}$
$K^-p \to \pi^0\Lambda^0$	[−2, 2][r, s]	p_{13}		$-\frac{1}{20}\sqrt{3}$	$\frac{1}{20}\sqrt{3}$	$\frac{1}{4\sqrt{3}}$		$-\frac{1}{4\sqrt{3}}$	$-\frac{1}{120\sqrt{3}}$	$\frac{1}{40\sqrt{3}}$
$K^-p \to \eta^0\Sigma^0$	[−2, 2][s, r]	p_{14}		$-\frac{1}{20}\sqrt{3}$	$\frac{1}{20}\sqrt{3}$	$\frac{1}{4\sqrt{3}}$		$\frac{1}{4\sqrt{3}}$	$\frac{1}{40\sqrt{3}}$	$-\frac{1}{120\sqrt{3}}$
$K^-p \to \eta^0\Lambda^0$	[−2, 2][s, s]	p_{15}		$\frac{1}{20}$	$\frac{9}{20}$	$\frac{1}{4}$		$\frac{1}{4}$	$-\frac{1}{120}$	$-\frac{1}{120}$
$K^+p \to K^+p$	[2, 2][2, 2]	e_4	$\frac{1}{8}$	$\frac{1}{5}$	$\frac{7}{40}$	$-\frac{1}{3}$	$-\frac{1}{12}$	$-\frac{1}{12}$		
$\overline{K}^0p \to \overline{K}^0p$	[1, 2][1, 2]	e_5	$\frac{1}{8}$	$-\frac{1}{10}$	$-\frac{1}{40}$	$\frac{1}{6}$	$-\frac{1}{12}$	$-\frac{1}{12}$	$\frac{1}{60}$	$\frac{1}{60}$
$\overline{K}^0p \to K^+\Xi^0$	[1, 2][2, 1]	p_{16}			$\frac{1}{2}$			$-\frac{1}{2}$		
$\overline{K}^0p \to \pi^0\Sigma^+$	[1, 2][r, −3]	p_{17}		$-\frac{3}{10\sqrt{2}}$	$\frac{3}{10\sqrt{2}}$	$-\frac{1}{6\sqrt{2}}$	$\frac{1}{3\sqrt{2}}$	$-\frac{1}{6\sqrt{2}}$	$-\frac{1}{60\sqrt{2}}$	$-\frac{1}{60\sqrt{2}}$
$\overline{K}^0p \to \pi^+\Sigma^0$	[1, 2][−3, r]	p_{18}		$\frac{3}{10\sqrt{2}}$	$-\frac{3}{10\sqrt{2}}$	$\frac{1}{6\sqrt{2}}$	$-\frac{1}{3\sqrt{2}}$	$\frac{1}{6\sqrt{2}}$	$\frac{1}{60\sqrt{2}}$	$\frac{1}{60\sqrt{2}}$
$\overline{K}^0p \to \eta^0\Sigma^+$	[1, 2][s, −3]	p_{19}		$-\frac{1}{10}\sqrt{\frac{3}{2}}$	$\frac{1}{10}\sqrt{\frac{3}{2}}$	$\frac{1}{2\sqrt{6}}$		$-\frac{1}{2\sqrt{6}}$	$\frac{1}{20\sqrt{6}}$	$-\frac{1}{60\sqrt{6}}$
$\overline{K}^0p \to \pi^+\Lambda^0$	[1, 2][−3, s]	p_{20}		$-\frac{1}{10}\sqrt{\frac{3}{2}}$	$\frac{1}{10}\sqrt{\frac{3}{2}}$	$\frac{1}{2\sqrt{6}}$		$-\frac{1}{2\sqrt{6}}$	$-\frac{1}{60\sqrt{6}}$	$\frac{1}{20\sqrt{6}}$
$K^0p \to K^0p$	[−1, 2][−1, 2]	e_6	$\frac{1}{8}$	$-\frac{1}{10}$	$-\frac{1}{40}$	$-\frac{1}{6}$	$\frac{1}{12}$	$\frac{1}{12}$	$-\frac{1}{60}$	$\frac{1}{60}$
$K^0p \to K^+n$	[−1, 2][2, −1]	p_{21}		$\frac{3}{10}$	$\frac{1}{5}$	$-\frac{1}{6}$	$-\frac{1}{6}$	$-\frac{1}{6}$	$\frac{1}{60}$	$-\frac{1}{60}$

3. For the weights of the four octuplets involved in the reaction we will use a convenient simplified notation given in fig. 4.6.

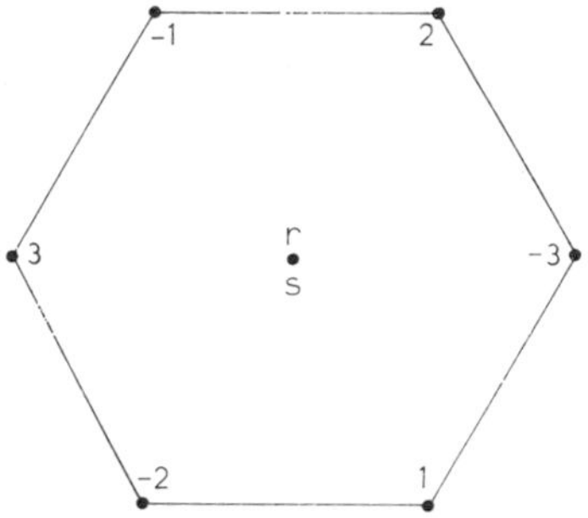

Fig. 4.6.

The numbers $P_{\alpha\beta;\,\gamma\delta}(\sigma, \chi_i, \chi_f)$ are tabulated in tables 4.14 and 4.15 for an expansion of the reaction amplitudes in eigenstates of the direct channel and of the crossed channel of baryonic number zero. In the crossed channel the consequence of time reversal invariance is simply $\mathscr{A}_{10} = \mathscr{A}_{\overline{10}}$.

4. The invariance with respect to I spin rotations (charge independence) gives 10 relations between the 27 amplitudes. Because of the spinor character of the proton in both I spin and U spin, it is trivial to exhibit 10 relations due to U spin rotations invariance.

TABLE 4.16

I spin invariance		U spin invariance
$e_3 - e_5 - p_9 = 0$	1	$e_3 - e_1 - p_{11} = 0$
$e_4 - e_6 - p_{21} = 0$	2	$e_4 - e_2 - p_6 = 0$
$p_7 - p_8 - p_{16} = 0$	3	$p_7 - p_{10} - p_1 = 0$
$e_1 - e_2 + \sqrt{2}p_2 = 0$	4	$e_5 - e_6 + \frac{1}{\sqrt{2}}p_{17} - \sqrt{\frac{3}{2}}p_{19} = 0$
$p_1 - p_6 + \sqrt{2}p_3 = 0$	5	$p_{16} - p_{21} + \frac{1}{\sqrt{2}}p_{18} - \sqrt{\frac{3}{2}}p_{20} = 0$
$p_{10} - p_{11} - \sqrt{2}p_{17} = 0$	6	$p_8 - p_9 - \frac{1}{\sqrt{2}}p_2 + \sqrt{\frac{3}{2}}p_4 = 0$
$p_{10} - p_{11} + \sqrt{2}p_{18} = 0$	7	$p_8 - p_9 + \frac{1}{\sqrt{2}}p_3 - \sqrt{\frac{3}{2}}p_5 = 0$
$p_{10} + p_{11} - 2p_{12} = 0$	8	$p_8 + p_9 + \frac{1}{2}\sqrt{3}(p_{13} + p_{14}) - \frac{1}{2}(p_{12} + 3p_{15}) = 0$
$p_{19} - \sqrt{2}p_{14} = 0$	9	$\sqrt{3}p_{13} + \sqrt{2}p_2 + p_9 - p_{12} = 0$
$p_{20} - \sqrt{2}p_{13} = 0$	10	$\sqrt{3}p_{14} + \sqrt{2}p_3 + p_8 - p_{12} = 0$

Only 19 of these relations are linearly independent. In other terms the consideration of unitary symmetry – and U spin rotation is sufficient – furnishes 9 new relations between the physical amplitudes.

Time reversal invariance gives one equality (RUEGG et al. [1962]):

$$p_8 = p_{10}$$

which can be combined with the previous relations 3_{I} and 3_{U} to obtain a second equality

$$p_{16} = p_1 .$$

Obviously, all these relations between amplitudes can be directly checked on the explicit expressions given in tables 4.14 and 4.15; but the knowledge of elementary Clebsch-Gordan coefficients of SU(2) is sufficient to compute the results given in table 4.16.

5. For a practical comparison with experiment of these predictions of U spin symmetry it is difficult to use relations where more than three amplitudes are involved.

In the present case we have two equalities:

$$A(\mathrm{K^-p} \Rightarrow \mathrm{K^0}\Xi^0) = A(\mathrm{K^-p} \Rightarrow \pi^+\Sigma^-)$$
$$A(\pi^-\mathrm{p} \Rightarrow \mathrm{K}^+\Sigma^-) = A(\mathrm{K^-n} \Rightarrow \mathrm{K^0}\Xi^-)$$

and two triangular relations:

$$A(\mathrm{K^-p} \Rightarrow \mathrm{K^-p}) = A(\pi^-\mathrm{p} \Rightarrow \pi^-\mathrm{p}) + A(\mathrm{K^-p} \Rightarrow \pi^-\Sigma^+)$$
$$A(\mathrm{K^+p} \Rightarrow \mathrm{K^+p}) = A(\pi^+\mathrm{p} \Rightarrow \pi^+\mathrm{p}) + A(\pi^+\mathrm{p} \Rightarrow \mathrm{K}^+\Sigma^+).$$

The first triangular relations have been recently studied in some detail by ABARBANEL and CALLAN [1965]; if agreement with experiment can be obtained for the total cross-sections (HARRARI and LIPKIN [1963]), it seems that for the differential cross-sections the triangle relations are violated.

6. Tables 4.14, 4.15 and 4.16 are useful to compute the production of vector mesons V in pseudoscalar meson-baryon scattering:

$$\mathrm{M+B \Rightarrow V+B}.$$

In this case where time reversal invariance cannot be used, there exist 8 reduced amplitudes to describe the set of reactions. The predictions of the U spin symmetry which can be compared with experiment are three triangular relations:

$$A(\mathrm{K^-p} \Rightarrow \mathrm{K^{*-}p}) = A(\pi^-\mathrm{p} \Rightarrow \rho^-\mathrm{p}) + A(\mathrm{K^-p} \Rightarrow \rho^-\Sigma^+)$$
$$A(\mathrm{K^+p} \Rightarrow \mathrm{K^{*+}p}) = A(\pi^+\mathrm{p} \Rightarrow \rho^+\mathrm{p}) + A(\pi^+\mathrm{p} \Rightarrow \mathrm{K^{*+}}\Sigma^+)$$
$$A(\mathrm{K^-p} \Rightarrow \mathrm{K^{*+}}\Xi^0) = A(\pi^-\mathrm{p} \Rightarrow \mathrm{K^{*+}}\Sigma^-) + A(\mathrm{K^-p} \Rightarrow \rho^+\Sigma^-).$$

Unfortunately the experimental data are too poor for such a comparison.

4.3.3. Baryon-baryon and antibaryon-baryon scattering

1. Let us first discuss the more general problem of elastic scattering of two spin $\frac{1}{2}$ particles.

As usual we denote as J, L, S respectively the total angular momentum, the orbital angular momentum and the total spin, adding an index f for the final state and i for the initial state.

For a given value of J, there exist, in general, four independent states:

$$J \begin{cases} S = 0 & L = J \\ S = 1 & \begin{cases} L = J+1 \\ L = J \\ L = J-1. \end{cases} \end{cases}$$

The conservation of the total angular momentum

$$J_{\mathrm{i}} = J_{\mathrm{f}} = J$$

allows us to define 16 amplitudes and the invariance with respect to space reflexion

$$(-1)^{L_{\mathrm{i}}} = (-1)^{L_{\mathrm{f}}} = \omega_P$$

reduces the number of non vanishing amplitudes to eight which we classify in the following way

Table 4.17

ΔS	ΔL	S_{i}	S_{f}	L_{i}	L_{f}
0	0	0	0	J	J
		1	1	J	J
				$J+1$	$J+1$
				$J-1$	$J-1$
	2	1	1	$J-1$	$J+1$
				$J+1$	$J-1$
1	0	0	1	J	J
		1	0	J	J

For the spin violating ($\Delta S = 1$) and for the L violating ($\Delta L = 2$) transitions it is convenient to define the symmetric and antisymmetric combinations:

$$A(\text{st}+\text{ts}) = A(S_i = 0 \Rightarrow S_f = 1)+A(S_i = 1 \Rightarrow S_f = 0)$$
$$A(\text{st}-\text{ts}) = A(S_i = 0 \Rightarrow S_f = 1)-A(S_i = 1 \Rightarrow S_f = 0)$$
$$A(\Delta L = 2 \text{ even}) = A(L_i = J+1 \Rightarrow L_f = J-1)+A(L_i = J-1 \Rightarrow L_f = J+1)$$
$$A(\Delta L = 2 \text{ odd}) = A(L_i = J+1 \Rightarrow L_f = J-1)-A(L_i = J-1 \Rightarrow L_f = J+1).$$

2. In the case of four identical particles, as for instance four protons, the Pauli principle forbids the spin violating amplitudes. The same result can be extended to four nucleons, using the isotopic spin invariance.

A generalized Pauli principle can be written also in the framework of SU(3) symmetry. We define $\omega_S = (-1)^S$ and we use the quantity $\varepsilon(\sigma, \chi)$ introduced in 4.3.1

$$\varepsilon(\sigma, \chi) = +1 \quad \text{for} \quad (\sigma, \chi) = 1, 8_s, 27$$
$$\varepsilon(\sigma, \chi) = -1 \quad \text{for} \quad (\sigma, \chi) = 8_a, 10, \overline{10}$$

and we obtain a Pauli principle in the form:

$$\omega_P \omega_S \varepsilon(\sigma, \chi) = 1.$$

The singulet-singulet (L even) and the triplet-triplet (L_i, L_f odd) transitions are described by the three reduced amplitudes A_1, A_{8ss}, A_{27}.

The singulet-singulet (L odd) and the triplet-triplet (L_i, L_f even) transitions are described by the three reduced amplitudes A_{8aa}, A_{10}, $A_{\overline{10}}$.

The singulet-triplet transitions are described by the two reduced amplitudes A_{8sa} and A_{8as}.

3. We now try to apply the time reversal invariance. In the particular case of four protons we obtain, as a new restriction, the vanishing of the odd $\Delta L = 2$ transitions.

The same result can easily be extended to the complete baryon octuplet. In fact the eigenamplitude $A_{8as}-A_{8sa}$, which is the only one odd when initial and final states are exchanged, describes only singulet-triplet transitions because of the Pauli principle and cannot be used for $\Delta L=2$, odd, transitions.

These results are summarized in table 4.18.

TABLE 4.18

$\Delta S = 0$	4 amplitudes	$\Delta L = 0$	A_1, A_{8ss}, A_{27} if $\omega_P\omega_S = 1$
	1 amplitude	$\Delta L = 2$ even	A_{8aa} A_{10} A_{10} if $\omega_P\omega_S = -1$
$\Delta S = 0$	1 amplitude	$\Delta L = 2$ odd	Forbidden by T
$\Delta S = 1$	1 amplitude	$A(\text{st}+\text{ts}) \Rightarrow A_{8as}+A_{8sa}$	
	1 amplitude	$A(\text{st}-\text{ts}) \Rightarrow A_{8as}-A_{8sa}$	

Taking into account spin and unitary spin, we have 32 scalar amplitudes to describe baryon-baryon scattering (RUEGG [1965]).

4. Tables 4.14 and 4.15 of the previous section allow us to compute all the possible baryon-baryon scattering amplitudes only by changing the attributions of the weights.

We now restrict ourselves to a more particular case where one particle in the initial state is a proton, the second baryon being a nucleon, a Λ or a charged Σ (DE SOUZA et al. [1964]). We give, in table 4.19, the expansion of the 9 amplitudes in terms of seven reduced amplitudes of the direct channel, the A_1 amplitude being not involved in these reactions.

TABLE 4.19

Reaction	A_{8ss}	A_{27}	A_{8aa}	A_{10}	A_{10}	A_{8sa}	A_{8as}
$pp \to pp$		1					
$np \to np$		$\frac{1}{2}$			$\frac{1}{2}$		
$\Sigma^+p \to \Sigma^+p$		$\frac{1}{2}$		$\frac{1}{2}$			
$\Sigma^-p \to \Sigma^-p$	$\frac{3}{10}$	$\frac{1}{5}$	$\frac{1}{6}$	$\frac{1}{6}$	$\frac{1}{6}$	$\frac{1}{60}$	$\frac{1}{60}$
$\Sigma^-p \to \Sigma^0n$	$-\frac{3}{10\sqrt{2}}$	$\frac{3}{10\sqrt{2}}$	$-\frac{1}{6\sqrt{2}}$	$\frac{1}{3\sqrt{2}}$	$-\frac{1}{6\sqrt{2}}$	$-\frac{1}{60\sqrt{2}}$	$-\frac{1}{60\sqrt{2}}$
$\Sigma^-p \to \Lambda n$	$-\frac{3}{10\sqrt{6}}$	$\frac{3}{10\sqrt{6}}$	$\frac{1}{2\sqrt{6}}$		$-\frac{1}{2\sqrt{6}}$	$\frac{1}{20\sqrt{6}}$	$-\frac{1}{60\sqrt{6}}$
$\Lambda p \to \Lambda p$	$\frac{1}{20}$	$\frac{9}{20}$	$\frac{1}{4}$		$\frac{1}{4}$	$-\frac{1}{120}$	$-\frac{1}{120}$
$\Lambda p \to \Sigma p$	$-\frac{3}{20}$	$\frac{3}{20}$	$\frac{1}{4\sqrt{3}}$		$-\frac{1}{4\sqrt{3}}$	$-\frac{1}{120\sqrt{3}}$	$-\frac{1}{40\sqrt{3}}$
$\Lambda p \to \Sigma^+n$	$-\frac{3}{10\sqrt{2}}$	$\frac{3}{10\sqrt{2}}$	$\frac{1}{2\sqrt{6}}$		$-\frac{1}{2\sqrt{6}}$	$-\frac{1}{60\sqrt{6}}$	$\frac{1}{20\sqrt{6}}$

These 9 amplitudes are related by 2 relations due to isotopic spin invariance

$$A(\Lambda p \Rightarrow \Sigma^+n) = \sqrt{2}A(\Lambda p \Rightarrow \Sigma^0 n)$$

$$A(\Sigma^+p \Rightarrow \Sigma^+p) - A(\Sigma^-p \Rightarrow \Sigma^-p) = \sqrt{2}A(\Sigma^-p \Rightarrow \Sigma^0 n)$$

and we do not have predictions from the unitary symmetry.

The baryon-baryon potential problem can be treated in a similar way and in an exact SU(3) symmetry the relations between these potentials are completely determined by the Clebsch-Gordan coefficients.

We must be extremely careful in this case and because of the large breaking of the symmetry for the pseudoscalar mesons, we expect very important differences in the ranges of the parts of the various potentials.

Let us compare for instance the nucleon-nucleon and the Λ-nucleon forces. To the one-pion exchange between two nucleons there corresponds a one K meson exchange between a Λ and a nucleon, of ranges respectively $\hbar/m_\pi c$ and $\hbar/m_K c$; it follows that the smallest range is obtained in the Λ-nucleon forces by a two π meson exchange. It becomes meaningless to compare these two potentials in the framework of an exact unitary symmetry.

5. The crossed channels of baryon-baryon scattering describe both anti-baryon-baryon scattering:

$$
\begin{aligned}
B_1+B_2 &\Rightarrow B_3+B_4 \quad &(\mathrm{I})\\
\bar{B}_1+B_2 &\Rightarrow B_3+\bar{B}_1 \quad &(\mathrm{II})\\
\bar{B}_3+B_2 &\Rightarrow \bar{B}_1+B_4. \quad &(\mathrm{III})
\end{aligned}
$$

It is interesting to study the crossing matrices between these three channels and we will separate the space time part and the unitary spin part.

The eight parity conserving amplitudes can be split into two sets closed by crossing. We have first the five classical amplitudes $\Delta S = 0$, $\Delta L = 0$ and $\Delta L = 2$ even, which are present in proton-proton scattering or in anti-proton-proton scattering.

The second set includes three amplitudes and the two crossing matrices of spin are shown in table 4.20:

TABLE 4.20

Reaction	Amplitudes		
$B_1+B_2 \Rightarrow B_3+B_4$	$A(\mathrm{st}+\mathrm{ts})$	$A(\mathrm{st}-\mathrm{ts})$	$A(\Delta L = 2 \text{ odd})$
$\bar{B}_4+B_2 \Rightarrow B_3+\bar{B}_1$	$A(\Delta L = 2 \text{ odd})$	$A(\mathrm{st}-\mathrm{ts})$	$A(\mathrm{st}+\mathrm{ts})$
$\bar{B}_3+B_2 \Rightarrow \bar{B}_1+B_4$	$A(\mathrm{st}+\mathrm{ts})$	$A(\Delta L = 2 \text{ odd})$	$A(\mathrm{st}-\mathrm{ts})$

The table 4.20 is written neglecting constant coefficients.

We are now able, using tables 4.12 and 4.20, to translate table 4.18 in terms of antibaryon-baryon scattering amplitudes, using for instance the eigenamplitudes of channel III (RUEGG [1965]).

TABLE 4.21

$\Delta S = 0$	$\begin{bmatrix} 4 \text{ amplitudes } \Delta L = 0 \\ 1 \text{ amplitude } \Delta L = 2 \text{ even} \end{bmatrix} \Rightarrow$	$A_1, A_{8ss}, A_{27}, A_{8aa}$ $A_{10}+A_{\overline{10}}, A_{8as}+A_{8sa}$
$\Delta S = 0$	1 amplitude $\Delta L = 2$ odd $\Rightarrow$	$A_{8as}-A_{8sa}$
$\Delta S = 1$	1 amplitude $A(\mathrm{st}+\mathrm{ts}) \Rightarrow$ 1 amplitude $A(\mathrm{st}-\mathrm{ts}) \Rightarrow$	$A_{10}-A_{\overline{10}}$ Forbidden by T

In this case also, of course, we have 32 scalar amplitudes. As a last remark, the results of table 4.21 can also be directly obtained using *PC* invariance in the antibaryon-baryon channel.

6. From a physical point of view, we are now interested in antiproton-proton scattering. One pure elastic reaction, e_4, and 9 pseudo elastic reactions $p_7, p_8, \ldots, p_{15}$ can be studied. The expansion of these ten amplitudes in eigenamplitudes of the direct and of the crossed channel is given in tables 4.22 and 4.23.

TABLE 4.22

Reaction	A_1	A_{8ss}	A_{27}	A_{8aa}	A_{10}	$A_{\overline{10}}$	A_{8sa}	A_{8as}
$\bar{p}p \to \bar{p}p$	$\frac{1}{8}$	$\frac{1}{5}$	$\frac{7}{40}$	$\frac{1}{3}$	$\frac{1}{12}$	$\frac{1}{12}$		
$\bar{p}p \to \bar{\Xi}^-\Xi^-$	$\frac{1}{8}$	$\frac{1}{5}$	$\frac{7}{40}$	$-\frac{1}{3}$	$-\frac{1}{12}$	$-\frac{1}{12}$		
$\bar{p}p \to \bar{\Xi}^0\Xi^0$	$\frac{1}{8}$	$-\frac{1}{10}$	$-\frac{1}{40}$	$-\frac{1}{6}$	$\frac{1}{12}$	$\frac{1}{12}$	$-\frac{1}{60}$	$+\frac{1}{60}$
$\bar{p}p \to \bar{n}n$	$\frac{1}{8}$	$-\frac{1}{10}$	$-\frac{1}{40}$	$\frac{1}{6}$	$-\frac{1}{12}$	$-\frac{1}{12}$	$+\frac{1}{60}$	$+\frac{1}{60}$
$\bar{p}p \to \bar{\Sigma}^-\Sigma^-$	$\frac{1}{8}$	$-\frac{1}{10}$	$-\frac{1}{40}$	$-\frac{1}{6}$	$\frac{1}{12}$	$\frac{1}{12}$	$+\frac{1}{60}$	$-\frac{1}{60}$
$\bar{p}p \to \bar{\Sigma}^+\Sigma^+$	$\frac{1}{8}$	$-\frac{1}{10}$	$-\frac{1}{40}$	$\frac{1}{6}$	$-\frac{1}{12}$	$-\frac{1}{12}$	$-\frac{1}{60}$	$-\frac{1}{60}$
$\bar{p}p \to \bar{\Sigma}^0\Sigma^0$	$\frac{1}{8}$	$-\frac{1}{10}$	$-\frac{1}{40}$					$-\frac{1}{60}$
$\bar{p}p \to \bar{\Sigma}^0\Lambda^0$		$\frac{1}{10}\sqrt{3}$	$-\frac{1}{10}\sqrt{3}$		$-\frac{1}{4\sqrt{3}}$	$\frac{1}{4\sqrt{3}}$		$-\frac{1}{60\sqrt{3}}$
$\bar{p}p \to \bar{\Lambda}^0\Sigma^0$		$\frac{1}{10}\sqrt{3}$	$-\frac{1}{10}\sqrt{3}$		$\frac{1}{4\sqrt{3}}$	$-\frac{1}{4\sqrt{3}}$		$-\frac{1}{60\sqrt{3}}$
$\bar{p}p \to \bar{\Lambda}^0\Lambda^0$	$\frac{1}{8}$	$\frac{1}{10}$	$-\frac{9}{40}$					$\frac{1}{60}$

TABLE 4.23

Reaction	$\mathscr{A}_1$	$\mathscr{A}_{8ss}$	$\mathscr{A}_{27}$	$\mathscr{A}_{8aa}$	$\mathscr{A}_{10}$	$\mathscr{A}_{\overline{10}}$	$\mathscr{A}_{8sa}$	$\mathscr{A}_{8as}$
$\bar{p}p \to \bar{p}p$	$\frac{1}{8}$	$\frac{1}{5}$	$\frac{7}{40}$	$\frac{1}{3}$	$\frac{1}{12}$	$\frac{1}{12}$		
$\bar{p}p \to \bar{\Xi}^-\Xi^-$			1					
$\bar{p}p \to \bar{\Sigma}^0\Sigma^0$			$\frac{1}{2}$			$\frac{1}{2}$		
$\bar{p}p \to \bar{n}n$		$\frac{3}{10}$	$\frac{1}{5}$	$\frac{1}{6}$	$\frac{1}{6}$	$\frac{1}{6}$	$-\frac{1}{60}$	$-\frac{1}{60}$
$\bar{p}p \to \bar{\Sigma}^-\Sigma^-$			$\frac{1}{2}$		$\frac{1}{2}$			
$\bar{p}p \to \bar{\Sigma}^+\Sigma^+$		$\frac{3}{10}$	$\frac{1}{5}$	$\frac{1}{6}$	$\frac{1}{6}$	$\frac{1}{6}$	$\frac{1}{60}$	$\frac{1}{60}$
$\bar{p}p \to \bar{\Sigma}^0\Sigma^0$		$\frac{3}{20}$	$\frac{7}{20}$	$\frac{1}{12}$	$\frac{1}{3}$	$\frac{1}{12}$	$\frac{1}{120}$	$\frac{1}{120}$
$\bar{p}p \to \bar{\Sigma}^0\Lambda^0$		$-\frac{1}{20}\sqrt{3}$	$\frac{1}{20}\sqrt{3}$	$\frac{1}{4\sqrt{3}}$		$-\frac{1}{4\sqrt{3}}$	$-\frac{1}{120\sqrt{3}}$	$\frac{1}{40\sqrt{3}}$
$\bar{p}p \to \bar{\Lambda}^0\Sigma^0$		$-\frac{1}{20}\sqrt{3}$	$\frac{1}{20}\sqrt{3}$	$\frac{1}{4\sqrt{3}}$		$-\frac{1}{4\sqrt{3}}$	$\frac{1}{40\sqrt{3}}$	$-\frac{1}{120\sqrt{3}}$
$\bar{p}p \to \bar{\Lambda}^0\Lambda^0$		$\frac{1}{20}$	$\frac{9}{20}$	$\frac{1}{4}$		$\frac{1}{4}$	$-\frac{1}{120}$	$-\frac{1}{120}$

We can write one relation due to isotopic spin invariance:

$$A(\bar{p}p \Rightarrow \bar{\Sigma}^-\Sigma^-)+A(\bar{p}p \Rightarrow \bar{\Sigma}^+\Sigma^+) = 2A(\bar{p}p \Rightarrow \bar{\Sigma}^0\Sigma^0)$$

and one complicated relation due to U spin invariance and extremely difficult to test experimentally:

$$A(\bar{p}p \Rightarrow \bar{\Lambda}\Lambda)-\tfrac{2}{3}A(\bar{p}p \Rightarrow \bar{n}n)+\tfrac{1}{3}A(\bar{p}p \Rightarrow \bar{\Sigma}^0\Sigma^0)-\tfrac{2}{3}A(\bar{p}p \Rightarrow \bar{\Xi}^0\Xi^0) =$$
$$= \tfrac{1}{3}[A(\bar{p}p \Rightarrow \bar{\Lambda}^0\Sigma^0)+A(\bar{p}p \Rightarrow \bar{\Sigma}^0\Lambda^0)].$$

4.3.4. Excited baryon production

1. We are now concerned with the second class of reactions defined in section 4.3.1 and where, in the final state, the decuplet B* associated to the excited baryons of spin $J = \frac{3}{2}^+$ is produced.

As a useful example we first consider the decuplet production in meson-baryon inelastic scattering:

$$M+B \Rightarrow M+B^*.$$

This set of reactions is described by four reduced amplitudes $A_{\sigma\chi_i}$. Using the Clebsch-Gordan coefficients as computed by Tarjanne [1963b] we have listed, in table 4.24, the values of the projection operators $P_{\alpha\beta\gamma\delta}(\sigma, \chi_i)$ for the 28 reactions generated by the same six initial states as considered in the elastic case (Gourdin [1964c]).

Table 4.24

Initial state	Final state	Notation	A_{27}	A_{8s}	A_{10}	A_{8a}
π^-p	$\pi^-N^{*+}_{\frac{3}{2}}$	α_1	$-\frac{1}{5}$	$-\frac{1}{5}$	$-\frac{1}{3\sqrt{2}}$	$-\frac{1}{3\sqrt{5}}$
	$\pi^+N^{*-}_{\frac{3}{2}}$	α_2	$\frac{1}{20}\sqrt{3}$	$-\frac{1}{5}\sqrt{3}$	$\frac{1}{2\sqrt{6}}$	$-\frac{1}{\sqrt{15}}$
	$\pi^0N^{*0}_{\frac{3}{2}}$	α_3	$\frac{3}{20\sqrt{2}}$	$\frac{1}{5}\sqrt{2}$	$\frac{1}{12}$	$\frac{1}{3}\sqrt{\frac{2}{5}}$
	$\eta^0N^{*0}_{\frac{3}{2}}$	α_4	$\frac{1}{4}\sqrt{\frac{3}{2}}$		$-\frac{1}{4\sqrt{3}}$	
	$K^+Y^{*-}_1$	α_5	$\frac{1}{20}$	$-\frac{1}{5}$	$\frac{1}{6\sqrt{2}}$	$-\frac{1}{3\sqrt{5}}$
	$K^0Y^{*0}_1$	α_6	$-\frac{3}{10\sqrt{2}}$	$\frac{1}{5\sqrt{2}}$	$\frac{1}{6}$	$\frac{1}{3\sqrt{10}}$

TABLE 4.24 (Continued)

Initial state	Final state	Notation	A_{27}	A_{8s}	A_{10}	A_{8a}
π^+p	$\pi^+N^{*+}_{\frac{3}{2}}$	α_7	$\frac{1}{4}$		$\frac{1}{2\sqrt{2}}$	
	$\pi^0N^{*++}_{\frac{3}{2}}$	α_8	$-\frac{1}{4}\sqrt{\frac{3}{2}}$		$\frac{1}{4}\sqrt{3}$	
	$\eta^0N^{*++}_{\frac{3}{2}}$	α_9	$\frac{3}{4\sqrt{2}}$		$-\frac{1}{4}$	
	$K^+Y^{*+}_1$	α_{10}	$-\frac{1}{4}$		$\frac{1}{2\sqrt{2}}$	
K^+p	$K^+N^{*+}_{\frac{3}{2}}$	α_{11}	$\frac{1}{2}$			
	$K^0N^{*++}_{\frac{3}{2}}$	α_{12}	$-\frac{1}{2}\sqrt{3}$			
K^0p	$K^0N^{*+}_{\frac{3}{2}}$	α_{13}	$-\frac{1}{2}$			
	$K^+N^{*0}_{\frac{3}{2}}$	α_{14}	$\frac{1}{2}$			
K^-p	$K^-N^{*+}_{\frac{3}{2}}$	α_{15}	$\frac{1}{20}$	$-\frac{1}{5}$	$-\frac{1}{6\sqrt{2}}$	$\frac{1}{3\sqrt{5}}$
	$\overline{K}^0N^{*0}_{\frac{3}{2}}$	α_{16}	$-\frac{1}{20}$	$\frac{1}{5}$	$\frac{1}{6\sqrt{2}}$	$-\frac{1}{3\sqrt{5}}$
	$K^+\Xi^{*-}_{\frac{1}{2}}$	α_{17}	$\frac{1}{20}$	$-\frac{1}{5}$	$\frac{1}{6\sqrt{2}}$	$-\frac{1}{3\sqrt{5}}$
	$K^0\Xi^{*0}_{\frac{1}{2}}$	α_{18}	$-\frac{1}{4}$		$\frac{1}{6\sqrt{2}}$	$\frac{2}{3\sqrt{5}}$
	$\pi^+Y^{*-}_1$	α_{18}	$\frac{1}{20}$	$-\frac{1}{5}$	$\frac{1}{6\sqrt{2}}$	$-\frac{1}{3\sqrt{5}}$
	$\pi^-Y^{*+}_1$	α_{20}	$-\frac{1}{4}$		$-\frac{1}{6\sqrt{2}}$	$-\frac{2}{3\sqrt{5}}$
	$\pi^0Y^{*0}_1$	α_{21}	$\frac{1}{10}$	$\frac{1}{10}$		$\frac{1}{2\sqrt{5}}$
	$\eta^0Y^{*0}_1$	α_{22}	$\frac{1}{10}\sqrt{3}$	$\frac{1}{10}\sqrt{3}$		$\frac{1}{2\sqrt{15}}$
$\overline{K}^0p$	$\overline{K}^0N^{*+}_{\frac{3}{2}}$	α_{23}	$-\frac{1}{20}$	$\frac{1}{5}$	$\frac{1}{6\sqrt{2}}$	$-\frac{1}{3\sqrt{5}}$
	$K^-N^{*++}_{\frac{3}{2}}$	α_{24}	$\frac{1}{20}\sqrt{3}$	$-\frac{1}{5}\sqrt{3}$	$-\frac{1}{2\sqrt{6}}$	$\frac{1}{\sqrt{15}}$
	$K^+\Xi^{*0}_{\frac{1}{2}}$	α_{25}	$-\frac{1}{5}$	$-\frac{1}{5}$	$\frac{1}{3\sqrt{2}}$	$\frac{1}{3\sqrt{5}}$
	$\pi^+Y^{*0}_1$	α_{26}	$\frac{3}{10\sqrt{2}}$	$-\frac{1}{5\sqrt{2}}$	$\frac{1}{6}$	$\frac{1}{3\sqrt{10}}$
	$\pi^0Y^{*+}_1$	α_{27}	$-\frac{3}{10\sqrt{2}}$	$\frac{1}{5\sqrt{2}}$	$-\frac{1}{6}$	$-\frac{1}{3\sqrt{10}}$
	$\eta^0Y^{*+}_1$	α_{28}	$\frac{1}{5}\sqrt{\frac{3}{2}}$	$\frac{1}{5}\sqrt{\frac{3}{2}}$		$-\frac{1}{\sqrt{30}}$

2. Due to charge independence only, these 28 amplitudes are submitted to 16 relations:

TABLE 4.25

$$\alpha_{11} = -\frac{\alpha_{12}}{\sqrt{3}} = -\alpha_{13} = \alpha_{14}$$

$$\alpha_{15} = -\alpha_{16} = -\alpha_{23} = \frac{\alpha_{24}}{\sqrt{3}}$$

$$\alpha_1\sqrt{3}+\alpha_2+\alpha_3\sqrt{6} = 0 \qquad 2\alpha_2+\alpha_3\sqrt{6}-\alpha_7\sqrt{3} = 0$$

$$\alpha_7\sqrt{3}+\alpha_8\sqrt{2} = 0 \qquad \alpha_4\sqrt{3}-\alpha_9 = 0$$

$$\alpha_5+\alpha_6\sqrt{2}-\alpha_{10} = 0 \qquad \alpha_{17}+\alpha_{18}-\alpha_{25} = 0$$

$$\alpha_{19}+\alpha_{20}+2\alpha_{21} = 0 \qquad \alpha_{19}-\alpha_{20}-\alpha_{26}\sqrt{2} = 0$$

$$\alpha_{26}+\alpha_{27} = 0 \qquad \alpha_{22}\sqrt{2}-\alpha_{28} = 0$$

We then have only 12 linearly independent amplitudes after application of isotopic invariance.

The consideration of U spin rotation invariance is sufficient to find the last 8 relations. In fact, U spin invariance alone gives 12 relations but only eight are linearly independent if we take into account charge independence:

TABLE 4.26

$$\frac{\alpha_2}{\sqrt{3}} = \alpha_5 = \alpha_{17} = \alpha_{19}$$

$$\alpha_7-\alpha_{10}-\alpha_{11} = 0 \qquad \alpha_3-\alpha_4\sqrt{3}-2\alpha_6 = 0$$

$$\alpha_1-\alpha_{15}-\alpha_{20} = 0 \qquad \alpha_6\sqrt{2}-\alpha_{16}-\alpha_{18} = 0$$

$$\alpha_3\sqrt{3}+\alpha_4-\alpha_{21}\sqrt{6}-\alpha_{22}\sqrt{2} = 0$$

$$\alpha_8-\alpha_9\sqrt{3}-\alpha_{13}\sqrt{6} = 0 \qquad \alpha_{14}+\alpha_{25}-\alpha_{26}\sqrt{2} = 0$$

$$\alpha_6\sqrt{2}-2\alpha_{16}-\alpha_{21}+\alpha_{22}\sqrt{3} = 0 \qquad \alpha_{13}\sqrt{2}-\alpha_{23}\sqrt{2}-\alpha_{27}+\alpha_{28}\sqrt{3} = 0$$

In the upper part of table 4.26 we give a possible choice of eight linearly independent relations predicted by U spin rotation invariance. Combining now these relations with charge independence as exhibited in table 4.25, it is easy to obtain the last four U spin relations indicated in the lower part of table 4.26.

3. Let us define a quantity $\tau = |\alpha|^2$ which is, up to a known phase space factor, the differential cross section. Besides the trivial U spin equalities:

$$\tfrac{1}{3}\tau(\pi^- p \Rightarrow \pi^+ N^{*-}_{\frac{3}{2}}) = \tau(\pi^- p \Rightarrow K^+ Y^{*-}_1) = \tau(K^- p \Rightarrow K^+ \Xi^*_{\frac{1}{2}}) = \\ = \tau(K^- p \Rightarrow \pi^+ Y^{*-}_1)$$

it is possible to find some relations between the differential cross-sections, because of the small number of reduced amplitudes. The first equality, due to MESHKOV, LEVINSON and LIPKIN [1963] seems to be difficult to compare with experiment:

$$\tau(\pi^- p \Rightarrow \pi^0 N^{*0}_{\frac{3}{2}}) + \tau(\pi^- p \Rightarrow \eta^0 N^{*0}_{\frac{3}{2}}) + \tau(K^- p \Rightarrow K^0 N^{*0}_{\frac{3}{2}}) + \tau(K^- p \Rightarrow K^0 \Xi^{*0}_{\frac{1}{2}}) = \\ = 2[\tau(\pi^- p \Rightarrow K^0 Y^{*0}_1) + \tau(K^- p \Rightarrow \pi^0 Y^{*0}_1) + \tau(K^- p \Rightarrow \eta^0 Y^{*1}_0)]. \quad \text{(a)}$$

The second equality, due to MESHKOV, SNOW and YODH [1964]:

$$3\tau(\pi^+ p \Rightarrow K^+ Y^{*+}_1) + \tau(K^+ p \Rightarrow K^0 N^{*++}_{\frac{3}{2}}) = 3\tau(\pi^+ p \Rightarrow \eta^0 N^{*++}_{\frac{3}{2}}) + \\ + \tau(\eta^+ p \Rightarrow \pi^0 N^{*++}_{\frac{3}{2}}) \quad \text{(b)}$$

is in reasonable agreement with experiment, for the total cross-sections at least.

4. The same considerations can be easily extended to the case where the final meson is a vector meson:

$$M + B \Rightarrow V + B^*.$$

Because of the large ω-φ mixing, we must simultaneously consider the reaction

$$8 + 8 \Rightarrow 1 + 10$$

which is described by one new amplitude B_{10}.

The transition amplitudes associated to φ and ω production are then given in terms of five reduced amplitudes and of the mixing angle λ previously defined. It follows that the relations between the transition amplitudes and between the cross sections are more complicated than in the previous case when φ and ω mesons are concerned.

The three equalities of table 4.16 take the form:

$$\frac{1}{\sqrt{3}} A(\pi^- p \Rightarrow \rho^+ N^{*-}_{\frac{3}{2}}) = A(\pi^- p \Rightarrow K^{*+} Y^{*-}_1) \\ = A(K^- p \Rightarrow K^{*+} \Xi^{*-}_{\frac{1}{2}}) = A(K^- p \Rightarrow \rho^+ Y^{*-}_1)$$

and the condition b on the cross-sections becomes an inequality:

$$3\tau(\pi^+ p \Rightarrow K^{*+} Y^{*+}_1) + (K^+ p \Rightarrow K^{*0} N^{*++}_{\frac{3}{2}}) - \tau(\pi^+ p \Rightarrow \rho^0 N^{*++}_{\frac{3}{2}}) \leqq \\ \leqq 3[\tau(\pi^+ p \Rightarrow \varphi + N^{*++}_{\frac{1}{2}}) + \tau(\pi^+ p \Rightarrow \omega + N^{*++}_{\frac{3}{2}})].$$

Following MESHKOV, SNOW and YODTH [1964], the agreement with experiment is quite good.

5. Baryon-baryon and antibaryon-baryon collisions offer a new way of producing a decuplet of excited baryons:

$$\mathrm{B}+\mathrm{B} \Rightarrow \mathrm{B}+\mathrm{B}^{*}$$
$$\overline{\mathrm{B}}+\mathrm{B} \Rightarrow \overline{\mathrm{B}}+\mathrm{B}^{*}.$$

The first reaction is not extremely interesting from the point of view of unitary symmetry, the actual available high energy beams of baryons being essentially proton beams. We concentrate our attention to the second type of reactions on antiproton-proton inelastic collisions. Using the results of tables 4.24, 4.25 and 4.26, we have eight physical amplitudes related by four relations; two are due to charge independence:

$$\alpha_{12}+\alpha_{16} = 0 \qquad \alpha_{19}+\alpha_{20}+2\alpha_{21} = 0$$

and the last two are consequences of U spin rotation invariance:

$$A(\bar{\mathrm{p}}\mathrm{p} \Rightarrow \overline{\Xi}^{-}\Xi_{\frac{1}{2}}^{*-}) = A(\bar{\mathrm{p}}\mathrm{p} \Rightarrow \overline{\Sigma}^{-}\mathrm{Y}_{1}^{*-})$$
$$3A(\bar{\mathrm{p}}\mathrm{p} \Rightarrow \overline{\Lambda}^{0}\mathrm{Y}_{1}^{*0})-A(\bar{\mathrm{p}}\mathrm{p} \Rightarrow \overline{\Sigma}^{0}\mathrm{Y}_{1}^{*0}) = A(\bar{\mathrm{p}}\mathrm{p} \Rightarrow \bar{\mathrm{n}}\mathrm{N}_{\frac{3}{2}}^{*0})-A(\bar{\mathrm{p}}\mathrm{p} \Rightarrow \overline{\Xi}^{0}\Xi_{\frac{1}{2}}^{*0}).$$

Experimentally, the observed reactions are of the type:

$$\bar{\mathrm{p}}+\mathrm{p} \Rightarrow \overline{\mathrm{B}}+\mathrm{B}+\pi$$

and one looks for some resonant $\mathrm{B}\pi$ or $\overline{\mathrm{B}}\pi$ systems; of course, the two types of processes are related by charge conjugation and we obtain the same type of predictions for the reactions $\bar{\mathrm{p}}\mathrm{p} \Rightarrow \mathrm{B}\overline{\mathrm{B}}^{*}$, in particular the equality:

$$A(\bar{\mathrm{p}}\mathrm{p} \Rightarrow \Xi^{-}\overline{\Xi_{\frac{1}{2}}^{*-}}) = A(\bar{\mathrm{p}}\mathrm{p} \Rightarrow \Sigma^{-}\overline{\mathrm{Y}_{1}^{*-}}).$$

4.3.5. TWO DECUPLET PRODUCTION

1. We consider the general reactions

$$8+8 \Rightarrow 10+\overline{10}$$

experimentally observed in antiproton-proton inelastic collisions:

$$\mathrm{B}+\overline{\mathrm{B}} \Rightarrow \mathrm{B}^{*}+\overline{\mathrm{B}}^{*}.$$

The product of the final state representations being decomposed into:

$$10 \otimes \overline{10} = 1 \oplus 8 \oplus 27 \oplus 64.$$

there exist, in general, linearly independent amplitudes which are convenient to quote as:

$$A_1, A_{8a}, A_{8s}, A_{27}.$$

2. We now restrict ourselves to the only interesting physical case of antiproton-proton collisions. We have ten processes and table 4.27 gives an expansion of these physical amplitudes in reduced amplitudes of the direct channel using the Clebsch-Gordan coefficients as computed by TARJANNE [1963b].

TABLE 4.27

Final state	A_{27}	A_{8s}	A_{8a}	A_1
$N_{\frac{3}{2}}^{*++}\overline{N_{\frac{3}{2}}^{*++}}$	$\frac{9}{20\sqrt{7}}$	$\frac{1}{5\sqrt{2}}$	$-\frac{1}{\sqrt{10}}$	$\frac{1}{10\sqrt{2}}$
$N_{\frac{3}{2}}^{*+}\overline{N_{\frac{3}{2}}^{*+}}$	$\frac{1}{4\sqrt{7}}$	0	$-\frac{1}{3}\sqrt{\frac{2}{5}}$	$\frac{1}{10\sqrt{2}}$
$N_{\frac{3}{2}}^{*0}\overline{N_{\frac{3}{2}}^{*0}}$	$\frac{1}{20\sqrt{7}}$	$-\frac{1}{5\sqrt{2}}$	$-\frac{1}{3\sqrt{10}}$	$\frac{1}{10\sqrt{2}}$
$N_{\frac{3}{2}}^{*-}\overline{N_{\frac{3}{2}}^{*-}}$	$-\frac{3}{20\sqrt{7}}$	$\sqrt{\frac{2}{5}}$	0	$\frac{1}{10\sqrt{2}}$
$Y_1^{*+}\overline{Y_1^{*+}}$	$-\frac{11}{20\sqrt{7}}$	$\frac{1}{5\sqrt{2}}$	$-\frac{1}{3\sqrt{10}}$	$\frac{1}{10\sqrt{2}}$
$Y_1^{*0}\overline{Y_1^{*0}}$	$-\frac{1}{4\sqrt{7}}$	0	0	$\frac{1}{10\sqrt{2}}$
$Y_1^{*-}\overline{Y_1^{*-}}$	$\frac{1}{20\sqrt{7}}$	$-\frac{1}{5\sqrt{2}}$	$\frac{1}{3\sqrt{10}}$	$\frac{1}{10\sqrt{2}}$
$\Xi_{\frac{1}{2}}^{*0}\overline{\Xi_{\frac{1}{2}}^{*0}}$	$-\frac{11}{20\sqrt{7}}$	$\frac{1}{5\sqrt{2}}$	$\frac{1}{3\sqrt{10}}$	$\frac{1}{10\sqrt{2}}$
$\Xi_{\frac{1}{2}}^{*-}\overline{\Xi_{\frac{1}{2}}^{*-}}$	$\frac{1}{4\sqrt{7}}$	0	$\frac{1}{3}\sqrt{\frac{2}{5}}$	$\frac{1}{10\sqrt{2}}$
$\Omega^-\overline{\Omega^-}$	$\frac{9}{20\sqrt{7}}$	$\frac{1}{5\sqrt{2}}$	$\frac{1}{2\sqrt{10}}$	$\frac{1}{10\sqrt{2}}$

3. The I spin and U spin rotation invariances give six relations between these ten amplitudes, which are easy to write symbolically as

TABLE 4.28

I spin invariance	U spin invariance
$\alpha(N^-)+\alpha(N^+) = 2\alpha(N^0)$	$\alpha(N^-)+\alpha(\Xi^-) = 2\alpha(Y^-)$
$\alpha(N^0)+\alpha(N^{++}) = 2\alpha(N^+)$	$\alpha(Y^-)+\alpha(\Omega^-) = 2\alpha(\Xi^-)$
$\alpha(Y^-)+\alpha(Y^+) = 2\alpha(Y^0)$	$\alpha(N^0)+\alpha(\Xi^0) = 2\alpha(Y^0)$

It is also possible to obtain two sets of equalities between four cross-sections. The first one is due to charge independence

$$3[\tau(N^+)-\tau(N^0)] = \tau(N^{++})-\tau(N^-)$$

and the second, first pointed out by LIPKIN, LEVINSON and MESHKOV [1963] is a prediction of U spin invariance:

$$3[\tau(Y^-)-\tau(\Xi^-)] = \tau(N^-)-\tau(\Omega^-).$$

CHAPTER V

ELECTROMAGNETIC INTERACTIONS

5.1. Electromagnetic current

1. The charge operator Q has the well known structure:

$$Q = I_3 + \tfrac{1}{2}Y$$

where I_3 is the third component of the isotopic spin operator and Y the hypercharge operator. For all the physical states, Q has a diagonal representation and the electric charge q of a state ψ is given by:

$$q = e\langle\psi|Q|\psi\rangle$$

where e is the unit charge.

2. The electromagnetic current is strongly connected with the charge operator Q. It can be divided into two parts:

the isovector current, related to I_3,
the isoscalar current, related to Y.

For the nucleons, for instance, we have $Y|\mathrm{N}\rangle = |\mathrm{N}\rangle$ and the isotopic spin operators are the Pauli matrices,

$$Q = \tfrac{1}{2}(\tau_3 + 1).$$

It follows that the matrix elements of the electromagnetic current are given by:

$$\langle \mathrm{N}|J_\mu^{\mathrm{em}}|\mathrm{N}\rangle = \tfrac{1}{2}\mathrm{i}[\bar{\psi}_\mathrm{N}\gamma_\mu\psi_\mathrm{N} + \bar{\psi}_\mathrm{N}\gamma_\mu\tau_3\psi_\mathrm{N}]$$

where ψ_N is a 4×2 components field describing the nucleon.

For the π meson, $Y|\pi\rangle = 0$ and the electric charge is known from the third component t_3 of the spin one isotopic spin $Q = t_3$. The matrix elements of the electromagnetic current of pions takes then the familiar form:

$$\langle\pi|J_\mu^{\mathrm{em}}|\pi\rangle = \varepsilon_{3jk}\frac{\partial\phi^j}{\partial x^\mu}\phi^k = \pi^+ \frac{\overleftrightarrow{\partial}}{\partial x^\mu}\pi^- .$$

3. The strong and electromagnetic interactions are invariant under I_3 and Y transformations. In the approximation where the weak interactions can be neglected, both isovector and isoscalar currents are separately conserved.

4. We now take into account renormalization effects due to strong interactions. We have now to consider induced coupling and invariant form factors.

Let us take, as a useful example, the case of the nucleon. The previous coupling is a Dirac type coupling and we now introduce a gauge invariant Pauli type invariant coupling. The electromagnetic properties of a spin $\frac{1}{2}$ particle are described by two electromagnetic form factors:

$$\langle K', \lambda' | J_\mu^{\mathrm{em}} | K, \lambda \rangle = \bar{u}(K', \lambda') \left[\mathrm{i}\gamma_\mu F_1(q^2) - \frac{1}{4M} [\gamma_\mu, \not{q}] F_2(q^2) \right] u(K, \lambda),$$

where $u(K, \lambda)$ is a Dirac free spinor for a nucleon of energy momentum K and helicity λ. The transfer q is defined by $q = K' - K$ and $\not{q} = \gamma^\rho q_\beta$. The Dirac form factor $F_1(q^2)$ is normalized to the electric charge in units e; the Pauli form factor is normalized to the abnormal magnetic moment in units $e/2M$ where M is the nucleon mass.

For a π-meson, the situation is more simple because of the spin zero value for a pion. We have only one electromagnetic form factor normalized to the electric charge, in units e:

$$\langle K' | J_\mu^{\mathrm{em}} | K \rangle = \mathrm{i}(K + K')_\mu F(q^2)$$

and the form factors for π^+ and π^- are opposite due to *TCP* invariance. For the same reason, the π^0 form factor is identically zero.

Due to the conservation of the electromagnetic current, the electric charge is not renormalized and is identical to the bare charge.

5. The universality of the electric charge is an experimental fact completely independent of the conservation of the current. For instance, due to the universality, the proton and the positron have the same electric charge.

5.2. Electromagnetic current in the unitary symmetry

1. The electromagnetic current is the sum of the hypercharge current and of the third component of the isotopic spin current. Both currents are conserved in the limit where the weak interactions are neglected.

2. The infinitesimal generator Q of the Lie algebra commutes with the three components of the U spin,

$$Q = H_1\sqrt{6} \qquad U^+ = E_{32}\sqrt{6} \qquad U^- = E_{23}\sqrt{6} \qquad U_3 = \tfrac{1}{2}\sqrt{6}(H_3 - H_2).$$

In the limit of an exact unitary symmetry, the electromagnetic interactions are assumed to be invariant under U spin rotations and the photon is a U spin scalar.

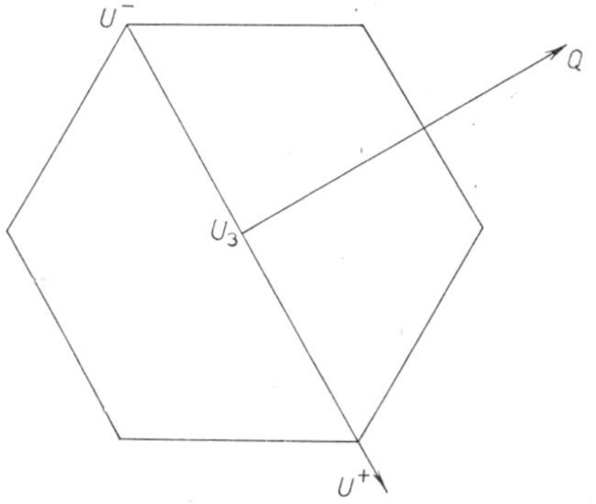

Fig. 5.1.

3. In the unitary symmetry model, we can define eight vector currents associated to an octuplet and one baryonic current associated to a singulet which are all conserved currents. A detailed treatment of this question will be given in the next chapter. The general form of a conserved U spin scalar current can be written as as superposition of an octuplet current transforming like a Q weight and a singulet current.

4. The assumption made by COLEMAN and GLASHOW [1961] is more restrictive: the electromagnetic current is constructed from the infinitesimal generator Q of the Lie algebra and the photon has the same transformations properties as the $U = Q = 0$ weight of an octuplet.

Such an assumption is completely similar to that made previously for the medium strong interactions H_Y. The invariance $[\boldsymbol{I}, Y]$ of medium strong interactions is now replaced by the invariance $[\boldsymbol{U}, Q]$ of the electromagnetic interactions valid only, of course, in the limit where the breaking due to the medium strong interactions can be neglected.

5. The isometries associated to the component $U = Q = 0$ of an octuplet are easily deduced from the isometries $I = Y = 0$ by the simple substitution:

$$Y \Rightarrow Q \quad \text{and} \quad I(I+1) \Rightarrow U(U+1)$$

and we have immediately:

$$\Omega_Q^{(8a)} = Q$$
$$\Omega_Q^{(8s)} = Q^2 - 4U(U+1) + \tfrac{2}{3}x.$$

As previously, the Casimir operator x is given by:

$$x = \tfrac{2}{3}(\lambda_1^2+\lambda_2^2+\lambda_1\lambda_2)+2(\lambda_1+\lambda_2).$$

6. We will restrict now to the study of the main important multiplets: spin $\frac{1}{2}^+$ baryons, spin $\frac{3}{2}^+$ excited baryons, pseudoscalar mesons and vector mesons. In each case we will define various approximations with respect to the medium strong interactions.

a. Zero order in H_Y: the U spin invariance helds for strong and electromagnetic interactions.

b. Arbitrary order in H_Y: we disregard the interference between H_Y and the electromagnetic interactions; the medium strong interactions are taken into account as an additional perturbation and the electromagnetic corrections satisfy U spin invariance.

c. First order in H_Y: as in the Gell-Mann-Okubo mass formula the unitary symmetry is broken at first order in H_Y but the effect of interference between H_Y and the electromagnetic interactions is conserved.

7. Some of the results are only the consequence of the U spin scalar character of the photon, for instance the calculation of the electromagnetic mass differences within an isotopic spin multiplet.

The property of the photon to belong to an octuplet is used only in first order electromagnetic problems and a large part of the results, even in this case, is still independent of such an assumption.

5.3. Electromagnetic properties of baryons

1. If the medium strong interactions are neglected, it is possible to define baryon multiplets with respect to U spin which are completely degenerated:

TABLE 5.1

Q	U	Multiplet
1	$\frac{1}{2}$	$[\Sigma^+, p]$
0	1	$[\Xi^0, B_3, n]$
	0	B_0
-1	$\frac{1}{2}$	Ξ^-, Σ^-

The two linear combinations of Λ^0 and Σ^0, B_0 and B_3 are defined by:

$$B_0 = \tfrac{1}{2}(\Sigma^0\sqrt{3}+\Lambda^0), \qquad B_3 = \tfrac{1}{2}(\Sigma^0-\Lambda^0\sqrt{3}).$$

The electromagnetic properties of the partners of a given U multiplet are identical and independent of the third U spin component.

2. We shall call as j the electromagnetic current which is associated to a real or virtual photon. More generally, j^n will represent an electromagnetic interaction taken at the order n. The U spin invariance of electromagnetic interactions gives us the following relations (COLEMAN and GLASHOW [1961] and CABIBBO and GATTO [1962]):

$$\langle \Sigma^+|j^n|\Sigma^+\rangle = \langle \mathrm{p}|j^n|\mathrm{p}\rangle$$
$$\langle \Sigma^-|j^n|\Sigma^-\rangle = \langle \Xi^-|j^n|\Xi^-\rangle$$
$$\langle \Xi^0|j^n|\Xi^0\rangle = \langle \mathrm{n}|j^n|\mathrm{n}\rangle.$$

The three unphysical relations:

$$\langle \mathrm{B}_3|j^n|\mathrm{B}_3\rangle = \langle \mathrm{n}|j^n|\mathrm{n}\rangle$$
$$\langle \mathrm{B}_3|j^n|\mathrm{B}_0\rangle = 0 = \langle \mathrm{B}_0|j^n|\mathrm{B}_3\rangle$$

can be transformed into matrix elements between the states Λ^0 and Σ^0 by using:

$$\Sigma^0 = \tfrac{1}{2}(\mathrm{B}_0\sqrt{3}+\mathrm{B}_3) \qquad \Lambda^0 = \tfrac{1}{2}(\mathrm{B}_0-\mathrm{B}_3\sqrt{3}).$$

We immediately deduce:

$$\langle \Sigma^0|j^n|\Sigma^0\rangle = \tfrac{3}{4}\langle \mathrm{B}_0|j^n|\mathrm{B}_0\rangle+\tfrac{1}{4}\langle \mathrm{B}_3|j^n|\mathrm{B}_3\rangle$$
$$\langle \Lambda^0|j^n|\Lambda^0\rangle = \tfrac{1}{4}\langle \mathrm{B}_0|j^n|\mathrm{B}_0\rangle+\tfrac{3}{4}\langle \mathrm{B}_3|j^n|\mathrm{B}_3\rangle$$
$$\langle \Lambda^0|j^n|\Lambda^0\rangle = \tfrac{1}{4}\sqrt{3}\langle \mathrm{B}_0|j^n|\mathrm{B}_0\rangle-\tfrac{1}{4}\sqrt{3}\langle \mathrm{B}_3|j^n|\mathrm{B}_3\rangle$$

and the previous relations can also be written as:

$$\langle \Lambda^0|j^n|\Sigma^0\rangle = \langle \Sigma^0|j^n|\Lambda^0\rangle$$
$$\langle \mathrm{n}|j^n|\mathrm{n}\rangle = \langle \Sigma^0|j^n|\Sigma^0\rangle-\sqrt{3}\langle \Lambda^0|j^n|\Sigma^0\rangle$$
$$\langle \Sigma^0|j^n|\Sigma^0\rangle-\langle \Lambda^0|j^n|\Lambda^0\rangle = \frac{2}{\sqrt{3}}\langle \Lambda^0|j^n|\Sigma^0\rangle.$$

The ten transition matrix elements are related by six relations as expected for an octuplet.

3. Let us now consider, as an immediate application of these results the problem of electromagnetic mass differences for the baryon octuplet.

The mass operator is written as:

$$m = m_0(I, Y)+\delta m(U, Q).$$

The leading term m_0 is invariant under I spin rotations and the correction δm

of electromagnetic nature is assumed to be invariant under U spin rotation. We have neglected the crossed terms corrections transforming for instance as a product YQ.

We define 8 diagonal quantities δm and two non diagonal quantities $\delta m_{\Sigma^0 \Lambda^0} = \delta m_{\Lambda^0 \Sigma^0}$, the mass matrix being symmetrical. We have five relations:

$$\delta m_{\Sigma^+} = \delta m_{\mathrm{p}} \qquad \delta m_{\Sigma^-} = \delta m_{\Xi^-}$$

$$\delta m_{\mathrm{n}} = \delta m_{\Xi^0} = \delta m_{\Sigma^0} - \sqrt{3}\,\delta m_{\Sigma^0 \Lambda^0} = \delta m_{\Lambda^0} - \frac{1}{\sqrt{3}}\,\delta m_{\Sigma^0 \Lambda^0}.$$

Taking into account the principal term $m_0(I, Y)$, we obtain the two following equalities:

$$m_{\mathrm{n}} - m_{\mathrm{p}} + m_{\Sigma^+} - m_{\Sigma^0} + \sqrt{3}\,\delta m_{\Sigma^0 \Lambda^0} = 0$$

$$m_{\Xi^-} - m_{\Xi^0} + m_{\Sigma^0} - m_{\Sigma^-} - \sqrt{3}\,\delta m_{\Sigma^0 \Lambda^0} = 0.$$

The elimination of $\delta m_{\Sigma^0 \Lambda^0}$ leads to the Coleman-Glashow relation (COLEMAN and GLASHOW [1961]):

$$(m_{\mathrm{n}} - m_{\mathrm{p}}) + (m_{\Xi^-} - m_{\Xi^0}) = (m_{\Sigma^-} - m_{\Sigma^+}).$$

The experimental mass differences are the following:

$$m_{\Sigma^-} - m_{\Sigma^+} = (8.25 \pm 0.25)\ \mathrm{MeV}$$

$$m_{\mathrm{n}} - m_{\mathrm{p}} = 1.3\ \mathrm{MeV}$$

$$m_{\Xi^-} - m_{\Xi^0} = (6.1 \pm 1.6)\ \mathrm{MeV}$$

and the data fit very well the Coleman-Glashow relation:

$$7.4 \pm 1.6 = 8.25 \pm 0.25.$$

The non diagonal term $\delta m_{\Sigma^0 \Lambda^0}$ is calculated using one of the two previous formulae and we choose the first ones because of smaller experimental errors. With

$$m_{\Sigma^0} - m_{\Sigma^+} = (3.38 \pm 0.28)\ \mathrm{MeV}$$

we find:

$$\delta m_{\Sigma^0 \Lambda^0} = (1.20 \pm 0.16)\ \mathrm{MeV}.$$

The mass matrix is not diagonal for the states Σ^0 and Λ^0. The physical observed states are the eigenstates of the mass matrix and are obtained by an electromagnetic mixing of Σ^0 and Λ^0. For instance, the physical Λ particle is not a pure isotopic spin scalar state but a linear superposition of Λ^0 and Σ^0 (DALITZ and VON HIPPEL [1964]):

$$\Lambda_{\text{phys}} = \Lambda^0 \cos\alpha - \Sigma^0 \sin\alpha$$
$$\Sigma_{\text{phys}} = \Lambda^0 \sin\alpha + \Sigma^0 \cos\alpha.$$

The mixing angle α is easily related to the matrix elements of the mass matrix by

$$\text{tg}\, 2\alpha_{\Sigma^0\Lambda^0} = \frac{2\delta m_{\Sigma^0\Lambda^0}}{m_{\Sigma^0} - m_{\Lambda^0}}$$

and we find for the mixing angle the numerical value:

$$\alpha_{\Sigma^0\Lambda^0} \simeq 0.0154 \pm 0.0020.$$

The excellent agreement of the Coleman-Glashow formula with experiment shows that the interference between medium strong interactions and electromagnetic interactions is certainly small, at least for the baryon case.

Nevertheless, it can be useful to calculate the prediction of the unitary symmetry if δm is perturbed at first order by H_Y. We then have only one relation between the electromagnetic mass corrections:

$$\delta m_{\text{n}} + \delta m_{\Xi^0} = 2\delta m_{\text{B}_3}.$$

This result, combined with the Gell-Mann-Okubo mass formula for $m_0(I, Y)$ gives (Okubo [1963a]):

$$2\sqrt{3}\,\delta m_{\Sigma^0\Lambda^0} = 3m_{\Lambda^0} + m_{\Sigma^0} - 2(m_{\text{n}} + m_{\Sigma^0}).$$

The numerical value of $\delta m_{\Sigma^0\Lambda^0}$ obtained in this way turns out to be large: $\delta m_{\Sigma^0\Lambda^0} \simeq 9$ MeV. We believe the previous value more accurate and the Coleman-Glashow approximation better than a first order perturbation in H_Y which is certainly not sufficient for the calculation of electromagnetic effects.

4. The electromagnetic form factors correspond to a first order electromagnetic interaction. The matrix elements of a given quantity to depend only of two reduced matrix elements α and β. The isometries have been given and in the case of the octuplet representation we have:

$$E = \alpha Q + \beta[4 - 4U(U+1) + Q^2].$$

Only two form factors are linearly independent and it is convenient to choose the proton and neutron form factors. We then obtain the expressions given in the table 4.2.

Of course, some of the relations, as for instance $F_{\Sigma^+} = F_{\text{p}}$, are due to U spin invariance and include all orders electromagnetic corrections.

TABLE 4.2

	E	F_{p}	F_{n}
F_{p}	$\alpha+2\beta$	1	0
F_{n}	-4β	0	1
F_{Σ^-}	$-\alpha+2\beta$	-1	-1
F_{Ξ^-}	$-\alpha+2\beta$	-1	-1
F_{Ξ^0}	-4β	0	1
F_{Σ^+}	$\alpha+2\beta$	1	0
F_{Σ^0}	$+2\beta$	0	$-\frac{1}{2}$
F_{Λ^0}	-2β	0	$+\frac{1}{2}$
$F_{\Sigma\Lambda}$	$-2\beta\sqrt{6}$	0	$-\sqrt{\frac{3}{2}}$

The experimental verification of the previous equalities is not possible in the actual situation.

The baryon magnetic moments obey the same relations and it is interesting to compare the values predicted by the unitary symmetry from μ_{p} and μ_{n} with the experimental data.

The five experimental determinations of the Λ^0 magnetic moment are not in perfect agreement. In units of the nucleon Bohr magneton $e/2M_{\text{N}}$, the experimental data are the following:

-1.5 ± 0.5 (COOL et al. [1962]), $0+0.6$ (KERMAN et al. [1963]), -1.39 ± 0.72 (ANDERSON and CRAWFORD [1964]), -0.5 ± 0.28 (CHARRIERE et al. [1965]), -0.77 ± 0.27 (HILL et al. [1965]).

The theoretical value, predicted by the unitary symmetry is:

$$\mu_{\Lambda} = \tfrac{1}{2}\mu_{\text{n}} = -0.95e/2M_{\text{N}}.$$

We have also a recent evaluation of the Σ^+ magnetic moment, in the same units, the experimental result is 4.3 ± 1.3 (MCINTURFF and ROOS [1964]). The theoretical value predicted by U spin symmetry is:

$$\mu_{\Sigma^+} = \mu_{\text{p}} = 1.71e/2M_{\text{N}}.$$

In both cases the agreement between theory and experiment is possible but it is difficult to give a definite conclusion.

If now we introduce the influence of the medium strong interactions as an additional perturbation, we obtain for the electromagnetic form factors, and therefore for the magnetic moments, relations analogous to those obtained in section 3 for the mass differences:

$$F_{\mathrm{n}} - F_{\mathrm{p}} + F_{\Sigma^+} - F_{\Sigma^0} + F_{\Sigma\Lambda}\sqrt{3} = 0$$
$$F_{\Xi^-} - F_{\Xi^0} + F_{\Sigma^0} - F_{\Sigma^-} - F_{\Sigma\Lambda}\sqrt{3} = 0.$$

The only additional relations due to the restriction to first order electromagnetic interaction is also obtained in the framework of isotopic spin symmetry and is simply:

$$F_{\Sigma^+} + F_{\Sigma^-} = 2F_{\Sigma^0}.$$

Finally, taking also into account the interference between the medium strong interactions restricted to first order and the electromagnetic interactions, we obtain only one relation (excepted the previous isotopic spin relation) (Okubo [1963a]):

$$2F_{\Sigma\Lambda}\sqrt{3} = 3F_{\Lambda^0} + F_{\Sigma^0} - 2F_{\mathrm{n}} - 2F_{\Xi^0}.$$

5.4. Electromagnetic properties of the baryon resonance decuplet

1. The decuplet has a very simple structure with respect to the U spin rotations:

TABLE 5.3

Q	U	Multiplet
2	0	$N^{*++}_{\frac{3}{2}}$
1	$\frac{1}{2}$	$[Y^{*+}_1, N^{*+}_{\frac{3}{2}}]$
0	1	$[\Xi^{*0}_{\frac{1}{2}}, Y^{*0}_1, N^{*0}_{\frac{3}{2}}]$
-1	$\frac{3}{2}$	$[\Omega^-, \Xi^{*-}_{\frac{1}{2}}, Y^{*-}_1, N^{*-}_{\frac{3}{2}}]$

If the medium strong interactions are neglected, the electromagnetic properties of the partners of a U spin multiplet are independent of the value of U_3.

2. We define ten diagonal matrix elements related by six relations because of U spin invariance (Cabibbo and Gatto [1962]):

$$\langle Y^{*+}_1|j^n|Y^{*+}_1\rangle = \langle N^{*+}_{\frac{3}{2}}|j^n|N^{*+}_{\frac{3}{2}}\rangle$$
$$\langle \Xi^{*0}_{\frac{1}{2}}|j^n|\Xi^{*0}_{\frac{1}{2}}\rangle = \langle Y^{*0}_1|j^n|Y^{*0}_1\rangle = \langle N^{*0}_{\frac{3}{2}}|j^n|N^{*0}_{\frac{3}{2}}\rangle$$
$$\langle \Omega^-|j^n|\Omega^-\rangle = \langle \Xi^{*-}_{\frac{1}{2}}|j^n|\Xi^{*-}_{\frac{1}{2}}\rangle = \langle Y^{*-}_1|j^n|Y^{*-}_1\rangle = \langle N^{*-}_{\frac{3}{2}}|j^n|N^{*-}_{\frac{3}{2}}\rangle.$$

We now study the problem of the electromagnetic mass differences. In all the triangular representations, the I spin is a linear function of the hypercharge and the U spin a linear function of the charge. We write in the first approximation the mass matrix in the form:

$$m = m_0(Y) + \delta m(Q).$$

The ten electromagnetic corrections δm are related by six relations from U spin invariance:

$$\begin{aligned} \delta m_{Y^{*+}} &= \delta m_{N^{*+}} \\ \delta m_{\Xi^{*0}} &= \delta m_{Y^{*0}} = \delta m_{N^{*0}} \\ \delta m_{\Omega^-} &= \delta m_{\Xi^{*-}} = \delta m_{Y^{*-}} = \delta m_{N^{*-}} \end{aligned}$$

and we obtain three relations between the electromagnetic mass differences (MACFARLANE and SUDARSHAN [1964])

$$\begin{aligned} m_{Y^{*0}} - m_{Y^{*+}} &= m_{N^{*0}} - m_{N^{*+}} \\ m_{\Xi^{*-}} - m_{\Xi^{*0}} &= m_{Y^{*-}} - m_{Y^{*0}} = m_{N^{*-}} - m_{N^{*0}}. \end{aligned}$$

We have now some preliminary measurements of the electromagnetic mass differences of the spin $\frac{3}{2}^+$ excited baryons.

$$m_{N^{*++}_{\frac{3}{2}}} - m_{N^{*0}_{\frac{3}{2}}} \simeq (-0.45 \pm 0.85)\ \text{MeV} \quad (\text{OLSSON [1965]})$$

$$m_{Y^{*-}_1} - m_{Y^{*+}_1} \simeq (4.3 \pm 2.2)\ \text{MeV} \quad (\text{HUWE [1964]})$$

$$m_{\Xi^{*-}_{\frac{1}{2}}} - m_{\Xi^{*0}_{\frac{1}{2}}} \simeq (5.7 \pm 3)\ \text{MeV} \quad (\text{PJERROU [1965]}).$$

The comparison with the prediction of the unitary symmetry is possible only if we assume a second order violation of isotopic spin to be sufficient to produce an electromagnetic mass splitting. We obtain a relation only for the quartet

$$m_{N^{*++}_{\frac{3}{2}}} - m_{N^{*-}_{\frac{3}{2}}} = 3(m_{N^{*+}_{\frac{3}{2}}} - m_{N^{*0}_{\frac{3}{2}}})$$

and the electromagnetic mass differences in the decuplet depend only of two parameters. The three measured quantities are then related by one relation:

$$(m_{\Xi^{*-}_{\frac{1}{2}}} - m_{\Xi^{*0}_{\frac{1}{2}}}) = \tfrac{3}{4}(m_{Y^{*-}_1} - m_{Y^{*0}_1}) - \tfrac{1}{4}(m_{N^{*++}_{\frac{3}{2}}} - m_{N^{*0}_{\frac{3}{2}}}).$$

The experimental value of the right hand side is (3.35 ± 1.85) MeV and is compatible, within the large errors with the $\Xi^*_{\frac{1}{2}}$ measurements.

Let us now introduce a first order violation with respect to medium strong interaction in the electromagnetic term δm,

$$\delta m = \delta m^{(0)}(Q) + Y \delta m^{(1)}(Q).$$

We obtain an equal spacing rule for the corrections δm:

$$\delta m_{\Xi^{*0}} - \delta m_{Y^{*0}} = \delta m_{Y^{*0}} - \delta m_{N^{*0}}$$

$$\delta m_{\Omega^-} - \delta m_{\Xi^{*-}} = \delta m_{\Xi^{*-}} - \delta m_{Y^{*-}} = \delta m_{Y^{*-}} - \delta m_{N^{*-}}$$

and only one relation between the electromagnetic mass differences:

$$(m_{\Xi^{*-}} - m_{\Xi^{*0}}) + (m_{N^{*-}} - m_{N^{*0}}) = 2(m_{Y^{*-}} - m_{Y^{*0}}).$$

We know that the non electromagnetic mass term $m_0(Y)$ can be accurately represented by a linear function of Y. The mass operator takes then the form:

$$m = [m_0^{(0)} + \delta m^{(0)}(Q)] + Y[m_0^{(1)} + \delta m^{(1)}(Q)].$$

The equal spacing rule in a given U spin multiplet follows immediately:

$$m_{\Xi^{*0}} - m_{Y^{*0}} = m_{Y^{*0}} - m_{N^{*0}}$$

$$m_{\Omega^-} - m_{\Xi^{*-}} = m_{\Xi^{*-}} - m_{Y^{*-}} = m_{Y^{*-}} - m_{N^{*-}}.$$

Finally if we use a quadratic dependence with respect to the hypercharge in the mass matrix we obtain only one relation:

$$m_{\Omega^-} - m_{N^{*-}} = 3m_{\Xi^{*-}} - m_{Y^{*-}}.$$

5. We study the electromagnetic form factors of the spin $\frac{3}{2}$ baryon resonances. For a spin $\frac{3}{2}$ particle, we have two electric and two magnetic form factors and consequently also for the static moments as the magnetic dipole moment, the electric quadrupole moment or the octupole magnetic moment.

If we neglect the medium strong interactions, the matrix elements of a first order electromagnetic quantity E are given, in the case of the decuplet – and more generally in the case of a triangular representation $\lambda_1 \lambda_2 = 0$ – by one reduced matrix element only:

$$E = \alpha Q.$$

As an immediate consequence, the form factors of the neutral particles are identically zero and all the non vanishing form factors are proportional.

We now take into account a first order violation with respect to the medium strong interactions. The matrix elements of E can then be written as:

$$E = \alpha Q + \beta + \gamma Y + \delta Y Q$$

because of the presence of isometries 1, 8, 10 and 27. The consequence of the previous expression is an equal spacing rule in each I spin multiplet and in each U spin multiplet because of a first order violation of I spin by Q and of U spin by Y:

$$F_{N^{*-}}+F_{N^{*+}} = 2F_{N^{*0}} \qquad F_{N^{*0}}+F_{N^{*++}} = 2F_{N^{*+}}$$

$$F_{N^{*-}}+F_{\Xi^{*-}} = 2F_{Y^{*-}} \qquad F_{Y^{*-}}+F_{\Omega^-} = 2F_{\Xi^{*-}}$$

$$F_{Y^{*+}}+F_{Y^{*-}} = 2F_{Y^{*0}} = F_{N^{*0}}+F_{\Xi^{*0}}.$$

6. We are now interested with the electromagnetic transitions between a baryon spin $\frac{3}{2}$ resonance B* and a spin $\frac{1}{2}$ baryon B. The U spin invariance of electromagnetic interaction gives, neglecting medium strong interactions:

$$\langle \Sigma^+|j''|Y_1^{*+}\rangle = \langle p|j''|N_{\frac{3}{2}}^{*+}\rangle$$

$$\langle \Xi^0|j''|\Xi_{\frac{1}{2}}^{*0}\rangle = \langle n|j''|N_{\frac{3}{2}}^{*0}\rangle$$

$$\langle \Sigma^0|j''|Y_1^{*0}\rangle = \tfrac{1}{2}\langle n|j''|N_{\frac{3}{2}}^{*0}\rangle$$

$$\langle \Lambda^0|j''|Y_1^{*0}\rangle = -\tfrac{1}{2}\sqrt{3}\langle n|j''|N_{\frac{3}{2}}^{*0}\rangle$$

$$\langle \Sigma^-|j''|Y_1^{*-}\rangle = 0 = \langle \Xi^-|j''|\Xi_{\frac{1}{2}}^{*-}\rangle.$$

Such a problem includes the study of the electromagnetic vertex B*Bγ for a virtual of a real photon and an interesting application is the radiative decay of baryon resonances: B* $\Rightarrow$ B$+\gamma$. If we restrict ourselves to first order electromagnetic interactions, the breaking of isotopic spin symmetry alone gives an additional relation due to the isovector character of the photon:

$$\langle p|j''|N_{\frac{3}{2}}^{*+}\rangle = \langle n|j''|N_{\frac{3}{2}}^{*0}\rangle$$

and all the matrix elements are proportionals.

If now we introduce a first order perturbation with respect to the medium strong interactions, the eight matrix elements are related by only 4 relations and we obtain (BARRET and TANAKA [1965]):

$$\langle p|j|N_{\frac{3}{2}}^{*+}\rangle = \langle n|j|N_{\frac{3}{2}}^{*0}\rangle$$

$$\langle \Sigma^-|j|Y_1^{*-}\rangle = \langle \Xi^-|j|\Xi_{\frac{1}{2}}^{*-}\rangle$$

$$\langle n|j|N_{\frac{3}{2}}^{*0}\rangle+\langle \Xi^0|j|\Xi_{\frac{1}{2}}^{*0}\rangle = \langle \Sigma^0|j|Y_1^{*0}\rangle-\sqrt{3}\langle \Lambda^0|j|Y_1^{*0}\rangle$$

$$\langle \Sigma^+|j|Y_1^{*+}\rangle+\langle \Sigma^-|j|Y_1^{*-}\rangle = 2\langle \Sigma^0|j|Y_1^{*0}\rangle.$$

5.5. Electromagnetic properties of the pseudoscalar mesons

1. The pseudoscalar mesons π, K, η, X^0 belong to an octuplet and a singulet. The U spin structure is very close to those obtained for the baryons.

TABLE 5.4

Q	U	Multiplet
1	$\frac{1}{2}$	$[\pi^+, K^+]$
0	1	$[\bar{K}^0, M_3, K^0]$
	0	M_0
		X_1^0
-1	$\frac{1}{2}$	$[K^-, \pi^-]$

The U spin eigenstates M_0 and M_3 are two linear combinations of π^0 and η^0:

$$M_0 = \tfrac{1}{2}(\pi^0\sqrt{3}-\eta^0) \qquad M_3 = \tfrac{1}{2}(\pi^0-\eta^0\sqrt{3}).$$

The mixing angle between η and X^0 has been found very small on the basis of mass considerations. In a very good approximation, X^0 is a unitary symmetry singulet state.

2. The relations due to U spin invariance are the following (CABIBBO and GATTO [1962]):

$$\begin{aligned}
\langle\pi^+|j^n|\pi^+\rangle &= \langle K^+|j^n|K^+\rangle\\
\langle\pi^-|j^n|\pi^-\rangle &= \langle K^-|j^n|K^-\rangle\\
\langle K^0|j^n|K^0\rangle &= \langle\bar{K}^0|j^n|\bar{K}^0\rangle\\
\langle\pi^0|j^n|\eta^0\rangle &= \langle\eta^0|j^n|\pi^0\rangle\\
\langle K^0|j^n|K^0\rangle &= \langle\pi^0|j^n|\pi^0\rangle-\sqrt{3}\langle\pi^0|j^n|\eta^0\rangle\\
2\langle\eta^0|j^n|\eta^0\rangle &= \langle\pi^0|j^n|\pi^0\rangle+2\langle K^0|j^n|K^0\rangle
\end{aligned}$$

for the octuplet-octuplet electromagnetic transitions and:

$$\begin{aligned}
\langle\pi^0|j^n|X_1^0\rangle &= \langle X_1^0|j^n|\pi^0\rangle\\
\langle\eta^0|j^n|X_1^0\rangle &= \langle X_1^0|j^n|\eta^0\rangle\\
\langle\pi^0|j^n|X_1^0\rangle &= \sqrt{3}\langle\eta^0|j^n|X_1^0\rangle
\end{aligned}$$

for the octuplet-singulet electromagnetic transitions.

The charge conjugation invariance of the electromagnetic interactions gives some new relations. The mesons π^0, η, X^0 are eigenstates of the charge conjugation operator C with the eigenvalue $+1$ whereas the charge parity of the photon is -1. Up to a phase we have:

$$C|\pi^\pm\rangle = |\pi^\mp\rangle; \qquad C|K^\pm\rangle = |K^\mp\rangle; \qquad C|K^0\rangle = |\bar{K}^0\rangle$$

and it follows immediately, from charge conjugation invariance only:

$$\langle\pi^0|j^{2m+1}|\pi^0\rangle = 0 \qquad \langle\eta|j^{2m+1}|\eta\rangle = 0 \qquad \langle X^0|j^{2m+1}|X^0\rangle = 0$$
$$\langle\pi^0|j^{2m+1}|\eta\rangle = 0 \qquad \langle\pi^0|j^{2m+1}|X^0\rangle = 0 \qquad \langle\eta|j^{2m+1}|X^0\rangle = 0$$

$$\langle K^0|j^n|K^0\rangle = (-1)^n\langle\overline{K}^0|j^n|\overline{K}^0\rangle$$
$$\langle\pi^\pm|j^n|\pi^\pm\rangle = (-1)^n\langle\pi^\mp|j^n|\pi^\mp\rangle$$
$$\langle K^\pm|j^n|K^\pm\rangle = (-1)^n\langle K^\mp|j^n|K^\mp\rangle.$$

These equalities, combined with U spin invariance, give the relation:

$$\langle K^0|j^{2m+1}|K^0\rangle = 0 = \langle\overline{K}^0|j^{2m+1}|\overline{K}^0\rangle.$$

The matrix elements, of odd order with respect to electromagnetic interactions vanish for all the neutral pseudoscalar mesons.

3. The problem of the electromagnetic mass differences can be treated, using the same technique as explained for the baryon octuplet case, but the *TCP* invariance which insures the equality of the masses for the particles and the antiparticles simplifies the calculations.

We first write the mass operator in the form:

$$m^2 = m^2(I, Y)+\delta m^2(U, Q)$$

and we obtain only one relation – instead of two for the baryons – the Coleman-Glashow relation becoming an identity by the *TCP* theorem (Barton and Rosen [1962])

$$-\sqrt{3}\,\delta m^2_{\eta^0\pi^0} = (m^2_{K^0}-m^2_{K})+(m^2_{\pi^+}-m^2_{\pi^0}).$$

The numerical value is:

$$\delta m^2_{\eta^0\pi^0} = -(2960\pm 365)\ \text{MeV}^2.$$

In a first approximation, we neglect the ηX^0 mixing and we use the previous value for the electromagnetic quantity $\delta m^2_{\eta^0\pi^0}$. We have an electromagnetic η-π^0 mixing and we define the physical states as (Dalitz and Von Hippel [1964]):

$$\pi^0_{\text{phys}} = \pi^0\cos\beta-\eta^0\sin\beta$$
$$\eta_{\text{phys}} = \pi^0\sin\beta+\eta^0\cos\beta.$$

The β angle is calculated from $\delta m^2_{\eta^0\pi^0}$ using:

$$\text{tg}\,2\beta = \frac{2\delta m^2_{\eta^0\pi^0}}{m^2_{\eta^0}-m^2_{\pi^0}}$$

and we obtain:

$$\beta_{\eta^0\pi^0} \simeq -0.0105 \pm 0.0013.$$

It can be interesting to take into account the interference terms between the medium strong interactions and the electromagnetic interactions. If we restrict ourselves to the first order in H_Y we obtain:

$$2\sqrt{3}\,\delta m^2_{\eta^0\pi^0} = 3m^2_{\eta^0} + m^2_{\pi^0} - 4m^2_{K^0}.$$

4. Due to the *TCP* invariance, we have the following relations for the electromagnetic form factors of the pseudoscalar mesons:

$$F_{\pi^0} = 0 \qquad F_{\eta} = 0 \qquad F_{X^0} = 0$$

$$F_{K^+} + F_{K^-} = 0 \qquad F_{\pi^+} + F_{\pi^-} = 0 \qquad F_{K^0} + F_{\bar{K}^0} = 0.$$

On the other hand, the electromagnetic vertices $\gamma_{\pi^0\eta}$, $\gamma_{\pi^0 X^0}$, $\gamma_{\eta X^0}$ vanish because of charge conjugation invariance:

$$F_{\pi^0\eta} = 0 \qquad F_{\pi^0 X^0} = 0 \qquad F_{\eta X^0} = 0.$$

If we neglect the medium strong interactions, the U spin invariance holds and we deduce two relations due to U spin invariance only:

$$F_{K^+} = F_{\pi^+} \qquad F_{K^0} = 0.$$

We introduce the influence of the medium strong interactions as an additional perturbation and we obtain only one relation:

$$F_{\pi^+} = F_{K^+} - F_{K^0}.$$

Finally, if we take into account the interference between the electromagnetic interactions and the medium strong interactions restricted to first order, there only remains the vanishing of the K^0 form factor:

$$F_{K^0} = 0.$$

5. The decays into photons of π^0, η and X^0 can be related in the framework of unitary symmetry. The charge conjugation invariance of electromagnetic interactions forbids a decay into an odd number of photons and the most frequent mode is a 2γ mode.

As a consequence of U spin invariance, the decay of the M_3 state into photons is forbidden and we obtain a relation between the radiative decay amplitudes for π^0 and η^0 (CABIBBO and GATTO [1962]),

$$A(\pi^0 \Rightarrow 2m\gamma) = \sqrt{3}A(\eta^0 \Rightarrow 2m\gamma).$$

The three decays of π^0, η, X^0 depend on two reduced amplitudes, one related to the octuplet, and one to the singulet. Using the $\eta^0 X_1^0$ mixing angle defined in chapter IX, we immediately obtain, taking into account the phase space factors:

$$\frac{\Gamma(\eta \Rightarrow 2\gamma)}{\Gamma(\pi^0 \Rightarrow 2\gamma)} = \left(\frac{m_\eta}{m_{\pi^0}}\right)^3 \frac{1}{3\cos^2\alpha}(1-\zeta\sqrt{3}\sin\alpha)^2$$

$$\frac{\Gamma(X^0 \Rightarrow 2\gamma)}{\Gamma(\pi^0 \Rightarrow 2\gamma)} = \left(\frac{m_{X^0}}{m_{\pi^0}}\right)^3 \zeta^2.$$

The phase space corrections are extremely large:

$$\left(\frac{m_\eta}{m_{\pi^0}}\right)^3 = 67.14 \qquad \left(\frac{m_{X^0}}{m_{\pi^0}}\right)^3 = 358.47$$

and if we neglect the $\eta^0 X_1^0$ mixing, the partial width $\Gamma(\eta \Rightarrow 2\gamma)$ predicted by the unitary symmetry is:

$$\Gamma(\eta \Rightarrow 2\gamma)_{\text{th}} = (140 \pm 25)\ \text{eV};$$

by using the experimental value (VON DARDEL et al. [1963]):

$$\Gamma(\pi^0 \Rightarrow 2\gamma)_{\text{exp}} = (6.3 \pm 1.1)\ \text{eV}.$$

Of course, the $\eta^0 X_1^0$ mixing can disturb the previous prediction in a large way if the $X^0 \Rightarrow 2\gamma$ amplitude turns out to be large (DALITZ and VON HIPPEL [1964]).

5.6. Electromagnetic properties of the vector mesons

1. The vector mesons ρ, K^*, ω, φ belong to an octuplet and to a singulet and we will use the following ω-φ mixing due to medium strong interactions:

$$\omega = \omega^0 \cos\lambda + \varphi^0 \sin\lambda$$
$$\varphi = -\omega^0 \sin\lambda + \varphi^0 \cos\lambda,$$

where φ^0 and ω^0 are respectively $I = Y = 0$ members of an octuplet and a singulet. We define, as usual the two linear U spin combinations:

$$V_0 = \tfrac{1}{2}(\rho^0\sqrt{3} + \varphi^0), \qquad V_3 = \tfrac{1}{2}(\rho^0 - \varphi^0\sqrt{3}).$$

TABLE 5.4

Q	U	Multiplet
1	$\frac{1}{2}$	$[\rho^+, K^{*+}]$
	1	$[\overline{K}^{0*}, V_3, K^{0*}]$
0	0	V_0
	0	ω_0
-1	$\frac{1}{2}$	$[K^{*-}, \rho^-]$

2. All the properties we have found for the pseudoscalar mesons can be extended in a very simple way to the vector mesons. We only remark that the charge conjugation acts in an opposite way on the neutral mesons:

$$C|\rho^0\rangle = -|\rho^0\rangle, \qquad C|\omega\rangle = -|\omega\rangle, \qquad C|\varphi\rangle = -|\varphi\rangle.$$

In particular, if the U spin invariance holds, the odd order electromagnetic matrix elements vanish for all the neutral vector mesons. The octuplet and the singulet can be connected via electromagnetic interactions. The U spin invariance forbids the ω^0-V_3 transition,

$$\langle\rho^0|j^n|\omega^0\rangle = 3\langle\varphi^0|j^n|\omega^0\rangle.$$

3. The problem of the electromagnetic mass differences of vector mesons is complicated because of the existence of the ω-φ mixing. We assume the electromagnetic corrections to be independent on the medium strong interactions and we obtain:

$$\begin{aligned} \delta m^2_{\rho^\pm} &= \delta m^2_{K^{*\pm}} \\ \delta m^2_{K^{*0}} = \delta m^2_{\overline{K}^{*0}} &= \delta m^2_{\rho^0} - \sqrt{3}\,\delta m^2_{\rho^0\varphi^0} \\ \sqrt{3}[\delta m^2_{\rho^0} - \delta m^2_{\varphi^0}] &= 2\delta m^2_{\rho^0\varphi^0} \\ \delta m^2_{\rho^0\omega^0} &= \sqrt{3}\,\delta m^2_{\varphi^0\omega^0} \end{aligned}$$

and the only relation in terms of physical masses is:

$$\sqrt{3}[\delta m^2_{\rho^0\varphi} \cos\lambda + \delta m^2_{\rho^0\omega} \sin\lambda] = (m^2_{\rho^0} - m^2_{\rho^+}) + (m^2_{K^*} - m^2_{K^{*0}}).$$

For the neutral particles of hypercharge $Y = 0$, the ρ^0, ω and φ mesons, we have a 3×3 mass matrix and the non diagonal matrix elements associated with φ-ω, φ-ρ^0 and ω-φ^0 electromagnetic transitions are related to the electromagnetic self energies of ρ^0, ω, φ by two relations only.

4. Due to *TCP* invariance, we have the following relations between the electromagnetic form factors of the vector mesons:

$$F_{\rho^0} = 0 \qquad F_{\omega} = 0 \qquad F_{\varphi} = 0$$
$$F_{\rho^+} + F_{\rho^-} = 0 \qquad F_{K^{*+}} + F_{K^{*-}} = 0 \qquad F_{K^{*0}} + F_{\bar{K}^{*0}} = 0.$$

On the other hand, the electromagnetic vertices $\gamma\rho^0\omega$, $\gamma\rho^0\varphi$ and $\gamma\varphi\omega$ vanish because of charge conjugation invariance:

$$F_{\rho^0\omega} = 0, \qquad F_{\rho^0\varphi} = 0, \qquad F_{\varphi\omega} = 0.$$

If we neglect the medium strong interactions, the U spin invariance holds and we deduce two relations:

$$F_{K^{*0}} = 0, \qquad F_{K^{*+}} = F_{\rho^+}.$$

We now introduce the influence of the medium strong interactions as an additional perturbation and we obtain only one relation:

$$F_{\rho^+} = F_{K^{*+}} - F_{K^{*0}}.$$

Finally, if we take into account the interference between the electromagnetic interactions and the medium strong interactions restricted to first order, there only remains the vanishing of the K^{*0} form factors.

5. The decays into a system of photons of the ρ^0, ω and φ mesons are related in the framework of unitary symmetry. The charge conjugation invariance forbids a decay into an even number of photons and the most frequent mode will be a 3γ mode.

If the photon is virtual, the transition V-γ can occur. Let us consider the decays:

$$V \Rightarrow e^+e^- \qquad \text{and} \qquad V \Rightarrow \mu^+\mu^-$$

which occur essentially through a one photon exchange, see fig. 5.2.

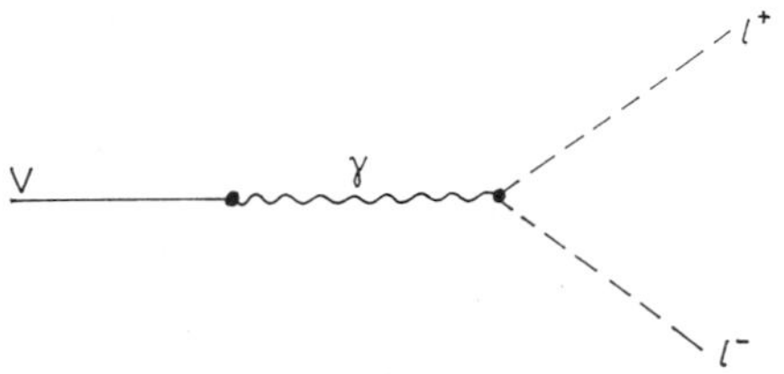

Fig. 5.2.

From Lorentz invariance, the matrix elements of the electromagnetic current between the vacuum and a one vector meson state has the following structure:

$$\langle 0|J_\alpha^{\mathrm{em}}|\mathrm{V}\rangle = eg(-m_{\mathrm{v}}^2)\rho_\alpha(K, \lambda)$$

where $\rho_\alpha(K, \lambda)$ is the polarization four vector for a meson of energy momentum K and helicity λ. Of course, we have to take into account the supplementary condition $K^\sigma \rho_\sigma(K, \lambda) = 0$.

We use the electromagnetic coupling at the $\gamma l^+ l^-$ vertex and the decay rate can then be written as (GOURDIN [1964c]):

$$\frac{\Gamma(\omega \Rightarrow \mathrm{e}^+\mathrm{e}^-)}{\Gamma(\rho^0 \Rightarrow \mathrm{e}^+\mathrm{e}^-)} = \tfrac{1}{3}\sin^2\lambda \left(\frac{m_\varphi}{m_\omega}\right)^3 \simeq 0.12$$

$$\frac{\Gamma(\omega \Rightarrow \mathrm{e}^+\mathrm{e}^-)}{\Gamma(\varphi \Rightarrow \mathrm{e}^+\mathrm{e}^-)} = \mathrm{tg}^2\lambda \left(\frac{m_\varphi}{m_\omega}\right)^3 \simeq 1.56.$$

The comparison of the ω and φ radiative decay rates will give a direct determination of the mixing angle (DASHEN and SHARP [1964]). But the experiments are too difficult to provide a good measurement of λ. The previous numbers are calculated for $\lambda = 41°$ as found previously.

It is possible to estimate the partial radiative decay widths by calculating first the $\rho^0 \Rightarrow \mathrm{e}^+\mathrm{e}^-$ transition. We follow GELL-MANN et al. [1962] to relate the $\rho^0\gamma$ coupling constant and the $f_{\rho\pi\pi}$ coupling constant previously used in the calculation of the $\rho \Rightarrow 2\pi$ decay width,

$$\frac{g_{\rho\gamma}}{m_\rho^2} \simeq \frac{1}{f_{\rho\pi\pi}}.$$

For a $\Gamma(\rho \Rightarrow 2\pi)$ width of 100 MeV, we found $f_{\rho\pi\pi}^2/4\pi \simeq 2$ and it follows immediately:

$$\Gamma(\rho^0 \Rightarrow \mathrm{e}^+\mathrm{e}^-) \simeq 6.6\ \mathrm{keV}.$$

A recent measurement of the branching ratio gives (ZDANIS et al. [1965]):

$$\frac{\Gamma(\rho^0 \Rightarrow \mathrm{e}^+\mathrm{e}^-)}{\Gamma(\rho \Rightarrow 2\pi)} \simeq 0.5\begin{array}{c}+0.6\\-0.3\end{array}\times 10^{-4}$$

in good agreement with the theoretical value:

$$\frac{\Gamma(\rho^0 \Rightarrow \mathrm{e}^+\mathrm{e}^-)}{\Gamma(\rho \Rightarrow 2\pi)} = 0.66\times 10^{-4}.$$

We are now able to give a prediction for the absolute ω and φ decay rates:

$$\Gamma(\omega \Rightarrow e^+e^-) = 0.8\ \text{keV}, \qquad \Gamma(\varphi \Rightarrow e^+e^-) \simeq 0.5\ \text{keV}.$$

The branching ratios can also be calculated. Assuming $\Gamma(\omega \Rightarrow 3\pi) \simeq 10$ MeV the theoretical and experimental values are in good agreement (ZDANIS et al. [1965]):

$$\left(\frac{\Gamma(\omega \Rightarrow e^+e^-)}{\Gamma(\omega \Rightarrow 3\pi)}\right)_{\text{th}} \simeq 0.8 \times 10^{-4} \quad \left(\frac{\Gamma(\omega \Rightarrow e^+e^-)}{\Gamma(\omega \Rightarrow 3\pi)}\right)_{\text{exp}} \simeq 1 \begin{array}{c} +1.2 \\ -0.8 \end{array} \times 10^{-4}.$$

Unfortunately the φ branching ratio is not known experimentally with enough accuracy to be compared with the theoretical prediction.

6. We are now interested in the radiative decay of the vector mesons into a pseudoscalar meson and a real photon. The U spin invariance gives some relations for the electromagnetic matrix elements analogous to those previously obtained for vector mesons or for pseudoscalar mesons.

The charge conjugation invariance gives some additionnal relations which are different from the two previous cases because of the opposite character of the pseudoscalar mesons and the vector mesons with respect to charge conjugation:

$$\begin{array}{ccc} \langle \pi^0 | j^{2m} | \rho^0 \rangle = 0 & \langle \pi^0 | j^{2m} | \omega \rangle = 0 & \langle \pi^0 | j^{2m} | \varphi \rangle = 0 \\ \langle \eta | j^{2m} | \rho^0 \rangle = 0 & \langle \eta | j^{2m} | \omega \rangle = 0 & \langle \eta | j^{2m} | \omega \rangle = 0 \\ \langle \rho^0 | j^{2m} | X^0 \rangle = 0 & \langle \omega | j^{2m} | X^0 \rangle = 0 & \langle X^0 | j^{2m} | \varphi \rangle = 0 \end{array}$$

$$\begin{aligned} \langle K^0 | j^n | K^{0*} \rangle &= (-1)^{n+1} \langle \overline{K}^0 | j^n | \overline{K}^{*0} \rangle \\ \langle \pi^\pm | j^n | \rho^\pm \rangle &= (-1)^{n+1} \langle \pi^\mp | j^n | \rho^\mp \rangle \\ \langle K^\pm | j^n | K^{*\pm} \rangle &= (-1)^{n+1} \langle K^\mp | j^n | K^{*\mp} \rangle. \end{aligned}$$

These equalities combined with U spin invariance gives the relation:

$$\langle K^0 | j^{2m} | K^{0*} \rangle = 0 = \langle \overline{K}^0 | j^{2m} | \overline{K}^{*0} \rangle$$

and the matrix elements of even order with respect to electromagnetic interactions vanish for all the neutral meson transitions.

We are now restricted to the special case of the first order electromagnetic transitions. Due to parity conservation and gauge invariance we have only one electromagnetic form factor if the photon is virtual and consequently one coupling for a real photon. The general structure of the Lorentz invariant matrix element is given by:

$$\langle K' | J^{\text{em}}_\alpha | K, \lambda \rangle = e G_{\text{VM}\gamma}(q^2) \varepsilon_{\alpha\beta\gamma\rho} K^\beta K'^\gamma \rho^\rho(K, \lambda).$$

The decay width is computed after summation over the photon and vector meson polarizations and the result takes the form:

$$\Gamma(\mathrm{V} \Rightarrow \mathrm{M}+\gamma) = \tfrac{1}{3}\alpha g^2_{\mathrm{VM}\gamma}\left(\frac{m_{\mathrm{V}}^2 - m_{\mathrm{M}}^2}{2m_{\mathrm{V}}}\right)^3,$$

where as usual α is the fine structure constant $\alpha = \frac{1}{137}$.

In the framework of unitary symmetry the octuplet-octuplet transitions are described by one reduced matrix element only because of charge conjugation invariance and only the symmetric isometry $\Omega_Q^{(8s)}$ can contribute. Due to U spin invariance, we have also only one reduced matrix element for the octuplet-singulet transition and only one for the singulet-octuplet transition:

$$A(\omega^0 \Rightarrow \mathrm{M}_3+\gamma) = 0, \qquad A(\mathrm{V}_3 \Rightarrow \mathrm{X}_1^0+\gamma) = 0.$$

Finally, the singulet-singulet transition is forbidden at first order if the photon belongs to an octuplet. It follows that the 15 coupling constants can be expressed in terms of three reduced quantities and the results are given in the table 5.5.

TABLE 5.5

Transition	g_{88}	g_{18}	g_{81}
$\rho^+\pi^-\gamma$	1		
$\rho^-\pi^+\gamma$	1		
$\rho^0\pi^0\gamma$	1		
$\mathrm{K}^{*+}\mathrm{K}^-\gamma$	1		
$\mathrm{K}^{*-}\mathrm{K}^+\gamma$	1		
$\mathrm{K}^{*0}\overline{\mathrm{K}}{}^0\gamma$	-2		
$\overline{\mathrm{K}}{}^{*0}\mathrm{K}^0\gamma$	-2		
$\varphi\pi^0\gamma$	$\sqrt{3}\cos\lambda$	$-\sqrt{3}\sin\lambda$	
$\omega\pi^0\gamma$	$\sqrt{3}\sin\lambda$	$\sqrt{3}\cos\lambda$	
$\rho^0\eta\gamma$	$\sqrt{3}\cos\alpha$		$-\sqrt{3}\sin\alpha$
$\varphi\eta\gamma$	$-\cos\lambda\cos\alpha$	$-\sin\lambda\cos\alpha$	$-\cos\lambda\sin\alpha$
$\omega\eta\gamma$	$-\sin\lambda\cos\alpha$	$\cos\lambda\cos\alpha$	$-\sin\lambda\sin\alpha$
$\rho^0\mathrm{X}^0\gamma$	$\sqrt{3}\sin\alpha$		$\sqrt{3}\cos\alpha$
$\varphi\mathrm{X}^0\gamma$	$-\cos\lambda\sin\alpha$	$-\sin\lambda\sin\alpha$	$\cos\lambda\cos\alpha$
$\omega\mathrm{X}^0\gamma$	$-\sin\lambda\sin\alpha$	$\cos\lambda\sin\alpha$	$\sin\lambda\cos\alpha$

The only experimental result:

$$\Gamma(\omega \Rightarrow \pi^0+\gamma) = (1.05\pm 0.1)\ \mathrm{MeV}$$

does not allow a comparison between theory and experiment at this stage of the symmetry.

Finally, the same table 5.5 gives the reduced matrix elements for the radiative decay of the X^0 meson into a vector meson and a photon.

5.7. Photoproduction

1. The photoproduction reactions:

$$\gamma + A \Rightarrow B + C$$

are first order electromagnetic interactions. The transition matrix elements can be computed in the general framework of a four body reaction in unitary symmetry as explained in chapter IX, by using, for the photon, the weight $U = Q = 0$ of an octuplet.

As a particular result, the reactions:

$$\gamma \oplus 8 \Rightarrow 8 \oplus 8 \qquad \text{(I)}$$

are described by eight linearly independent amplitudes and the reaction

$$\gamma \oplus 8 \Rightarrow 8 \oplus 10$$

by four linearly independent amplitudes.

2. In the case where medium strong interactions are neglected, the U spin scalar character of the photon plays an important role to exhibit relations between some photoproduction amplitudes.

Let us first consider the case where the target is a proton. There exist six possible reactions of the type I, due to charge and hypercharge conservation. The U spin invariance allows us to write two relations which, for instance, take the form (LEANSON et al. [1963]):

$$\sqrt{2}A(\gamma p \Rightarrow \pi^+ n) = \sqrt{3}A(\gamma p \Rightarrow K^+ \Lambda^0) - A(\gamma p \Rightarrow K^+ \Sigma^0)$$

$$\sqrt{2}A(\gamma p \Rightarrow K^0 \Sigma^+) = \sqrt{3}A(\gamma p \Rightarrow \eta^0 p) - A(\gamma p \Rightarrow \pi^0 p).$$

In the case of type II reactions, we have also two relations between the six physical reactions with a proton target (LEANSON et al. [1963]):

$$A(\gamma p \Rightarrow \pi^+ N^{*0}_{\frac{3}{2}}) = -2A(\gamma p \Rightarrow K^+ Y^{*0}_1)$$

$$\sqrt{2}A(\gamma p \Rightarrow K^0 Y^{*+}_1) = \sqrt{3}A(\gamma p \Rightarrow \eta^0 N^{*+}_{\frac{3}{2}}) - A(\gamma p \Rightarrow \pi^0 N^{*+}_{\frac{3}{2}}).$$

The photoproduction reactions on neutron are reached experimentally using a deuteron target. We obtain reactions of different types because of the U spin character of the neutron. In the case of type I reactions we have for instance:

$$\sqrt{3}A(\gamma n \Rightarrow K^0 \Lambda^0) - A(\gamma n \Rightarrow K^0 \Sigma^0) = \sqrt{3}A(\gamma n \Rightarrow \eta^0 n) - A(\gamma n \Rightarrow \pi^0 n)$$

and for the type II reactions, two equalities:

$$A(\gamma n \Rightarrow K^+Y_1^{*-}) = -\sqrt{3}A(\gamma n \Rightarrow \pi^+N_{\frac{3}{2}}^{*-})$$
$$2A(\gamma n \Rightarrow K^0Y_1^{*0}) = A(\gamma n \Rightarrow \pi^0N_{\frac{3}{2}}^{*0}) - \sqrt{3}A(\gamma n \Rightarrow \eta^0N_{\frac{3}{2}}^{*0}).$$

5.8. Electromagnetic π–Λ coupling

1. The $\Lambda\Lambda\pi^0$ vertex is identically zero in the absence of electromagnetic interactions; we now introduce the physical Λ and π^0 states as defined in sections 5.3 and 5.5, in order to calculate the effective coupling constant following a method due to DALITZ and VON HIPPEL [1964]. In a calculation at first order in $\delta m_{\Sigma^0\Lambda^0}$ and first order in $\delta m^2_{\eta^0\pi^0}$, the $\Lambda\Lambda\pi^0$ transition can be represented as the sum of three contributions corresponding to the three diagrams drawn in fig. 5.3:

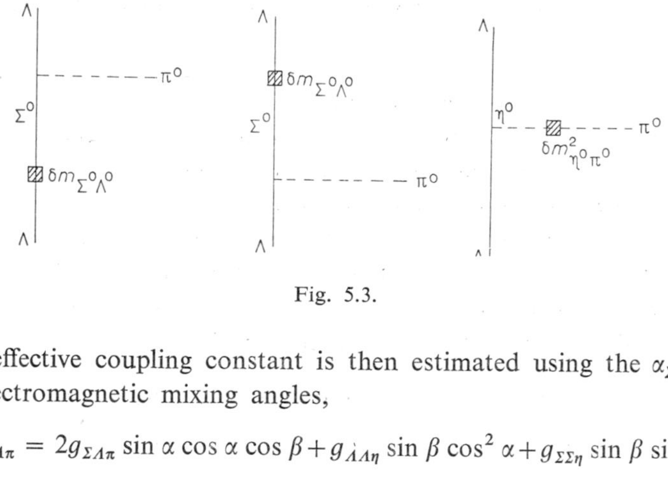

Fig. 5.3.

The effective coupling constant is then estimated using the $\alpha_{\Sigma^0\Lambda^0}$ and $\beta_{\eta^0\pi^0}$ electromagnetic mixing angles,

$$-g_{\Lambda\Lambda\pi} = 2g_{\Sigma\Lambda\pi}\sin\alpha\cos\alpha\cos\beta + g_{\Lambda\Lambda\eta}\sin\beta\cos^2\alpha + g_{\Sigma\Sigma\eta}\sin\beta\sin^2\alpha.$$

In an exact unitary symmetry we have:

$$g_{\Sigma\Lambda\pi} = -g_{\Lambda\Lambda\eta} = g_{\Sigma\Sigma\eta}$$

and it follows:

$$g_{\Lambda\Lambda\pi} = g_{\Sigma\Lambda\pi}\sin(\beta - 2\alpha).$$

Using the previous expressions for the mixing angles α and β we obtain:

$$g_{\Lambda\Lambda\pi} \simeq \left\{\frac{\delta m^2_{\eta^0\pi^0}}{m^2_{\eta^0} - m^2_{\pi^0}} - 2\frac{\delta m_{\Sigma^0\Lambda^0}}{m_{\Sigma^0} - m_{\Lambda^0}}\right\} g_{\Sigma\Lambda\pi}$$

and the numerical value is given by:

$$-\frac{g_{\Lambda\Lambda\pi}}{g_{\Sigma\Lambda\pi}} \simeq 0.041 \pm 0.005.$$

The unitary symmetry relates the $\Sigma\Lambda\pi$ and $NN\pi$ coupling constants following:

$$\frac{g_{\Sigma\Lambda\pi}}{g_{NN\pi}} = \frac{2}{\sqrt{3}} \frac{\rho_s}{1+\rho_s}$$

where ρ_s is the D/F ratio for the pseudoscalar meson-baryon coupling. Experimentally ρ_s is not very well defined: $1 \lesssim \rho_s \lesssim 2.5$ and the previous ratio of the coupling constants lies between 0.6 and 0.8. We then deduce for $g_{\Lambda\Lambda\pi}$ the following estimate:

$$-g_{\Lambda\Lambda\pi} \simeq 0.38 \pm 0.04.$$

CHAPTER VI

WEAK INTERACTIONS

Weak interactions seem to be one of the most interesting domains of applicability of unitary symmetry. The use of symmetries of strong interactions, destroyed by weak interactions as the isotopic spin rotations of the hypercharge gauge, has been extremely useful in the past to obtain some empirical rules and the same power of symmetries is true also with unitary symmetry.

Weak interactions do not conserve P (space reflection) and C (charge conjugation) and the violation in both cases is extremal. The recent observation of a $K_L^0 \Rightarrow 2\pi$ decay mode for the long lived component of the neutral K meson can be interpreted as a violation of PC invariance or equivalently, because of the PCT theorem, of time reversal invariance. Such a violation appears to be small and extremely difficult to detect in processes where a selection rule connected with PC symmetry cannot be involved. The PC invariant terms dominate weak interactions and in what follows we will use exact PC invariance as a first reasonable approximation.

Weak interactions are generally divided into two classes according to the appearance of leptons: the leptonic processes and the non leptonic processes. From the point of view of symmetries such a splitting is useful also. In many models the leptons are assumed to be scalar particles with respect to the transformations associated with the symmetry. The basic fact, in order to exclude leptons from many classification schemes, is the non appearance in nature of neutral leptonic currents comparable to the charged leptonic currents. We will adopt this viewpoint here and therefore study only as leptonic processes the semi-leptonic processes and completely disregard the pure leptonic processes where hadrons are not involved.

6.1. Currents

6.1.1. Conserved currents

1. *Noether theorem.* Let us first briefly recall the results known as the Noether theorem. We consider a lagrangian density L as a function of some

fields $\psi^\alpha(x)$ and of their first derivatives $\psi^\alpha_\mu(x) = \partial\psi^\alpha(x)/\partial x^\mu$. If the lagrangian L is invariant under a variation $\delta\psi^\alpha(x)$ of the fields, it is possible to define a current

$$j^\mu(x) = \frac{\partial L}{\partial \psi^\alpha_\mu}\, \delta\psi^\alpha,$$

which is divergenceless. The integral of such a current over a space like 3-dimensional surface Σ is independent of Σ:

$$G = \int_\Sigma j^\mu(x) \mathrm{d}\sigma_\mu .$$

It is then convenient to choose, for practical calculations, the surface Σ as the ordinary three-dimensional euclidian space taken at a given time t. The integral G is time-independent

$$G = \int j^0(x) \mathrm{d}\boldsymbol{r}.$$

2. Let us now introduce a Lie algebra Λ with the infinitesimal generators X_σ:

$$[X_\sigma, X_\rho] = C^\tau_{\sigma\rho} X_\tau .$$

The fields $\psi^\alpha(x)$ are assumed to belong to an irreducible representation of Λ. The infinitesimal variation of $\psi^\alpha(x)$ is given by:

$$\delta\psi^\alpha(x) = \mathrm{i}\varepsilon^\rho [X_\rho]^\alpha_\beta \psi^\beta(x),$$

where $[X_\rho]^\alpha_\beta$ is a matrix representation of the Lie algebra Λ and ε^ρ a set of infinitesimal parameters. It is then convenient to introduce a current for each infinitesimal transformation:

$$J^\mu_\rho(x) = \frac{1}{\mathrm{i}} \frac{\partial L}{\partial \psi^\alpha_\mu(x)} [X_\rho]^\alpha_\beta \psi^\beta(x).$$

If the lagrangian L is invariant under the transformations associated to the Lie algebra Λ then we obtain, as a consequence of the Noether theorem the two equivalent results:

a) the currents are divergenceless:

$$\frac{\partial}{\partial x^\mu} J^\mu_\rho(x) = 0;$$

b) the space integral of the current is time independent:

$$F_\rho = \int J^0_\rho(x)\mathrm{d}\boldsymbol{r}.$$

3. Let us define as usual:

$$\pi^\alpha_\mu(x) = \frac{\partial L}{\partial \psi^\mu_\alpha(x)}.$$

The fields $\psi^\alpha(x)$ and $\pi_{\alpha\mu}(x)$ belong to contragradient representations because of the invariant character of L.

The time component of the current is then written as:

$$J^0_\rho(x) = \frac{1}{\mathrm{i}}\,\pi_\alpha(x)[X_\rho]^\alpha_\beta\psi^\beta(x),$$

where $\pi_\alpha(x) = \pi^0_\alpha(x)$. The fields $\psi^\alpha(x)$ and $\pi_\alpha(x)$ are called conjugate fields and satisfy, in the Heisenberg representation, the equal time commutation relations:

$$\begin{aligned}[][\psi^\alpha(\boldsymbol{r}, t), \pi_\beta(\boldsymbol{r}', t)]_\pm &= \mathrm{i}\delta^\alpha_\beta\delta_3(\boldsymbol{r}-\boldsymbol{r}')\\ [\psi^\alpha(\boldsymbol{r}, t), \psi^\beta(\boldsymbol{r}', t)]_\pm &= 0\\ [\pi_\alpha(\boldsymbol{r}, t), \pi_\beta(\boldsymbol{r}', t)]_\pm &= 0\end{aligned}$$

where $\pm$ depends on the statistics.

Using these relations it is easy to calculate the equal time commutator of the time components of the densities:

$$[J^0_\rho(\boldsymbol{r}, t), J^0_\sigma(\boldsymbol{r}', t)] = \delta_3(\boldsymbol{r}-\boldsymbol{r}')C^\tau_{\rho\sigma}J^0_\tau(\boldsymbol{r}, t)$$

and we finally obtain:

$$[F_\rho(t), F_\sigma(t)] = C^\tau_{\rho\sigma}F_\tau(t).$$

The $F_\rho(t)$'s give a representation of the Lie algebra Λ in the Hilbert space.

4. As a useful illustration of these considerations, we give the explicit expression of the isotopic spin current, retaining only in the first approximation the nucleons and the π mesons. The fields are represented by their symbols only and the x dependence has been dropped for simplicity,

$$\begin{aligned}J^0_\alpha &= \mathrm{i}\left\{\tfrac{1}{2}(\bar{\mathrm{p}}\gamma_\mu\mathrm{p}-\bar{\mathrm{n}}\gamma_\mu\mathrm{n})+\left(\frac{\partial\pi^-}{\partial x^\alpha}\pi^+ - \frac{\partial\pi^+}{\partial x^\alpha}\pi^-\right)\right\}\\ J^+_\alpha &= \mathrm{i}\left\{\bar{\mathrm{n}}\gamma_\alpha\mathrm{p}+\sqrt{2}\left(\frac{\partial\pi^+}{\partial x^\alpha}\pi^0 - \frac{\partial\pi^0}{\partial x^\alpha}\pi^+\right)\right\}\\ J^-_\alpha &= \mathrm{i}\left\{\bar{\mathrm{p}}\gamma_\alpha\mathrm{n}-\sqrt{2}\left(\frac{\partial\pi^-}{\partial x^\alpha}\pi^0 - \frac{\partial\pi^0}{\partial x^\alpha}\pi^-\right)\right\}.\end{aligned}$$

6.1.2. PHENOMENOLOGY OF WEAK CURRENTS

1. We are first interested by the hypercharge conserving transitions. Let us consider the neutron β decay and the μ meson decay as two useful examples:

$$\mathrm{n} \Rightarrow \mathrm{p}+\mathrm{e}^{-}+\bar{\nu}_{\mathrm{e}}, \qquad \mu^{-} \Rightarrow \nu_{\mu}+\mathrm{e}^{-}+\bar{\nu}_{\mathrm{e}}.$$

In the FERMI [1933, 1934] theory the effective weak hamiltonian is written as a sum of products of weak currents:

$$H_{\mathrm{eff}}^{\beta} = \frac{G_{\mathrm{V}}}{\sqrt{2}}[J^{\mathrm{V}+}j^{l-}+J^{\mathrm{V}-}j^{l+}]-\frac{G_{\mathrm{A}}}{\sqrt{2}}[J^{\mathrm{A}+}j^{l-}+J^{\mathrm{A}-}j^{l+}]$$

$$H_{\mathrm{eff}} = \frac{G}{\sqrt{2}}[j^{\mu+}j^{\mathrm{e}-}+j^{\mu-}j^{\mathrm{e}+}].$$

For simplicity the four-vector index α has been dropped in the previous expressions where the leptonic currents j^{l} and the hadronic currents J are given by:

$$\begin{aligned} J_{\alpha}^{\mathrm{V}-} &= \mathrm{i}\bar{\mathrm{p}}\gamma_{\alpha}\mathrm{n} & J_{\alpha}^{\mathrm{V}+} &= \mathrm{i}\bar{\mathrm{n}}\gamma_{\alpha}\mathrm{p} \\ J_{\alpha}^{\mathrm{A}-} &= \mathrm{i}\bar{\mathrm{p}}\gamma_{\alpha}\gamma_{5}\mathrm{n} & J_{\alpha}^{\mathrm{A}+} &= \mathrm{i}\bar{\mathrm{n}}\gamma_{\alpha}\gamma_{5}\mathrm{p} \\ j_{\alpha}^{l-} &= \mathrm{i}\bar{\nu}_{l}(1-\gamma_{5})\gamma_{\alpha}l & j_{\alpha}^{l+} &= \mathrm{i}\bar{l}\gamma_{\alpha}(1+\gamma_{5})\nu_{l} \end{aligned}$$

with $l = \mathrm{e}^{-}$ or μ^{-}.

We have the two experimental results:

$$\frac{G_{\mathrm{V}}}{G} \simeq 0.978; \qquad -\frac{G_{\mathrm{A}}}{G_{\mathrm{V}}} \simeq 1.16 \pm 0.04.$$

2. The conserved vector current (C.V.C.) theory assumes that the charged vector currents appearing in β decay, $J_{\alpha}^{\mathrm{V}-}$ and $J_{\alpha}^{\mathrm{V}+}$ are the charged components of the isotopic spin current.

This hypothesis is due to GERNSTEIN and ZELDOVITCH [1955] and to FEYNMAN and GELL-MANN [1958].

All the implications of the C.V.C. theory will not be discussed here and we restrict ourselves to some consequences only:

a) The vector coupling constant G_{V} is not renormalized by strong interactions and only small electromagnetic effects can be expected. The axial vector currents cannot be conserved currents and the observed difference between the physical coupling constants G_{A} and G_{V} can be attributed to a renormalization effect if the bare coupling constants are assumed to be equal in a pure V-A theory as it is the case for the leptonic currents,

$$G_{\mathrm{V}}^{0} = G_{\mathrm{A}}^{0}, \qquad G_{\mathrm{V}} = G_{\mathrm{V}}^{0}, \qquad G_{\mathrm{A}} \neq G_{\mathrm{A}}^{0}.$$

b) The rate for the β decay of the charged π mesons:

$$\pi^+ \Rightarrow \pi^0 + e^+ + \nu_e$$

is completely known from the vector coupling constant G_V. The T matrix element is the product of two currents:

$$T_{fi} = i \frac{G}{\sqrt{2}} [\bar{u}_e \gamma_\alpha (1+\gamma_5) u_\nu] \langle \pi^0 | J_\alpha | \pi^- \rangle .$$

The transition is of the pure vector type and the matrix element of the hadronic current is given by the C.V.C. theory:

$$\langle \pi^0 | J_\alpha^V | \pi^+ \rangle = \frac{1}{i} \frac{G_V}{G} \sqrt{2} F_\pi(q^2)(p_{\pi^0} + p_{\pi^+}),$$

where p_{π^0} and p_{π^+} are the energy momentum of the π mesons; q^2 is the square of the transfer of momentum $q^2 = (p_{\pi^+} - p_{\pi^0})^2$ and $F_\pi(q^2)$ is the π-meson electromagnetic form factor normalized as usual to $F_\pi(0) = 1$.

The theoretical branching ratio:

$$\frac{\Gamma(\pi^+ \Rightarrow \pi^0 + e^+ + \nu_e)_{th}}{\Gamma(\pi^+ \Rightarrow \mu^+ + \nu_\mu)_{exp}} \simeq \left(\frac{G_V}{G}\right)^2 1.03 \times 10^{-8}$$

agrees with the experimental measurements within the errors:

$$\frac{\Gamma(\pi^+ \Rightarrow \pi^0 + e^+ + \nu_e)_{exp}}{\Gamma(\pi^+ \Rightarrow \mu^+ + \nu_\mu)} \simeq (1.13 \pm 0.09) \times 10^{-8}.$$

c) The effect of strong interactions is described by the appearance of induced couplings and of form factors. Let us consider for instance the case of nucleons. The C.V.C. theory tells us that the matrix elements of the weak currents are deduced from those of the isovector electromagnetic current and we have only to change the coupling constant. The matrix elements of the conserved vector current are then given for the nucleons by:

$$\langle K', \lambda' | J_\alpha^{V\pm} | K, \lambda \rangle = \bar{u}_N(K', \lambda') \left[i\gamma_\alpha F_1^V(q^2) - \frac{1}{4M} [\gamma_\alpha, \not{q}] F_2^V(q^2) \right] \tau^\pm u_N(K, \lambda)$$

where the isovector nucleon electromagnetic form factors are normalized following:

$$F_1^V(0) = 1, \qquad F_2^V(0) = \kappa_P - \kappa_N .$$

The 4×2 component spinor $u_N(K, \lambda)$ describes a nucleon of energy momentum K and helicity λ. The transfer of momentum q is defined by $q = K' - K$

and we have put $\not{q} = \gamma^\rho q_\rho$. The anomalous proton and neutron magnetic moments κ_P and κ_N are in unit $e/2M$.

The neutral component of the isotopic spin current is the isovector part of the electromagnetic current and the coupling constant is then the electric charge e.

The two charged components of the isotopic spin current are the weak vector currents and the coupling constant is $G_V/\sqrt{2}$.

3. The very close values of G_V and G can be understood in the framework of the C.V.C. theory if we add a new assumption, of different nature, about some form of universality in weak interactions.

Nevertheless, as will be seen later, the remaining 2 % of discrepancy can be significant and unitary symmetry will give a possible explanation for such a difference.

4. We have assumed the leptonic currents for electron and muon to be formally identical. The electron-muon universality in weak interactions is strongly suggested by the ratio of the two π decay rates. The theoretical value predicted by the V-A theory is simply given by

$$R = \frac{\Gamma(\pi \Rightarrow e+\nu_e)}{\Gamma(\pi \Rightarrow \mu+\nu_\mu)} = \left(\frac{m_e}{m_\mu}\right)^2 \left[\frac{1-m_e^2/m_\pi^2}{1-m_\mu^2/m_\pi^2}\right]^2 \simeq 1.28\times 10^{-4}$$

and agrees very well with the experimental value:

$$R_{\text{exp}} \simeq (1.247 \pm 0.028)\times 10^{-4}.$$

5. The T matrix element of the charged pion decay $\pi^- \Rightarrow \mu^- + \nu_\mu$ can be written, in the Fermi theory, as the product of two currents:

$$T_{\text{fi}} = \mathrm{i}\frac{G}{\sqrt{2}}[\bar{u}_\mu \gamma_\alpha(1+\gamma_5)u_\nu]\langle 0|J_\alpha^{\text{A}}|\pi^-\rangle.$$

The general structure of the matrix element of the hadronic current between the vacuum and the one π-meson state is extremely simple:

$$\langle 0|J_\alpha^{\text{A}}|\pi^-\rangle = \mathrm{i}k_\alpha f_\pi$$

where k_α is the energy momentum four-vector of the real incident π-meson. The decay rate is then easily calculated:

$$\Gamma(\pi^- \Rightarrow \mu^- + \bar{\nu}_\mu) = \tfrac{1}{2}G^2 \frac{f_\pi^2}{4\pi} m_\pi m_\mu^2 \left(1-\frac{m_\mu^2}{m_\pi^2}\right)^2.$$

The coupling constant f_π is the value at $k^2 = -m_\pi^2$ of an analytic function $f_\pi(k^2)$. It can be shown that $f_\pi(k^2)$ is analytic in the k^2 complex plane except for a cut on the real negative axis from $-(3m_\pi)^2$ to $-\infty$.

GOLDBERGER and TREIMAN [1958] write an unsubtracted relation for $f_\pi(k^2)$. The spectral function is determined from the unitarity relation in the approximation where only the $n\bar{p}$ intermediate state is retained. Such a calculation involves the axial vector coupling constant G_A and the π-meson-nucleon strong coupling constant $g(g^2/4\pi \simeq 14)$. The main important result is the so-called Goldberger-Treiman relation (GOLDBERGER and TREIMAN [1958]):

$$f_\pi = -\frac{G_A}{G}\frac{2M}{g\sqrt{2}}.$$

The experimental π^- decay rate is:

$$\Gamma(\pi^- \Rightarrow \mu^- + \bar{\nu}_\mu)_{\text{exp}} \simeq (1.84 \pm 0.04) \times 10^{-16} m_\pi$$

and the experimental value of f_π is then:

$$f_\pi \simeq 0.95 m_\pi.$$

The theoretical value of f_π calculated by the Goldberger-Treiman formula:

$$(f_\pi)_{\text{th}} \simeq (0.85 \pm 0.06) m_\pi$$

is in surprising agreement with the experimental one despite the crude approximations involved in the original dispersive approach.

6. The matrix elements of the axial vector current for the nucleons take the form (the coupling constant is as previously $G/\sqrt{2}$):

$$\langle K', \lambda' | J_\alpha^{A\pm} | K, \lambda \rangle = \bar{u}_N(K', \lambda') \left[i\gamma_\alpha \gamma_5 F_1^A(q^2) + \frac{q_\alpha}{2M} \gamma_5 F_2^A(q^2) \right] \tau^\pm u_N(K, \lambda)$$

if we retain only the two "normal" terms of G parity -1.

The axial form factor $F_1^A(q^2)$ is normalized so that:

$$F_1^A(0) = -G_A/G.$$

Let us now calculate, with GOLDBERGER and TREIMAN [1958], the weak axial form factors in the one-pion approximation as described in fig. 6.1.

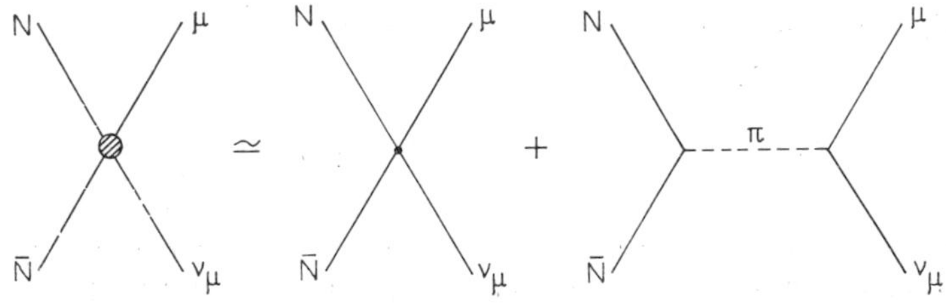

Fig. 6.1.

The first diagram corresponds to the local Fermi interaction and gives the normalization condition for F_1^A.

The second diagram contributes only to $F_2^A(q^2)$ and we obtain the one-pion pole formula:

$$F_2^A(q^2) \simeq \frac{2Mgf_\pi\sqrt{2}}{q^2+m_\pi^2}.$$

Taking into account the Goldberger-Treiman formula, this expression can be transformed into:

$$F_2^A(q^2) = -\frac{G_A}{G}\frac{4M^2}{q^2+m_\pi^2}.$$

An interesting application of such a model as given by the μ^- meson capture at rest on a proton:

$$\mu^- + \mathrm{p} \Rightarrow \mathrm{n} + \nu_\mu.$$

The transfer of momentum is very close to $q^2 \simeq m_\mu^2$ and the term $F_2^A(q^2)$ simulates a pseudoscalar interaction and the equivalent pseudoscalar coupling constant is defined by:

$$\frac{G_P}{G} \simeq -\frac{m_\mu}{2M} F_2^A(m_\mu^2).$$

Using the previous expression for the axial form factor we obtain the theoretical value:

$$G_P \simeq 7G_A$$

which is in reasonable agreement with experiment.

7. The theory of the partially conserved axial vector current as proposed by GELL-MANN and LÉVY [1960] provides a natural scheme to understand the Goldberger-Treiman formula and the one-pion pole approximation.

The divergence of the axial vector current is assumed to be proportional to the π meson field:

$$\frac{\partial J_\alpha^A(x)}{\partial x_\alpha} = a\phi(x).$$

By comparing the matrix elements of the two operators in the following situations:

between the vacuum and the one-pion state;
between two one-nucleon states;

it is possible to eliminate the unknown quantity a and we obtain:

$$F_1^{\mathrm{A}}(q^2) - \frac{q^2}{4M^2} F_2^{\mathrm{A}}(q^2) \simeq \frac{g\sqrt{2}}{2M} \frac{m_\pi^2}{m_\pi^2 + q^2} f_\pi K(q^2)$$

where $K(q^2)$ is the πNN vertex function for a virtual pion, normalized so that:

$$K(-m_\pi^2) = 1.$$

By considering first the case $q^2 = 0$ we obtain the Goldberger-Treiman formula:

$$f_\pi = -\frac{G_{\mathrm{A}}}{G} \frac{2M}{g\sqrt{2}} \frac{1}{K(0)}$$

modified only by the factor $K(0)$. The comparison between theory and experiment for the π decay shows that $K(0)$ is very close to unity.

The limiting case $q^2 = -m_\pi^2$ gives the residue of the one-pion pole term contained in the axial form factor $F_2^{\mathrm{A}}(q^2)$:

$$\lim_{q^2 + m_\pi^2 \Rightarrow 0} (q^2 + m_\pi^2) F_2^{\mathrm{A}}(q^2) = 2M\, g\sqrt{2} f_\pi .$$

8. For the hypercharge violating leptonic transitions some empirical rules have been experimentally observed:

a) The transitions $|\Delta Y| = 1$ satisfy the rule $\Delta Y = \Delta Q$ and the processes with $\Delta Y = -\Delta Q$ seem to occur only at second order. For $\Sigma\beta$ decay and K_{e_4} decay the experimental situation is the following:

$$\frac{\Gamma(\Sigma^+ \Rightarrow \mathrm{n} + \mathrm{e}^+ + \nu_{\mathrm{e}}) + \Gamma(\Sigma^+ \Rightarrow \mathrm{n} + \mu^+ + \nu_\mu)}{\Gamma(\Sigma^- \Rightarrow \mathrm{n} + \mathrm{e}^- + \bar{\nu}_{\mathrm{e}}) + \Gamma(\Sigma^- \Rightarrow \mathrm{n} + \mu^- + \bar{\nu}_\mu)} < \tfrac{1}{3}$$

$$\frac{\Gamma(\mathrm{K}^+ \Rightarrow \pi^+ + \pi^+ + \mathrm{e}^- + \bar{\nu}_{\mathrm{e}})}{\Gamma(\mathrm{K}^+ \Rightarrow \pi^+ + \pi^- + \mathrm{e}^+ + \nu_{\mathrm{e}})} > \tfrac{1}{40} .$$

b) The transitions $|\Delta Y| = 1$ have the isotopic spin $|\boldsymbol{\Delta I}| = \frac{1}{2}$. For instance, in K_{l_3} decay we have the following predictions:

$$\Gamma(\mathrm{K}_1^0 \Rightarrow \pi^\pm + l^\mp + \nu_l) = \Gamma(\mathrm{K}_2^0 \Rightarrow \pi^\pm + l^\mp + \nu_l) = 2\Gamma(\mathrm{K}^+ \Rightarrow \pi^0 + l^+ + \nu_l).$$

The first equality is a consequence of CP invariance and of the $\Delta Y = \Delta Q$ rule while the second is due to the $|\boldsymbol{\Delta I}| = \frac{1}{2}$ rule. The agreement with experiment is satisfactory.

c) The transitions $|\Delta Y| = 2$ do not occur at first order and experimentally the decay mode $\Xi^0 \Rightarrow \mathrm{p} + \mathrm{e}^- + \bar{\nu}_{\mathrm{e}}$ is strongly inhibited with respect to the normal mode experimentally measured $\Xi^- \Rightarrow \Lambda + \mathrm{e}^- + \bar{\nu}_{\mathrm{e}}$.

We assume, as previously, a current $\times$current structure for each term of the effective weak hamiltonian and the non leptonic current $J^{\Delta Y=\pm 1}$ will satisfy the same empirical rules because of the invariant character of the leptonic current under hypercharge and isotopic spin transformations.

As a last remark we note that the $\Delta Y = \Delta Q$ rule is a necessary condition to obtain the rule $|\boldsymbol{\Delta I}| = \frac{1}{2}$ but the converse is not true and the two rules are not equivalent.

6.1.3. Weak currents in the SU(3) symmetry

1. The charged vector currents $\Delta Y = 0$ are constructed from the isotopic spin generators I^+ and I^- and under the unitary symmetry transformations they behave like two components of an octuplet.

2. A natural extension of such a result is the following: the weak vector currents are associated to the weights of an octuplet of currents. In the limit of an exact symmetry, all the vector currents are divergenceless as the $\Delta Y = 0$ current and the C.V.C. theory is extended to the complete octuplet.

3. The same type of assumption can be used for the axial vector current empirically justified on the basis of a partially conserved axial vector current hypothesis.

The matrix elements of the weak currents can then be expressed in terms of the two isometries 8:

a) $\Omega^{(8a)}$ represented by the generators;

b) $\Omega^{(8s)}$ represented by symmetrical products of generators.

Of course, only $\Omega^{(8a)}$ is used for the conserved vector currents and conversely, due to the presence of $\Omega^{(8s)}$ the axial vector currents are not conserved.

4. The justification of the previous assumptions can be understood in terms of the empirical selection rules now very well satisfied:

a) there are no $\Delta Y = \pm 2$ currents,

b) the currents $|\Delta Y| = 1$ satisfy $|\boldsymbol{\Delta I}| = \frac{1}{2}$ and $\Delta Y = \Delta Q$,

c) the currents $\Delta Y = 0$ satisfy $|\boldsymbol{\Delta I}| = 1$.

The infinitesimal generators associated to the conserved charged vector currents are the following:

$$\Delta Q = +1 \begin{cases} \Delta Y = 0 & I^+ = \sqrt{6}E_{12} \\ \Delta Y = 1 & V^+ = \sqrt{6}E_{13} \end{cases}$$

$$\Delta Q = -1 \begin{cases} \Delta Y = 0 & I^- = \sqrt{6}E_{21} \\ \Delta Y = -1 & V^- = \sqrt{6}E_{31}\,. \end{cases}$$

The leptonic current is assumed to be invariant under unitary symmetry and the previous selection rules are also valid for the leptonic transitions in the current × current picture.

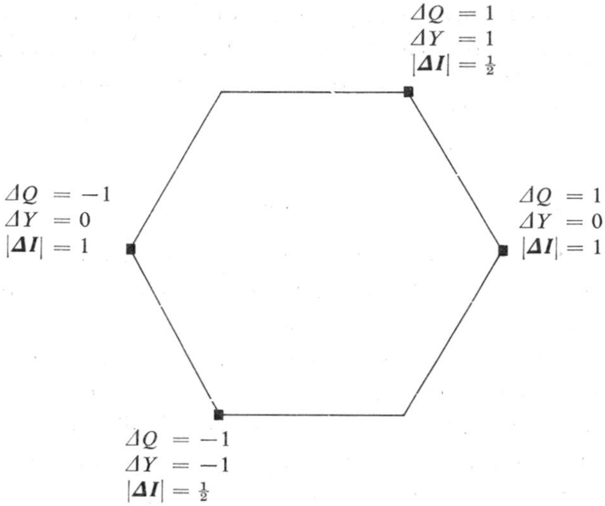

Fig. 6.2. Charged currents of an octuplet.

5. *Matrix elements of the charged baryonic currents.* The conserved vector current J^{V} depends only on the antisymmetric isometry $\Omega^{(8\mathrm{a})}$ and it is constructed from the infinitesimal generators. The axial vector current J^{A} depends on the two isometries $\Omega^{(8\mathrm{a})}$ and $\Omega^{(8\mathrm{s})}$.

The four possible weights of the octuplet associated to the charged currents are quoted by the index ρ.

The direct matrix elements are given by:

$$\langle \mathrm{B}|J^{\mathrm{V}}_{\alpha,\,\rho}|\mathrm{B}\rangle = \mathrm{i}(\overline{\mathrm{B}}_j\gamma_\alpha \mathrm{B}_k)\Omega^{(8\mathrm{a})kj}_{\rho}F^{\mathrm{V}}_{\mathrm{a}}$$

$$\langle \mathrm{B}|J^{\mathrm{A}}_{\alpha,\,\rho}|\mathrm{B}\rangle = \mathrm{i}(\overline{\mathrm{B}}_j\gamma_\alpha\gamma_5 B_k)[\Omega^{(8\mathrm{a})kj}_{\rho}F^{\mathrm{A}}_{\mathrm{a}}+\Omega^{(8\mathrm{s})kj}_{\rho}F^{\mathrm{A}}_{\mathrm{s}}]$$

where B is the 4×8 component baryon field and $F^{\mathrm{V}}_{\mathrm{a}}$, $F^{\mathrm{A}}_{\mathrm{a}}$ and $F^{\mathrm{A}}_{\mathrm{s}}$, three reduced matrix elements.

The computation of the isometry is straightforward.

a) In the antisymmetric case, we use the generators and the result is the following:

$$\Omega^{(8\mathrm{a})}_{12} = |\mathrm{p}\rangle\langle \mathrm{n}| - |\Xi^0\rangle\langle\Xi^-| + \sqrt{2}|\Sigma^0\rangle\langle\Sigma^-| - \sqrt{2}|\Sigma^+\rangle\langle\Sigma^0|,$$

$$\Omega^{(8\mathrm{a})}_{13} = |\Sigma^+\rangle\langle\Xi^0| - |\mathrm{n}\rangle\langle\Sigma^-| + \frac{1}{\sqrt{2}}|\Sigma^0\rangle\langle\Xi^-| - \frac{1}{\sqrt{2}}|\mathrm{p}\rangle\langle\Sigma^0| + \\ + \sqrt{\tfrac{3}{2}}|\Lambda^0\rangle\langle\Xi^-| - \sqrt{\tfrac{3}{2}}|\mathrm{p}\rangle\langle\Lambda^0|.$$

b) In the symmetric case, the isometries are easily obtained by using the 3×3 matrix form of the octuplet:

$$\Omega_{12}^{(8s)} = |\mathrm{p}\rangle\langle \mathrm{n}| + |\Xi^0\rangle\langle\Xi^-| + \sqrt{\tfrac{2}{3}}|\Lambda^0\rangle\langle\Sigma^-| + \sqrt{\tfrac{2}{3}}|\Sigma^+\rangle\langle\Lambda^0|,$$

$$\Omega_{13}^{(8s)} = |\Sigma^+\rangle\langle\Xi^0| + |\mathrm{n}\rangle\langle\Sigma^-| + \frac{1}{\sqrt{2}}|\Sigma^0\rangle\langle\Xi^-| + \frac{1}{\sqrt{2}}|\mathrm{p}\rangle\langle\Sigma^0| + \\ - \frac{1}{\sqrt{6}}|\Lambda^0\rangle\langle\Xi^-| - \frac{1}{\sqrt{6}}|\mathrm{p}\rangle\langle\Lambda^0|.$$

6. *Matrix elements of the charged mesonic currents.* In the conserved vector current theory, the matrix elements of the vector current between two one pseudoscalar meson states, are given by:

$$\langle \mathrm{M}|J^{\mathrm{V}}_{\alpha,\rho}|\mathrm{M}\rangle = \mathrm{i}\,\frac{\partial M_j}{\partial x^\alpha}\, M_k\, \Omega_\rho^{(8a)(kj)} F^{\mathrm{V}}_{\mathrm{a}}.$$

The antisymmetric isometries are given by:

$$\Omega_{12}^{(8a)} = |\mathrm{K}^+\rangle\langle\mathrm{K}^0| - |\overline{\mathrm{K}}^0\rangle\langle\mathrm{K}^-| + \sqrt{2}|\pi^0\rangle\langle\pi^-| - \sqrt{2}|\pi^+\rangle\langle\pi^0|,$$

$$\Omega_{13}^{(8a)} = |\pi^+\rangle\langle\overline{\mathrm{K}}^0| - |\mathrm{K}^0\rangle\langle\pi^-| + \frac{1}{\sqrt{2}}|\pi^0\rangle\langle\mathrm{K}^-| - \frac{1}{\sqrt{2}}|\mathrm{K}^+\rangle\langle\pi^0| + \\ + \sqrt{\tfrac{3}{2}}|\eta^0\rangle\langle\mathrm{K}^-| - \sqrt{\tfrac{3}{2}}|\mathrm{K}^+\rangle\langle\eta^0|.$$

6.1.4. Universality

1. There exist essentially three types of charged weak currents:
a) the leptonic current j_α;
b) the hypercharge conserving current $J_\alpha^{\Delta Y=0}$;
c) the hypercharge violating current $J_\alpha^{|\Delta Y|=1}$.
The original form of the universality of weak interactions postulates the same coupling constant for all three types of currents.

Such an assumption, combined with the C.V.C. theory, predicts the same value for the coupling constant associated to μ decay, G, and for the Fermi vector coupling constant of β decay G_{V}. The experimental values of G and G_{V} being very close, this result seems to support the idea of universality.

Unfortunately, the $\Delta Y = 0$ transitions are considerably more frequent than the $|\Delta Y| = 1$ transitions and this experimental fact contradicts the universality as presented in its original form.

2. Another weaker form of universality has been proposed by Gell-Mann

and LÉVY [1960] and used by CABIBBO [1963] in the framework of unitary symmetry.

We consider only two currents: the leptonic current and the hadronic current now defined by:

$$J_\alpha = aJ_\alpha^{\Delta Y=0} + bJ_\alpha^{|\Delta Y|=1}.$$

The universality in such a scheme assigns the same strength for the leptonic. Using the coupling constant $G/\sqrt{2}$ for both we obtain the restriction:

$$a^2+b^2 = 1.$$

The Cabibbo angle θ is then defined by:

$$a = \cos\theta \qquad b = \sin\theta.$$

In particular the vector coupling constant for neutron β decay is given by

$$G_V = G\cos\theta_V.$$

Qualitatively the Cabibbo angle must be small for two independent reasons:

α) to explain why the hypercharge violating part is depreciated with respect to the hypercharge conserving part by a factor of damping tg θ;

β) to explain the very close experimental values of G_V and G. Quantitatively of course the problem is more complicated and the conditions α and β must be consistent with the Cabibbo universality condition $a^2+b^2 = 1$.

3. In Cabibbo's original paper the same assumption is extended to the axial vector current, using the same angle $\theta_A = \theta_V$, by analogy with the leptonic current where the vector part and the axial vector parts have the same structure. For instance, the quark current will have the simple form as suggested by GELL-MANN [1964a]:

$$J_\alpha^+(x) = \bar{q}_1(x)\gamma_\alpha(1+\gamma_5)[\cos\theta\, q_2(x)+\sin\theta\, q_3(x)]$$

where q_1, q_2, q_3 are the three Dirac quark fields with the weights as distributed in fig. 6.3.

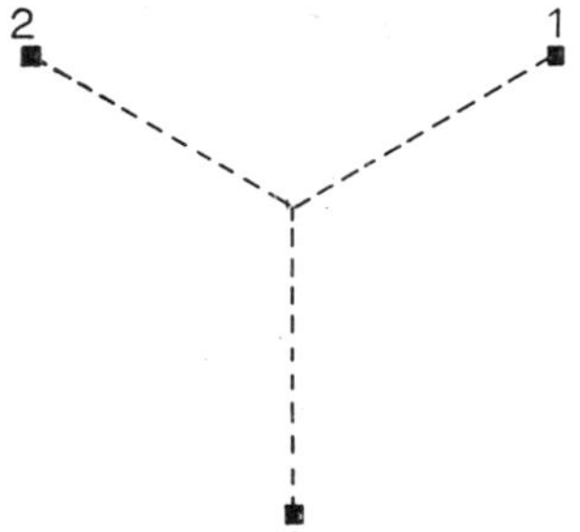

Fig. 6.3.

Of course the $(1+\gamma_5)$ structure will be modified by the presence of strong interactions.

4. The equality $\theta_A = \theta_V$ agrees very well with experiment as will be seen later. It is then possible to relate the Cabibbo angle θ to a rotation in the weight space. More precisely, if we perform a rotation of angle 2θ around the second U spin axis U_2 the weights of an octuplet are transformed according:

$$\begin{aligned} I'^{+} &= I^{+} \cos\theta + V^{+} \sin\theta & I'^{-} &= I^{-} \cos\theta + V^{-} \sin\theta \\ V'^{+} &= V^{+} \cos\theta - I^{+} \sin\theta & V'^{-} &= V^{-} \cos\theta - I^{-} \sin\theta \\ U'_1 &= U_1 \cos 2\theta + U_3 \sin 2\theta & U'_2 &= U_2 \\ U'_3 &= U_3 \cos 2\theta - U_1 \sin 2\theta & Q' &= Q. \end{aligned}$$

The positive hadronic current:

$$J_\alpha^+ = J_\alpha^{+\Delta Y=0} \cos\theta + J_\alpha^{+\Delta Y=1} \sin\theta$$

can then be interpreted as the positive component of the I′ spin current and we obtain, for the hadronic current, two selection rules:

$$|\Delta I'| = 1, \qquad \Delta Y' = 0$$

where the new hypercharge Y' is given by:

$$Y' = \tfrac{1}{2}Q - U_3 \cos 2\theta + U_1 \sin 2\theta.$$

In the new frame of reference the hadronic current is simply:

$$J_\alpha^+ = J_\alpha^{+\Delta Y'=0}.$$

Unfortunately the conservation of Y' in weak interactions is extremely difficult to check experimentally. The hadronic states are defined by strong interactions and do not possess a unique value of Y' but are linear superpositions of eigenstates of Y'.

6.1.5. Renormalization

1. The hypercharge conserving current is strictly conserved only in the limit where the electromagnetic and the weak interactions can be ignored. Nevertheless, the mass splitting inside an isotopic spin multiplet is not negligible and a small renormalization of the vector coupling constant G_V is expected because of the electromagnetic interactions.

Behrends and Sirlin [1960] have shown that such a renormalization occurs only at second order with respect to the electromagnetic interactions.

The proof is extremely simple and uses the G parity operator defined as usually by $G = C \exp(i\pi I_2)$.

The vector current is restricted to the first class of weak currents commuting with the G parity operator:

$$GJ_\alpha^V G^{-1} = J_\alpha^V.$$

Such a condition is satisfied for instance in the case of nucleons by the two operators γ_α and $[\gamma_\alpha, \not{q}]$ of the electromagnetic current.

Let us now call H_3 an operator invariant under charge conjugation and transformed like the third component of an isotopic spin vector under isotopic spin rotations. We then have

$$GH_3 G^{-1} = -H_3.$$

This operator H_3 is responsible for the breaking of the isotopic spin invariance by the electromagnetic interactions and it follows immediately that, *at first order*, the coupling constant G_V is not renormalized by the electromagnetic interactions.

2. We now go back to unitary symmetry and we look for a modification of the vector coupling constants due to the presence of medium strong interactions. As usual the effective hamiltonian H_Y responsible for the breaking of the symmetry is assumed, at first order, to be the Y component of a regular C conserving octuplet.

Of course, H_Y is an isoscalar quantity and the isotopic spin current cannot be affected by the medium strong interactions, and G_V is not renormalized at any order.

For the hypercharge violating vector current coupling constant ADEMOLLO and GATTO [1964] have pointed out that the renormalization can only occur at second order in H_Y.

In unitary symmetry the hypercharge violating current is the V spin current. The operator can obviously be decomposed into a V spin scalar H_Y^0 and the third component of a V spin vector H_Y^3. The scalar part does not give any renormalization to the V spin current and for the vector part H_Y^3 the same arguments as those given in the previous section apply immediately, using the G_V operator defined as $G_V = C \exp(i\pi V_2)$.

The same problem has also been studied by BOUCHIAT and MEYER [1964] using a Lagrangian formalism and slightly different assumptions. Finally FUBINI and FURLAN [1965] have given a very elegant method for the practical evaluation of renormalization effects due to the breaking of a symmetry. The method is quite general and will be studied in more detail in a next chapter.

6.2. Leptonic processes

6.2.1. Generalities

1. The leptonic processes are generally described by a current-current picture and the effective hamiltonian is written as the product of the leptonic current by the non leptonic current.

The leptonic current is assumed to be invariant with respect to the unitary transformations and it follows that the effective hamiltonian has the same transformation laws as the non leptonic current.

2. The detailed structure of the true hamiltonian can be ignored in a group-theoretical approach. In particular, we disregard the possibility of the existence of intermediate vector bosons which have not yet been experimentally discovered, and we are concerned only with unitary symmetry consequences.

3. We use the hypothesis of weak universality as formulated by Cabibbo [1963]. The mixing angles θ_V and θ_A can be phenomenologically determined by comparing $\Delta Y = 0$ and $\Delta Y = 1$ transitions. The simplest way seems to be the study of the leptonic decays of the pseudoscalar mesons because of the simplicity of the mesonic currents with respect to unitary symmetry.

6.2.2. Leptonic decays of pseudoscalar mesons

1. We first compare the decay rates for the two reactions:

$$K^+ \Rightarrow \mu^+ + \nu_\mu, \qquad \pi^+ \Rightarrow \mu^+ + \nu_\mu$$

in order to determine the axial vector angle θ_A.

The matrix element of the axial vector current between the vacuum and the one-meson state has been written in section 6.1.2.

$$\langle 0|J_\alpha^A|M\rangle = ik_\alpha f_M, \qquad M = \pi, K.$$

The ratio of the two rates takes the form:

$$\frac{\Gamma(K^+ \Rightarrow \mu^+ + \nu_\mu)}{\Gamma(\pi^+ \Rightarrow \rho^+ + \nu_\mu)} = \frac{m_K}{m_\pi}\left[\frac{1-m_\mu^2/m_K^2}{1-m_\mu^2/m_\pi^2}\right]^2 \frac{f_K^2}{f_\pi^2}.$$

If we apply unitary symmetry to the coupling constants f_K and f_π we obtain

$$\operatorname{tg}\theta_A = \frac{f_K}{f_\pi}.$$

Comparison with experiment gives the value $\theta_A \simeq 0.26 \pm 0.01$.

2. The breaking of unitary symmetry is particularly large when π mesons and K mesons are involved. Moreover, the coupling constants f_K and f_π have the dimension of a mass and there always exists some ambiguity in the application of unitary symmetry.

3. We are now interested in the determination of the vector angle θ_V and we compare the decay rates of the two reactions

$$\pi^+ \Rightarrow \pi^0 + e^+ + \nu_e, \qquad K^+ \Rightarrow \pi^0 + e^+ + \nu_e.$$

In the framework of an exact unitary symmetry the two vector currents involved in these reactions are conserved and the matrix elements are given by:

$$\langle \pi^0 | J^V_\alpha | \pi^+ \rangle = \frac{1}{i} \cos \theta_V \sqrt{2} F_\pi(q^2)(p_{\pi^0} + p_{\pi^+})_\alpha$$

$$\langle \pi^0 | J^V_\alpha | K^+ \rangle = \frac{1}{i} \sin \theta_V \frac{1}{\sqrt{2}} F_\pi(q^2)(p_{\pi^0} + p_{K^+})_\alpha .$$

The momentum transfer is defined as $q = p_{\pi^+} - p_{\pi^0}$ for the first reaction and $q = p_{K^+} - p_{\pi^0}$ for the second reaction.

Comparison with experiment gives: $\theta_V \simeq 0.24$.

4. With this value of θ_V essentially the same as θ_A the Fermi coupling constant for neutron decay becomes

$$\frac{G_V}{G} = \cos \theta_V \simeq 0.971,$$

and a small discrepancy between theory and experiment remains but now in the opposite direction.

The previous procedure due to CABIBBO [1963] has been criticized by SAKURAI [1964] for the following reason: if the vector current responsible for $\pi\beta$-decay is divergenceless the hypercharge violating vector current involved in K_{e_3} decay cannot be exactly conserved because of the presence of medium strong interactions. Sakurai then gives a very elegant procedure to estimate the effect due to medium strong interactions by looking at the decays of the vector mesons ρ and K*. The result is simply:

$$\text{tg}\, \theta_{SAK} \simeq 0.9\, \text{tg}\, \theta_{CAB}$$

reducing the mixing angle to $\theta_{SAK} \simeq 0.21$ and the Fermi coupling constant for neutron β decay is now in extraordinary agreement with experiment:

$$\cos \theta_{SAK} \simeq 0.977.$$

6.2.3. Leptonic decays of baryons

1. We use the explicit expressions given above for the isometries and we normalize the reduced matrix elements in the following way:

$$f_a = \frac{F_a^A}{F_a^V}, \qquad f_s = \frac{F_s^A}{F_a^V}.$$

For the various observable reactions, we obtain the following table (the factors cos θ and sin θ have been dropped for simplicity):

Table 6.1

		Vector part	Axial vector part
	$n \Rightarrow p+e^-+\bar{\nu}$	1	f_a+f_s
	$\Sigma^- \Rightarrow \Lambda^0+e^-+\bar{\nu}$	0	$\sqrt{\frac{2}{3}}f_s$
$\Delta Y = 0$	$\Sigma^- \Rightarrow \Sigma^0+e^-+\bar{\nu}$	$\sqrt{2}$	$\sqrt{2}f_a$
	$\Xi^- \Rightarrow \Xi^0+e^-+\bar{\nu}$	-1	$-f_a+f_s$
	$\Lambda^0 \rightarrow p+e^-+\bar{\nu}$	$-\sqrt{\frac{3}{2}}$	$-\sqrt{\frac{3}{2}}(f_a+\frac{1}{3}f_s)$
	$\Sigma^- \Rightarrow n+e^-+\bar{\nu}$	-1	$-f_a+f_s$
$\Delta Y = 1$	$\Xi^- \Rightarrow \Lambda^0+e+\bar{\nu}$	$\sqrt{\frac{3}{2}}$	$\sqrt{\frac{3}{2}}(f_a-\frac{1}{3}f_s)$
	$\Xi^- \Rightarrow \Sigma^0+e^-+\bar{\nu}$	$\sqrt{\frac{1}{2}}$	$\frac{1}{\sqrt{2}}(f_a+f_s)$
	$\Xi^0 \Rightarrow \Sigma^++e^-+\nu$	1	f_a+f_s

In the case of the $|\Delta Y| = 1$ transitions, the leptonic decays with the production of μ^- mesons are in general allowed by the phase space and have been experimentally observed with a branching ratio only due to phase space considerations.

2. Comparison with experiment has first been performed by Cabibbo [1963] in order to determine f_a and f_s at zero momentum transfer. We need two relations. The first one is given by the neutron β decay:

$$f_a+f_s = -\frac{G_A}{G_V}$$

and, for the second one, Cabibbo uses the $\Sigma^- \Rightarrow \Lambda^0+e^-+\bar{\nu}_e$ pure axial vector and unitary symmetry symmetric transition.

A more recent and more systematic analysis due to Willis and collaborators [1964] gives the following numerical values:

$$f_a = 0.437, \qquad f_s = 0.742$$

for a common mixing angle $\theta_V = \theta_A = 0.264$ and the coupling constants given by:

$$\frac{G_V}{G} \simeq 0.974 \pm 0.010, \qquad -\frac{G_A}{G_V} = 1.18.$$

The branching ratios obtained with these parameters are given in table 6.2 and are compared to the experimental values.

TABLE 6.2

Decay mode	Theoretical ratio	Experimental ratio
$\dfrac{\Sigma^- \Rightarrow \Lambda^0 + e^- + \bar{\nu}_e}{\text{all } \Sigma^-}$	0.61×10^{-4}	$(0.8 \pm 0.3) \times 10^{-4}$
$\dfrac{\Lambda \Rightarrow p + e^- + \bar{\nu}_e}{\text{all } \Lambda}$	0.91×10^{-3}	$(0.86 \pm 0.09) \times 10^{-3}$
$\dfrac{\Sigma^- \Rightarrow n + e^- + \bar{\nu}_e}{\text{all } \Sigma^-}$	1.32×10^{-3}	$(1.2 \pm 0.2) \times 10^{-3}$
$\dfrac{\Xi^- \Rightarrow \Lambda + e^- + \bar{\nu}_e}{\text{all } \Xi^-}$	0.65×10^{-3}	$(2.4 \pm 1.3) \times 10^{-3}$

3. The D/F ratio obtained for baryon leptonic decay

$$\rho_W = \frac{f_s}{f_a} \simeq 1.7$$

is compatible with the strong D/F ratio ρ_S used in the pseudoscalar meson baryon coupling.

Such a result suggests the possibility of extending the Goldberger-Treiman formula and the partially conserved axial vector current hypothesis to the complete octuplet.

Let us consider the weak decay of baryons:

$$B_j \Rightarrow B_k + e + \nu$$

which proceed via the component ρ of the hadronic current octuplet. The axial vector coupling constant is given by

$$G_A^{B_j B_k} = G_A^{\rho}[\Omega_{\rho}^{(8a)jk} f_a + \Omega_{\rho}^{(8s)jk} f_s] \frac{1}{f_a + f_s}.$$

Let us now assume an exact unitary symmetry to calculate the $B_j B_k P_{\rho}$ coupling constant:

$$g_{B_jB_kP_\rho} = \sqrt{2}g[\Omega_\rho^{(8a)jk}g_a + \Omega_\rho^{(8s)jk}g_s]\frac{1}{g_a+g_s}$$

where g is the usual π-N coupling constant ($g^2/4\pi \simeq 14$).

The Goldberger-Treiman formula, in this language is simply:

$$f_\rho = -\frac{G_A^{B_jB_k}}{G}\frac{M_j+M_k}{g_{B_jB_kP_\rho}}.$$

Using the previous expressions we obtain:

$$\frac{G_A^{B_jB_k}}{g_{B_jB_kP_\rho}} = \frac{G_A^\rho}{\sqrt{2}g}\left[\frac{\Omega_\rho^{(8a)jk}f_a + \Omega_\rho^{(8s)jk}f_s}{\Omega_\rho^{(8a)jk}g_a + \Omega_\rho^{(8s)jk}g_s} \times \frac{g_a+g_s}{f_a+f_s}\right].$$

If the D/F ratio is the same for weak and strong interactions:

$$\frac{f_s}{f_a} \simeq \frac{g_s}{g_a},$$

the bracket of the above formula is unity and, neglecting the baryon mass differences we obtain:

$$f_\rho = -\frac{G_A^\rho}{G}\frac{2M}{g\sqrt{2}}$$

for the Goldberger-Treiman generalized formula.

It is more convenient to use a coupling constant f, independent of the weight ρ and defined by:

$$Gf_\rho = G_V^\rho f.$$

The coupling constants for π decay and K decay are then simply given by:

$$f_\pi = f\cos\theta \qquad f_K = f\sin\theta$$

and the Goldberger-Treiman relation is written as:

$$f = -\frac{G_A}{G_V}\frac{2M}{g\sqrt{2}}.$$

6.2.4. High energy neutrino reactions

1. We first study the same type of problem by looking at the reaction in a different channel:

$$n \Rightarrow p + e^- + \bar{\nu}_e \qquad \bar{\nu}_\mu + n \Rightarrow \mu^- + p$$
$$\Lambda \Rightarrow p + e^- + \bar{\nu}_e \qquad \bar{\nu}_\mu + p \Rightarrow \mu^+ + \Lambda.$$

In the case of leptonic decays of baryons, the transfer of momentum q between the baryons is always very small. For high energy neutrino reactions this transfer q is large; the reduced matrix elements F_a^V, F_a^A and F_s^A are now form factor functions of q^2 and the analysis of the leptonic decays of baryons gives only their normalization at $q^2 = 0$.

Moreover we have also to consider other induced couplings due to strong interactions. We will restrict ourselves to first-class currents defined by Weinberg according to their G parity properties:

$$GJ_\alpha^V G^{-1} = J_\alpha^V, \qquad GJ_\alpha^A G^{-1} = -J_\alpha^A.$$

These currents have been introduced in section 6.1.2 for the case of strangeness conserving currents.

2. The weak form factors of the vector current part are related to the electromagnetic form factors in the conserved vector current theory. Due to the U spin invariance of electromagnetic interactions, the four charged vector currents are characterized by the same weak form factors.

For the axial vector current weak form factors, we can only make assumptions as, for instance, the partially conserved axial current hypothesis. The problem is the same as discussed in 6.1.2.

3. Some new processes can be studied by the high energy neutrino reactions as, for instance the production of the $J = \frac{3}{2}^+$ isobars (Block [1964]):

$$\begin{aligned} \Delta Y = 0 \qquad & \nu_\mu + \mathrm{p} = \mu^- + \mathrm{N}_{\frac{3}{2}}^{*++} \\ \Delta Y = -1 \qquad & \bar{\nu}_\mu + \mathrm{p} = \mu^+ + \mathrm{Y}_1^{*0}. \end{aligned}$$

The main difference with the previous case is that now the $J = \frac{3}{2}^+$ isobars are in a decuplet and there exists only one isometry relating the representations 8 and 10 by an octuplet. The calculation of these isometries is straightforward:

$$\begin{aligned} \Omega_{12}^{(8)} = {} & \sqrt{6}|\mathrm{N}_{\frac{3}{2}}^{*++}\rangle\langle \mathrm{p}| - \sqrt{2}|\mathrm{N}_{\frac{3}{2}}^{*+}\rangle\langle \mathrm{n}| - \sqrt{3}|\mathrm{Y}_1^{*+}\rangle\langle \Lambda^0| - |\mathrm{Y}_1^{*+}\rangle\langle \Sigma^0| + \\ & + |\mathrm{Y}_1^{*0}\rangle\langle \Sigma^-| + \sqrt{2}|\Xi_{\frac{1}{2}}^{*0}\rangle\langle \Xi^-|, \end{aligned}$$

$$\begin{aligned} \Omega_{13}^{(8)} = {} & -\sqrt{6}|\mathrm{N}_{\frac{3}{2}}^{*++}\rangle\langle \Sigma^+| - 2|\mathrm{N}_{\frac{3}{2}}^{*+}\rangle\langle \Sigma^0| + \sqrt{2}|\mathrm{N}_{\frac{3}{2}}^{*0}\rangle\langle \Sigma^-| + \\ & - \sqrt{2}|\mathrm{Y}_1^{*+}\rangle\langle \Xi^0| - |\mathrm{Y}_1^{*0}\rangle\langle \Xi^-|, \end{aligned}$$

$$\begin{aligned} \Omega_{21}^{(8)} = {} & -\sqrt{6}|\mathrm{N}_{\frac{3}{2}}^{*-}\rangle\langle \mathrm{n}| - \sqrt{2}|\mathrm{N}_{\frac{3}{2}}^{*0}\rangle\langle \mathrm{p}| - \sqrt{3}|\mathrm{Y}_1^{*-}\rangle\langle \Lambda^0| - |\mathrm{Y}_1^{*0}\rangle\langle \Sigma^+| + \\ & + |\mathrm{Y}_1^{*-}\rangle\langle \Sigma^0| + \sqrt{2}|\Xi_{\frac{1}{2}}^{*-}\rangle\langle \Xi^0|, \end{aligned}$$

$$\begin{aligned} \Omega_{31}^{(8)} = {} & \sqrt{6}|\Omega^-\rangle\langle \Xi^0| + \sqrt{2}|\mathrm{Y}_1^{*-}\rangle\langle \mathrm{n}| + |\mathrm{Y}_1^{*0}\rangle\langle \mathrm{p}| + \\ & + \sqrt{3}|\Xi_{\frac{1}{2}}^{*-}\rangle\langle \Lambda^0| + |\Xi_{\frac{1}{2}}^{*-}\rangle\langle \Sigma^0| - \sqrt{2}|\Xi_{\frac{1}{2}}^{*0}\rangle\langle \Sigma^+|. \end{aligned}$$

4. The matrix elements of the vector current between a spin $\frac{1}{2}$ baryon state of energy momentum K' and helicity λ' and a spin $\frac{3}{2}$ resonance state of energy momentum K and helicity λ, have the following structure due to Lorentz invariance:

$$G\langle K', \lambda' | J^{V}_{\alpha, \rho} | K, \lambda\rangle = G^{\rho}_{V}[\bar{u}_k(K', \lambda') V^{\sigma}_{\alpha} u_{\sigma, r}(K, \lambda)]\Omega^{(8)kr}_{\rho}$$

where $u(K', \lambda')$ is the spin $\frac{1}{2}$ Dirac spinor and $u(K, \lambda)$ the spin $\frac{3}{2}$ Rarita Schwinger spinor. We have the following constraints:

$$(\gamma^{\rho} K'_{\rho} - iM_k) u_k(K', \lambda') = 0$$
$$(\gamma^{\rho} K_{\rho} - iM^{*}_{r}) u_{\sigma, r}(K, \lambda) = 0$$
$$\gamma^{\sigma} u_{\sigma, r}(K, \lambda) = 0$$
$$K^{\sigma} u_{\sigma, r}(K, \lambda) = 0.$$

The vector coupling constants are defined by

$$G^{12}_{V} = G^{21}_{V} = G\cos\theta = G_V$$
$$G^{13}_{V} = G^{31}_{V} = G\sin\theta.$$

The general form of V^{σ}_{α} involves then four weak form factors:

$$V^{\sigma}_{\alpha} = \delta^{\sigma}_{\alpha}\gamma_5 h^{V}(q^2) + [i\gamma_{\alpha} f^{V}_{1}(q^2) - P_{\alpha} f^{V}_{2}(q^2) - q_{\alpha} f^{V}_{3}(q^2)] q^{\sigma}\gamma_5$$

where

$$q = K - K', \qquad 2P = K + K'.$$

If the current is conserved the four form factors are not linearly independent and we find the relation:

$$h^{V}(q^2) + (M + M^{*}) f^{V}_{1}(q^2) - \tfrac{1}{2}(M^{*2} - M^2) f^{V}_{2}(q^2) - q^2 f^{V}_{3}(q^2) = 0.$$

It is convenient to define a divergenceless form of V^{σ}_{α} following:

$$V^{\sigma}_{\alpha} = \{[i\gamma_{\alpha} q^{\sigma} - (M + M^{*})\delta^{\sigma}_{\alpha}] f^{V}_{1}(q^2) - [P_{\alpha} q^{\sigma} - \tfrac{1}{2}(M^{*2} - M^2)\delta^{\sigma}_{\alpha}] f^{V}_{2}(q^2) + \\ - [q_{\alpha} q^{\sigma} - q^2 \delta^{\sigma}_{\alpha}] f^{V}_{3}(q^2)\}\gamma_5 .$$

In the conserved vector current theory, the weak vector form factors are related to the corresponding electromagnetic form factors and we are naturally interested in the study of the γBB^{*} electromagnetic vertex. It is possible to define the Lorentz invariant, gauge invariant, parity conserving couplings associated to the physical electric, magnetic and longitudinal transitions. We first introduce three effective hamiltonians (Gourdin and Salin [1963a, b]):

$$H_3 = -e\frac{C_3}{m_\pi}\{\bar{\psi}_N\gamma_\mu\gamma_5\psi_\nu - \bar{\psi}_\nu\gamma_\mu\gamma_5\psi_N\}F^{\mu\nu}$$

$$H_4 = -e\frac{C_4}{m_\pi^2}\left\{\bar{\psi}_N\gamma_5\frac{\partial\psi_\nu}{\partial x^\mu} + \frac{\partial\bar{\psi}_\nu}{\partial x^\mu}\gamma_5\psi_N\right\}F^{\mu\nu}$$

$$H_5 = e\frac{C_5}{m_\pi^2}\left\{\frac{\partial\bar{\psi}_N}{\partial x^\mu}\gamma_5\psi_\nu + \bar{\psi}_\nu\gamma_5\frac{\partial\psi_N}{\partial x^\mu}\right\}F^{\mu\nu}.$$

After comparison of these expressions with the general form, given above, of the vector current we easily relate the weak and electromagnetic form factors following

$$f_1^V(q^2) = \frac{C_M(q^2)}{m_\pi} \qquad f_2^V(q^2) = \frac{C_E(q^2)}{m_\pi^2} \qquad f_3^V(q^2) = \frac{C_L(q^2)}{m_\pi^2}$$

where:

$$C_M = C_3 \qquad C_E = C_4 + C_5 \qquad C_L = \tfrac{1}{2}(C_4 - C_5).$$

In front of the vector current, the electric charge e is replaced by the convenient vector coupling constant G_V^v.

The phenomenological analysis of π meson photoproduction with an isobaric model gives the normalization values of the form factors at $q^2 = 0$

$$C_M(0) = 0.37 \qquad C_E(0) = -0.0086 \qquad C_L(0) = 0.$$

We immediately see that, in a very good approximation, the H_3 type coupling is dominant for photoproduction and can be interpreted as a covariant magnetic coupling. By analogy, the weak form factor $f_1^V(q^2)$ will dominate the weak vector current matrix elements.

The analysis of photoproduction has been performed on the reaction $\gamma + p \Rightarrow N_{\frac{3}{2}}^{*+}$. The matrix element for the $p \Rightarrow N_{\frac{3}{2}}^{*++}$ transition will then contain an extra Clebsch-Gordan coefficient $\sqrt{3}$. Under the hypothesis of one form factor only, we obtain (BERMAN and VELTMAN [1964]):

$$G\langle N_{\frac{3}{2}}^{*++}|J_\alpha^V|p\rangle = G_V\sqrt{3}\frac{C_3}{m_\pi}\bar{u}_{\sigma,N^*}[i\gamma_\alpha q^\sigma - (M_N + M_{N^*})\delta_\alpha^\sigma]\gamma_5 u_p.$$

As a practical way to analyze the π meson electroproduction we can assume a proportionality between the $\gamma BB^*C_3(q^2)$ form factor and the nucleon isovector magnetic form factor. The same type of approximation can be extended also to the weak form factor f_1^V and we have then:

$$f_1^V(q^2) \simeq 0.37\frac{G_1^V(q^2)}{G_1^V(0)}.$$

6. The matrix elements of the axial vector current between a spin $\frac{1}{2}$ baryon and a spin $\frac{3}{2}$ resonance can be easily deduced from the previous results only by replacing γ_5 by 1. From Lorentz invariance we have:

$$G\langle K', \lambda'|J^{A}_{\alpha,\rho}|K, \lambda\rangle = -G^{\rho}_{A}\bar{u}_k(K', \lambda')A^{\sigma}_{\alpha}u_{\sigma,r}(K, \lambda)\Omega^{(8)kr}_{\rho}.$$

The axial vector coupling constants G^{σ}_{A} are defined by

$$G^{12}_{A} = G^{21}_{A} = G_A$$
$$G^{13}_{A} = G^{31}_{A} = G_A \operatorname{tg}\theta.$$

The general form of A^{σ}_{α} involves four weak axial vector form factors which it is convenient to define as

$$A^{\sigma}_{\alpha} = \delta^{\sigma}_{\alpha}h^{A}(q^2) - q_{\alpha}q^{\sigma}f^{A}_{1}(q^2) + [i\gamma_{\alpha}q^{\sigma} - (M^* - M)\delta^{\sigma}_{\alpha}]f^{A}_{2}(q^2) + [P_{\alpha}q^{\sigma} - \tfrac{1}{2}(M^{*2} - M^2)\delta^{\sigma}_{\alpha}]f^{A}_{3}(q^2).$$

It can be useful to calculate the one pseudoscalar meson pole contribution to these form factors. An equivalent procedure is to use a partially conserved axial vector current hypothesis where the matrix elements of the divergence of the axial vector current are assumed to be proportional to the matrix elements of the pseudoscalar meson field.

We first obtain:

$$G\langle K', \lambda'|\operatorname{div} J^{A}_{\rho}|K, \lambda\rangle = -G_A\bar{u}_k(K', \lambda')u_{\sigma,r}(K, \lambda)iq^{\alpha}A^{\sigma}_{\alpha}\Omega^{(8)kr}_{\sigma}$$

with:

$$iq^{\alpha}A^{\sigma}_{\alpha} = iq^{\sigma}[h^{A}(q^2) - q^2f^{A}_{1}(q^2)].$$

The computation of the matrix element $\langle B|\phi_{\rho}|B^*\rangle$ necessitates the knowledge of the B*BP vertex. We then introduce an effective hamiltonian to describe the vertex

$$H_{B^*BP} = \frac{\lambda}{m}\bar{B}_k B_{\sigma,r}\frac{\partial\phi^{\rho}}{\partial x_{\sigma}}\Omega^{(8)kr}_{\rho}$$

where m is the meson mass and ϕ_{ρ} the pseudoscalar field normalized so that

$$\langle 0|\phi_{\rho}|M\rangle = 1.$$

The dimensionless coupling constant λ is determined by the decay width $\Gamma(B^* \Rightarrow B+P)$. For virtual mesons we introduce a vertex function $L(q^2)$ normalized so that $L(-m^2) = 1$. We then obtain

$$\langle K', \lambda'|\phi_{\rho}|K, \lambda\rangle = \bar{u}_k(K', \lambda')iq^{\sigma}u_{\sigma,r}(K, \lambda)\frac{\lambda}{m}\frac{L(q^2)}{q^2+m^2}$$

and using the coupling constant f_ρ for meson decay:

$$\langle 0|J^{\mathrm{A}}_{\alpha,\rho}|\mathrm{M}\rangle = \mathrm{i}k_\alpha f_\rho$$
$$\langle 0|\mathrm{div}\, J^{\mathrm{A}}|\mathrm{M}\rangle = m^2 f_\rho$$

we deduce the following approximate equality:

$$-\frac{G_{\mathrm{A}}}{G}\left[h^{\mathrm{A}}(q^2)-q^2 f_1^{\mathrm{A}}(q^2)\right] \simeq \frac{\lambda}{m}\frac{m^2}{q^2+m^2}L(q^2)f_\rho$$

which can also be written, taking into account the Goldberger-Treiman relation

$$h^{\mathrm{A}}(q^2)-q^2 f_1^{\mathrm{A}}(q^2) \simeq \frac{1}{\sqrt{2}}\frac{\lambda}{f}\frac{m^2}{q^2+m^2}L(q^2)$$

where

$$f = \frac{m}{2M}g.$$

We first consider the case $q^2 = 0$ to obtain the normalization of the form factor h^{A}:

$$h^{\mathrm{A}}(0) = \frac{1}{\sqrt{2}}\frac{\lambda}{f}L(0).$$

On the other hand it can be easily checked that only the form factor $f_1^{\mathrm{A}}(q^2)$ contains a one-meson pole singularity. By looking at the limiting case $q^2 = -m^2$ we obtain the residue of the one-meson pole contribution to the axial vector form factor $f_1^{\mathrm{A}}(q^2)$:

$$\lim_{q^2+m^2\Rightarrow 0}(q^2+m^2)f_1^{\mathrm{A}}(q^2) = \frac{1}{\sqrt{2}}\frac{\lambda}{f}.$$

Let us now consider, for simplicity, the $\mathrm{N}^*_{\frac{3}{2}}$-N transition. The intermediate pseudoscalar meson involved is a π meson and the experimental values of the involved coupling constants are

$$\frac{f^2}{4\pi} \simeq 0.08, \qquad \frac{\lambda^2}{4\pi} \simeq 0.35.$$

The matrix element for the $\mathrm{p}\Rightarrow\mathrm{N}^{*++}_{\frac{3}{2}}$ transition is then given, in the partially conserved axial vector current hypothesis, by (BERMAN and VELTMAN [1964]):

$$G\langle \mathrm{N}^{*++}_{\frac{3}{2}}|J^{\mathrm{A}}_\alpha|\mathrm{p}\rangle = -G_{\mathrm{A}}\frac{1}{\sqrt{2}}\frac{\lambda}{f}\bar{u}_{\sigma,\mathrm{N}^*}\left[\delta^\sigma_\alpha - \frac{q_\alpha q^\sigma}{q^2+m^2_\pi}\right]u_{\mathrm{p}}.$$

7. The Ω^- particle is not a resonance of the meson-baryon system and it is possible, experimentally, to observe the Ω^- leptonic decay:

$$\Omega^- \Rightarrow \Xi^0 + l^- + \bar{\nu}_l .$$

It is possible to compute the Ω^- decay rate as an interesting application of the previous considerations. As explained above, we retain only the C_3 type coupling for the vector transition and for the axial vector contribution we use the normalization value $h^{\mathrm{A}}(0)$ obtained in the partially conserved axial vector current hypothesis. The matrix element is then given by (GLASHOW and SOCOLOW [1964])

$$\langle \Xi l \nu | T | \Omega^- \rangle = \frac{G}{\sqrt{2}} \sin\theta \, (\bar{u}_\Xi T_\alpha^\sigma u_{\sigma\Omega}) l^\alpha$$

with:

$$T_\alpha^\sigma = \sqrt{3}\frac{C_3}{m_\pi}[\mathrm{i}\gamma_\alpha q^\sigma - (M_\Xi + M_\Omega)\delta_\alpha^\sigma]\gamma_5 - \frac{G_\mathrm{A}}{G_\mathrm{V}}\frac{1}{\sqrt{2}}\frac{\lambda}{f}\delta_\alpha^\sigma .$$

CHAPTER VII

NON-LEPTONIC WEAK INTERACTIONS

7.1. Non-leptonic hamiltonian

1. The effective hamiltonian for medium strong interactions transforms like the Y component of an octuplet; only $\boldsymbol{I}$ and Y transformations commute with Y.

The effective hamiltonian for electromagnetic interactions transforms like the Q component of an octuplet; only $\boldsymbol{U}$ and Q transformations commute with Q.

2. We assume the effective hamiltonian for non-leptonic weak processes to transform like the neutral components of an octuplet (D'ESPAGNAT and PRENTKI [1962] and BACKER and GLASHOW [1962]).

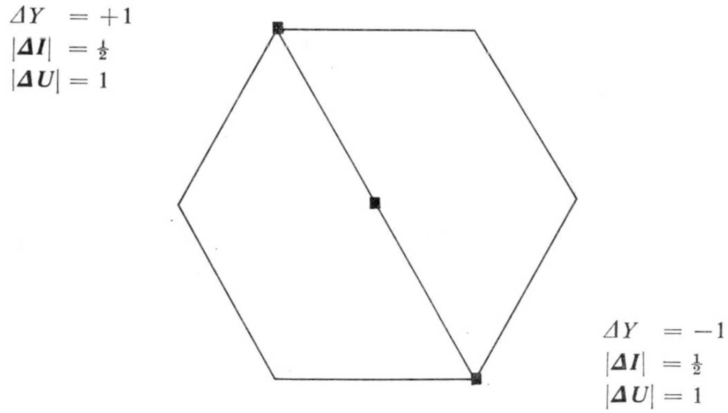

Fig. 7.1.

The hypercharge conserving part is a superposition of an isoscalar term which transforms like the Y component of an octuplet and of an isovector term which transforms like the I_3 component of the same octuplet. An equivalent description can be made with a reference to U spin instead to I spin. We have a U spin scalar term transforming like the Q component and a U spin vector term transforming like the U_3 component of the same octuplet.

The hypercharge violating part, $\Delta Y = 1$ transforms like the U^- component of an octuplet; and the part $\Delta Y = -1$, as the U^+ component of an octuplet.

3. The first consequence of such an hypothesis in the obtaining of the well-known selection rules for the non-leptonic processes, valid of course only in the first order with respect to the effective non-leptonic hamiltonian:

a) we do not have $\Delta Y = 2$ transitions;

b) the $\Delta Y = 1$ transitions are of the $|\boldsymbol{\Delta I}| = \frac{1}{2}$ type only.

4. The more natural realization of such a hamiltonian is obtained in a current-current picture. One can use for instance the current previously defined and its hermitian conjugate belonging to the same octuplet or two currents, each of them belonging with this hermitian conjugate to one octuplet.

In both cases, we have to consider the product of two octuplets:

$$8 \otimes 8 = 1 \oplus 8_a \oplus 8_s \oplus 10 \oplus \overline{10} \oplus 27.$$

The previous assumption made in 2 regarding the non-leptonic hamiltonian is called the octet enhancement. We now have to project the current × current terms on the adjoint representation and we have two possibilities to do this: the first symmetric, the second antisymmetric with respect to the unitary symmetry couplings.

The general structure of H_{NL} is then given by:

$$H_{\mathrm{NL}} = \alpha J_\mu^{(1)} J^{(2)*\mu} + \beta J_\mu^{(2)} J^{(1)*\mu}.$$

If we use only one octuplet of current, the Bose-Einstein statistics excludes the possibility of an antisymmetric coupling and H_{NL} belongs to the 8_s part only

$$H_{\mathrm{NL}} = J_\mu J^{*\mu} + J^{*\mu} J_\mu .$$

5. The non-leptonic hamiltonian can be divided into a parity conserving part and a parity violating part:

$$H_{\mathrm{NL}} = H_{\mathrm{pc}} + H_{\mathrm{pv}}$$

If we assume the current × current structure, we have an explicit form for the two parts:

$$H_{\mathrm{pc}} = J_\mu^{\mathrm{V}} J^{\mathrm{V}*\mu} + J_\mu^{\mathrm{A}} J^{\mathrm{A}*\mu}$$
$$H_{\mathrm{pv}} = J_\mu^{\mathrm{V}} J^{\mathrm{A}*\mu} + J_\mu^{\mathrm{A}} J^{\mathrm{V}*\mu}.$$

6. The non-leptonic hamiltonian has been also divided in 2 into a hypercharge conserving part and two hypercharge violating parts:

$$H_{\mathrm{NL}} = H_{\Delta Y=0}+H_{\Delta Y=1}+H_{\Delta Y=-1}\,.$$

Such a splitting is easily obtained in a current × current structure by combining, in convenient ways, the $\Delta Y = 0$ and the $\Delta Y = \pm 1$ currents. If we now use only one octuplet of currents, the unitary symmetry coupling being symmetrical, the hypercharge violating hamiltonian transforms like the U_1 component of the octuplet. This result is due to GELL-MANN [1964c].

7. The hamiltonian H_{NL} is hermitian and we have the conditions:

$$H^*_{\Delta Y=0} = H_{\Delta Y=0}\,, \qquad H^*_{\Delta Y=\pm 1} = H_{\Delta Y=\pm 1}\,.$$

We assume the non-leptonic hamiltonian H_{NL} to be PC invariant and we obtain:

$$(PC)H_{\Delta Y=0}(PC)^{-1} = H_{\Delta Y=0}$$
$$(PC)H_{\Delta Y=\pm 1}(PC)^{-1} = H_{\Delta Y=\mp 1}\,.$$

In what follows we do not use the complete unitary symmetry but only the U spin invariance of strong interactions.

As a reference, we consider the neutral pseudoscalar mesons K^0, $\overline{\mathrm{K}}{}^0$, π^0, η^0; they can be classified into a U spin scalar M_0 and a U spin vector M_j with

$$M_0 = \tfrac{1}{2}(\pi^0\sqrt{3}+\eta^0) \qquad M_3 = \tfrac{1}{2}(\pi^0 \;\; \eta^0\sqrt{3})$$
$$\mathrm{V}_+ = \overline{\mathrm{K}}{}^0_0 \qquad \mathrm{V}_- = \mathrm{K}^0.$$

It is convenient to define the G_u operation related to U spin rotations as the G parity to isotopic spin rotations:

$$G_u = C \exp(\mathrm{i}\pi U_2)$$

and also the PG_u transformation

$$PG_u = PC \exp(\mathrm{i}\pi U_2).$$

For the π^0 and η^0 mesons or their linear combinations M_0 and M_3 we have $C = +1$ and $PC = -1$. It follows immediately

$$G_u|M_0\rangle = |M_0\rangle \qquad PG_u|M_0\rangle = -|M_0\rangle$$
$$G_u|M_j\rangle = -|M_j\rangle \qquad PG_u|M_j\rangle = |M_j\rangle.$$

The neutral K meson states K^0_1 and K^0_2 are defined as eigenstates of the PC operator with the respective eigenvalues $+1$ and -1. As a consequence,

K_1^0 is transformed like the second component M_2 of the U spin vector and K_2^0 like the first component M_1.

We now go back to the non leptonic PC conserving hamiltonian. It can be decomposed into a U spin scalar H_0 and a U spin vector H_j. Whereas for the pseudoscalar mesons M_0 and M_3 we have $PC = -1$, now for the hypercharge conserving parts H_0 and H_3 we have $PC = +1$. It follows that the results of a PG_u operator must be inverted:

$$(PG_u)H_0(PG_u)^{-1} = H_0$$
$$(PG_u)H_j(PG_u)^{-1} = -H_j.$$

The components H_0, H_1, H_3 are associated to $PC = +1$ and the component H_2 to $PC = -1$ and we obtain the very important result: in a PC conserving theory, the hypercharge violating part of H_{NL} is transformed under U spin rotations like the first component of a U spin vector.

Such a result has been obtained by CABIBBO [1964] and by GELL-MANN [1964c] on the basis of much stronger assumptions. In fact, to prove it, we have used PC invariance of weak interactions and the invariance of strong interactions with respect to U_2 rotations only (GOURDIN [1964]).

If now, we allow $|\boldsymbol{\Delta U}| > 1$ components in the non-leptonic hamiltonian, the same technique can be used to separate the $PC = +1$ and the $PC = -1$ components of an arbitrary U spin tensor $H_{\alpha\beta\gamma\ldots}$ constructed by symmetric tensor product of U spin vectors. The components α, β, γ, . . . can take the three values 1, 2, 3 and components are characterized in the following way:

a) $PC = +1$ components: even number of indices 2

b) $PC = -1$ components: odd number of indices 2.

8. The medium strong interactions are invariant under $\boldsymbol{I}$ and Y transformations. The electromagnetic interactions are invariant under $\boldsymbol{U}$ and Q transformations.

D'ESPAGNAT and PRENTKI [1962] and also BACKER and GLASHOW [1962] have suggested that the non-leptonic interactions can be invariant under a third subgrup $\mathscr{G}$ of SU(3) and a third gauge group.

In order to construct $\mathscr{G}$, we perform a change of basis from the standard frame in which I_3 and Y are diagonal. The charge Q being conserved in all types of interactions, the previous transformation can only be a U spin rotation if one neglects possible phases introduced by a Q gauge transformation.

With respect to U spin rotations, the weights of an octuplet are classified following:

(I^+, V^+) spinor $\qquad$ (V^-, I^-) spinor

(U^+, U_3, U^-) vector $\qquad$ Q scalar.

Introducing a 2×2 matrix for the U rotation:

$$R = \begin{vmatrix} \alpha & \beta \\ -\bar{\beta} & \bar{\alpha} \end{vmatrix} \qquad \text{with } |\alpha|^2+|\beta|^2 = 1,$$

we immediately obtain:

$$\begin{aligned}
I'^{+} &= \alpha I^{+}+\beta V^{+} \\
V'^{+} &= -\bar{\beta} I^{+}+\bar{\alpha} V^{+} \\
I'^{-} &= \bar{\alpha} I^{-}+\bar{\beta} V^{-} \\
V'^{-} &= -\beta I^{-}+\alpha V^{-} \\
U'^{+} &= \alpha^2 U^{+}-\bar{\beta}^2 U^{-}+\bar{\alpha}\beta U_3 \\
U'^{-} &= \bar{\alpha}^2 U^{-}-\beta^2 U^{+}+\alpha\beta U_3 \\
U'_3 &= (|\alpha|^2-|\beta|^2)U_3-\alpha\bar{\beta}U^{+}-\bar{\alpha}\beta U^{-} \\
Q' &= Q.
\end{aligned}$$

The two conserved quantities associated to the $\mathscr{G}$ invariance are I'_3 and Y'. By using the relations:

$$I_3 = \tfrac{3}{4}Q+\tfrac{1}{2}U_3, \qquad Y = \tfrac{1}{2}Q-U_3$$

we find:

$$\begin{aligned}
I'_3 &= \tfrac{3}{4}Q+\tfrac{1}{2}(|\alpha|^2-|\beta|^2)U_3-\tfrac{1}{2}\alpha\bar{\beta}U^{+}-\tfrac{1}{2}\bar{\alpha}\beta U^{-} \\
Y' &= \tfrac{1}{2}Q-(|\alpha|^2-|\beta|^2)U_3+\alpha\bar{\beta}U^{+}+\bar{\alpha}\beta U^{-}.
\end{aligned}$$

The non leptonic hamiltonian H_{NL} is invariant under $\mathscr{G}$ rotations and Y' gauge transformations. Under unitary symmetry, it transforms like the Y' component of an octuplet.

Let us now go back to PC invariance. As it has been shown in the previous section, the component U_2 is associated to the part $PC = -1$. The only rotations $R(\alpha, \beta)$ preserving PC invariance are those where α and β have the same phase. By putting now $|\alpha| = \cos\theta$, $|\beta| = \sin\theta$ we obtain:

$$\begin{aligned}
I'_3 &= \tfrac{3}{4}Q+\tfrac{1}{2}(U_3\cos 2\theta-U_1\sin 2\theta) \\
Y' &= \tfrac{1}{2}Q-U_3\cos 2\theta+U_1\sin 2\theta.
\end{aligned}$$

The $\mathscr{G}$ spin invariance of H_{NL} does not give any supplementary information about the hypercharge conserving part and the hypercharge violating part separately. We only obtain a relation between the magnitude of the various coupling constants via the mixing parameters α and β.

The special case studied by D'ESPAGNAT and PRENTKI [1962] and also by CABIBBO [1964] is a rotation of 2θ around the second U spin axis U_2 and corresponds to $\alpha = \cos\theta$, $\beta = \sin\theta$.

7.2. Non-leptonic decays of baryons

1. All the non-leptonic decays of baryons experimentally observed satisfy very well the $|\Delta Y| = 1$ rule. We consider only this case in what follows.

The phase space considerations allow only the following possibilities:

$$\begin{array}{ll} \Lambda^0 \Rightarrow p+\pi^- & \Lambda^0 \Rightarrow n+\pi^0 \\ \Sigma^+ \Rightarrow n+\pi^+ & \Sigma^+ \Rightarrow p+\pi^0 \\ \Sigma^0 \Rightarrow n+\pi^0 & \Sigma^0 \Rightarrow p+\pi^- \\ \Sigma^- \Rightarrow n+\pi^- & \\ \Xi^0 \Rightarrow \Lambda^0+\pi^0 & \Xi^- \Rightarrow \Lambda^0+\pi^-. \end{array}$$

We note of course that the most frequent decay mode of Σ^0 decay is of electromagnetic nature following $\Sigma^0 \Rightarrow \Lambda^0+\gamma$.

2. The $|\boldsymbol{\Delta I}| = \frac{1}{2}$ rule seems to be satisfied by experiment. We then obtain five relations between the amplitudes:

$$A(\Lambda^0 \Rightarrow p\pi^-)+\sqrt{2}A(\Lambda^0 \Rightarrow n\pi^0) = 0,$$
$$A(\Xi^- \Rightarrow \Lambda^0\pi^-)-\sqrt{2}A(\Xi^0 \Rightarrow \Lambda^0\pi^0) = 0,$$
$$A(\Sigma^+ \Rightarrow n\pi^+)-A(\Sigma^- \Rightarrow n\pi^-)+\sqrt{2}A(\Sigma^+ \Rightarrow p\pi^0) = 0,$$
$$A(\Sigma^+ \Rightarrow n\pi^+)+A(\Sigma^- \Rightarrow n\pi^-)-2A(\Sigma^0 \Rightarrow n\pi^0) = 0,$$
$$A(\Sigma^0 \Rightarrow p\pi^-)-A(\Sigma^+ \Rightarrow p\pi^0) = 0.$$

We then have four independent physical amplitudes

3. In the unitary symmetry model, the hypercharge violating part of the non-leptonic effective hamiltonian transforms like the U_1 component of a U spin vector in an octuplet. We then have as a consequence the $|\boldsymbol{\Delta I}| = \frac{1}{2}$ rule.

In the strict framework of the unitary symmetry it is only possible to obtain an additional relation between the parity violating amplitudes (S wave of the final meson-baryon system) of three relations (GELL-MANN [1964c]):

$$A_S(\Lambda^0 \Rightarrow p\pi^-)+\sqrt{3}A_S(\Sigma^+ \Rightarrow p\pi^0) = 2A_S(\Xi^- \Rightarrow \Lambda^0\pi^-).$$

We first use the $|\boldsymbol{\Delta I}| = \frac{1}{2}$ rule:

$$A(\Sigma^+ \Rightarrow p\pi^0) = A(\Sigma^0 \Rightarrow p\pi^-)$$

to transform the left hand side into:

$$A(\Lambda^0 \Rightarrow p\pi^-)+\sqrt{3}A(\Sigma^+ \Rightarrow p\pi^0) = 2A(B_0 \Rightarrow p\pi^-)$$

where B_0 is the U spin scalar combination of Λ^0 and Σ^0.

It is then convenient to introduce a spurion octuplet S and to work in an exact symmetry. We define two amplitudes:

$$a = A(\mathrm{B}_0+\mathrm{S}_{23} \Rightarrow \mathrm{p}+\pi^-)$$
$$b = A(\Xi^-+\mathrm{S}_{23} \Rightarrow \Lambda^0+\pi^-)$$

where S_{23} is the component $Y = 1$, $I_3 = -\frac{1}{2}$ of the spurion.

We now perform a rotation of π along the second V spin axis V_2 and we obtain a second expression for a:

$$a = A(\Lambda_0+\mathrm{S}_{21} \Rightarrow \Xi^- +\mathrm{K}_0).$$

After comparison of the weights of a and b, it follows immediately that $b = a_\mathrm{T}$ where a_T is the reversed amplitude of a; it is well known that one goes from a to a_T by exchanging the non diagonal transition eigenamplitudes of the direct channel $A_{8\mathrm{as}}$ and $A_{8\mathrm{sa}}$. In this language, the relation we have to prove is simply $a = a_\mathrm{T}$.

It is obvious that the space properties of the spurion S are needed at this stage. For a S wave decay the spurion is pseudoscalar as the π-meson and for a P wave decay it is scalar. For weak decays we use explicitly *PC* invariance to obtain:

$$(A_{8\mathrm{as}})_\mathrm{S} = (A_{8\mathrm{sa}})_\mathrm{S}$$
$$(A_{8\mathrm{as}})_\mathrm{P} - -(A_{8\mathrm{sa}})_\mathrm{P}$$

and the expected equality follows immediately (GOURDIN [1964a]).

4. For completeness, we give the expansion of the physical transitions in eigenamplitudes of the direct channel.

TABLE 7.1

	A_{27}	A_{10}	$A_{\overline{10}}$	$A_{8\mathrm{ss}}$	$A_{8\mathrm{aa}}$	$A_{8\mathrm{sa}}$	$A_{8\mathrm{as}}$
$\Lambda^0 \Rightarrow \mathrm{p}+\pi^-$	$\frac{1}{10}\sqrt{\frac{3}{2}}$	—	$\frac{1}{2\sqrt{6}}$	$-\frac{1}{10}\sqrt{\frac{3}{2}}$	$-\frac{1}{2\sqrt{6}}$	$-\frac{1}{2}\sqrt{\frac{3}{10}}$	$-\frac{1}{2\sqrt{30}}$
$\Sigma^+ \Rightarrow \mathrm{n}+\pi^+$	$\frac{1}{5}$	$-\frac{1}{6}$	$-\frac{1}{6}$	$\frac{3}{10}$	$-\frac{1}{6}$	$\frac{1}{2\sqrt{5}}$	$-\frac{1}{2\sqrt{5}}$
$\Sigma^+ \Rightarrow \mathrm{p}+\pi^0$	$\frac{3}{10\sqrt{2}}$	$-\frac{1}{3\sqrt{2}}$	$\frac{1}{6\sqrt{2}}$	$-\frac{3}{10\sqrt{2}}$	$\frac{1}{6\sqrt{2}}$	$-\frac{1}{2\sqrt{10}}$	$\frac{1}{2\sqrt{10}}$
$\Sigma^- \Rightarrow \mathrm{n}+\pi^-$	$\frac{1}{2}$	$-\frac{1}{2}$	—	—	—	—	—
$\Xi^- \Rightarrow \Lambda^0+\pi^-$	$\frac{1}{5}\sqrt{\frac{3}{2}}$	$-\frac{1}{2\sqrt{6}}$	$\frac{1}{2\sqrt{6}}$	$-\frac{1}{5}\sqrt{\frac{3}{2}}$	—	—	$-\frac{1}{\sqrt{30}}$

5. The Lee relation for P wave amplitudes (LEE [1964]):

$$A_P(\Lambda^0 \Rightarrow p\bar{\pi})+\sqrt{3}A_P(\Sigma^+ \Rightarrow p\pi^0) = 2A_P(\Xi^- \Rightarrow \Lambda^0\pi^-)$$

works if and only if:

$$(A_{8sa})_P = (A_{8as})_P = 0.$$

Such a relation can be obtained in the framework of an additional symmetry which is not an operation of the group, the *R* symmetry, defined as the symmetry of the weight diagrams with respect to the origin.

It seems that, for strong interactions, the *R* invariance is not satisfied. Nevertheless, if we assume the non-leptonic weak hamiltonian to be *RP* invariant we obtain for the eigenvalues amplitudes the relations:

$$\begin{aligned}(A_{8as})_P &= (A_{8sa})_P = 0\\ (A_{10})_P &= (A_{\overline{10}})_P\\ (A_{27})_S &= (A_{8ss})_S = (A_{8aa})_S = 0\\ (A_{10})_S &= -(A_{\overline{10}})_S\,.\end{aligned}$$

Of course the Lee relation is satisfied and we obtain an additional relation which seems also in agreement with experiment:

$$A(\Sigma^+ \Rightarrow n\pi^+)_S = 0.$$

We have now to understand why the *RP* symmetry appears to be good in the non-leptonic baryon decays.

7.3. Weak radiative decays of baryons

1. Due to phase space considerations only, the following reactions are observable:

$$\begin{array}{lll}\Lambda^0 \Rightarrow n+\gamma & \Sigma^+ \Rightarrow p+\gamma & \Sigma^0 \Rightarrow n+\gamma\\ \Xi^- \Rightarrow \Sigma^-+\gamma & \Xi^0 \Rightarrow \Lambda^0+\gamma & \Xi^0 \Rightarrow \Sigma^0+\gamma.\end{array}$$

In the framework of unitary symmetry, it is possible to prove that the two amplitudes $A(\Sigma^+ \Rightarrow p+\gamma)$ and $A(\Xi^- \Rightarrow \Sigma^-+\gamma)$ are parity conserving. The proof is exactly the same in both cases and we restrict ourselves to the first reaction.

2. In order to study the radiative decay $B_1 \Rightarrow B_2+\gamma$, it is more convenient to consider the transition amplitude $B_1+\overline{B}_2 \Rightarrow \gamma$.

The total angular momentum is $J = 1$. For the parity violating amplitudes *PC* conservation implies *C* violation and the state $B_1\overline{B}_2$ has $C = +1$.

This result, combined with $J = 1$ gives a pure $^3P_1$ state. It follows immediately that:

$$A_{pv}(B_1+\overline{B}_2 \Rightarrow \gamma)+A_{pv}(B_2+\overline{B}_1 \Rightarrow \gamma) = 0.$$

3. We now consider the U spin spinor $[\Sigma^+, p]$. The G_u parity acts on the spinor in the following way:

$$G_u|\Sigma^+\rangle = |\overline{p}\rangle \qquad G_u|\overline{p}\rangle = -|\Sigma^+\rangle$$
$$G_u|p\rangle = -|\overline{\Sigma^+}\rangle \qquad G_u|\overline{\Sigma^+}\rangle = |p\rangle.$$

On the other hand, the photon is odd under charge conjugation and is invariant under U spin rotations. It follows that $G_u = -1$ for the photon.

The hypercharge violating, parity violating part of the non-leptonic hamiltonian commutes with the operator G_u and we immediately deduce the relation (Gourdin [1964b]):

$$A_{pv}(\Sigma^+\overline{p} \Rightarrow \gamma) = A_{pv}(\overline{p}\Sigma^+ \Rightarrow \gamma).$$

By combining this equality with the previous ones we see that the parity violating amplitude for the radiative decay $\Sigma^+ \Rightarrow p+\gamma$ is zero. As a consequence, the asymmetry parameter is also zero.

4. This property has been established by Hara [1964] using a complete unitary symmetry. In fact the PC invariance and the G_u invariance are sufficient to obtain it.

7.4. The K ⇒ 2π transition

1. We now study the two-pion decay of the K meson:

$$K \Rightarrow \pi+\pi.$$

The spin of the K meson is $J = 0^-$ and a 2π system in an S state has an even parity. The $K \Rightarrow 2\pi$ transition is parity violating and hypercharge violating.

2. The K meson has isotopic spin $I = \frac{1}{2}$. A 2π system in an S state can only have isotopic spin $I = 0$ or 2 because of the generalized Pauli principle.

It follows that the decay of the charged K mesons in a 2π system:

$$K^\pm \Rightarrow \pi^\pm+\pi^0$$

is forbidden if the $|\Delta I| = \frac{1}{2}$ rule is valid whereas the decay of the neutral K mesons in a 2π system of isotopic spin zero is allowed.

If the $|\Delta I| = \frac{1}{2}$ rule strictly holds, the $K^\pm \Rightarrow \pi^\pm+\pi^0$ decays can take place only with an additional electromagnetic interaction. On this basis, the ratio of the decay rates is expected to be:

$$\frac{\Gamma(K^+ \Rightarrow \pi^+ + \pi^0)}{\Gamma(K_1^0 \Rightarrow 2\pi)} \simeq (\tfrac{1}{137})^2.$$

The experimental value of this ratio is $\frac{1}{650}$ and we have to explain the large difference between the two numbers.

3. GELL-MANN [1964c] has shown that the neutral K mesons decay into a 2π system is forbidden in the framework of an exact unitary symmetry with *PC* invariance. In fact such a result is related to *PC* invariance and G_u invariance only (GOURDIN [1964]).

The hypercharge violating parity, violating part of the weak hamiltonian commutes with the operator G_u. As an immediate consequence the decays of the neutral K mesons into $2M_0$ or $2M_3$ systems are forbidden. The only possibility allowed by G_u invariance is a $M_0 + M_3$ system.

It is more convenient to work with a transition amplitude relating the vacuum to a $K_1^0(K_2^0)$, M_0, M_3 system. From space time properties, the $K_1^0(K_2^0)M_3$ system must be symmetrical with respect to space variables; K_1^0, $(K_2^0)M_3$ belonging to the same U spin multiplet, the system $K_1^0(K_2^0)M_3$ must also by symmetrical with respect to U spin variables and the only possible U spin state is then $U = 2$. The transitions allowed by the previous hamiltonian are only $|\Delta U| = 1$ transitions and it follows immediately that:

$$K_1^0 \not\Rightarrow M_0 + M_3 \qquad K_2^0 \not\Rightarrow M_0 + M_3 .$$

Finally, we combine all the results to obtain only the physical ones

$$K_1^0 \not\Rightarrow 2\pi^0 \qquad K_2^0 \not\Rightarrow 2\pi^0 .$$

By using the $|\Delta I| = \frac{1}{2}$ rule, we extend this result to the $\pi^+\pi^-$ mode of the two-pion neutral system.

4. The $|\Delta U| = 1$ rule is unimportant to forbid the $K_1^0 \Rightarrow 2\pi^0$ transition as pointed out by ITABASHI [1964]. Let us consider the three states:

$$|K_1^0, M_0, M_0\rangle \qquad |K_1^0, M_3, M_0\rangle \qquad |K_1^0, M_3, M_3\rangle.$$

They are completely symmetrical in space and because of the Bose-Einstein statistics they are also symmetrical in the exchange of two components of the U spin vector M_j. These three states can then be associated to three U spin tensors with symmetrized indices. The index 2 is present only one time and the three tensors transform like H_2, H_{23}, H_{233}. By using the previous *PC* invariant non-leptonic hamiltonian as studied in 7.1,7 we immediately see that the three transitions are forbidden.

5. It is relatively difficult to understand the real significance of such a result in the physical situation where the symmetry must be largely destroyed, in such a way that the phase-space allows the decay $K \Rightarrow 2\pi$.

Let us consider, for instance, the matrix element of the K meson current between the vacuum and a 2π state.

$$\langle 2\pi | J_K | 0 \rangle = V_K(q^2)$$

where q is the energy momentum of the virtual K meson.

In this language, the previous result is simply

$$V_K(-m_\pi^2) = 0.$$

The physical coupling constant is $V_K(-m_K^2)$.

Unfortunately we do not know the variation of the vertex function with respect to its argument q^2. But such a variation can be expected to be large because of the large difference between the K meson and the π meson masses and in a real physical situation, the $K_1^0 \Rightarrow 2\pi$ decay can be relatively important.

It is possible, of course, to use phenomenological models to calculate the function $V_K(q^2)$ and to estimate the damping factor due to unitary symmetry. The results seem to be too model dependent to be reliable.

6. Experimentally, the 2π decay of the long lived component K_L^0 of the neutral K meson has been observed with a branching ratio versus the 2π decay of the short lived component K_S^0 given by (Christenson [1964]):

$$\frac{(K_L^0 \Rightarrow 2\pi)}{(K_S^0 \Rightarrow 2\pi)} \simeq (2 \pm 0.4) \times 10^{-3}.$$

It follows that the physical states K_L^0 and K_S^0 are no longer the eigenstates K_2^0 and K_1^0 of the *PC* operator. The weak interactions exhibit here a small violation of the *PC* invariance and using the *TCP* theorem we conclude to a violation of time reversal invariance.

Of course the magnitude of such a violation is compatible with the other experimental data on weak interactions and it seems actually that the observation of processes forbidden by *PC* invariance is the only way to detect and to measure the *PC* violation.

The effective weak interaction hamiltonian is not a pure $PC = +1$ eigenstate and contains a $PC = -1$ part responsible for the observed violation. At least the hypercharge violating part responsible for $K \Rightarrow 2\pi$ decay is *PC* violating and from the previous results it is sufficient to introduce a part transforming like the second component of a U spin vector H_2 besides the component H_1 as previously.

Many theories have been proposed to explain the experimental observation of a $K_L^0 \Rightarrow 2\pi$ decay. The question of C conservation in strong and electromagnetic interactions has been examined in connection with the present problem, both from theoretical and experimental point of view. We do not discuss this important problem here and we refer the reader to specialized papers.

CHAPTER VIII

THE UNITARY GROUP SU(6)

8.1. Lie algebra

1. The Lie algebra A_5 is simple and the root diagram is five dimensional. The roots α_{ij} have the general form $\alpha_{ij} = e_i - e_j$ where the e_j's are six orthogonal vectors of equal norm in a six dimensional space. The root diagram lies then in the hyperplane $X_1+X_2+X_3+X_4+X_5+X_6 = 0$. The use of 6 coordinates of sum zero will be convenient in the following.

2. The Cartan tensor is regular and normalized so that $g_{\alpha-\alpha} = 1$. Using this condition the common normalization of the roots is given by:

$$(\alpha, \alpha) = \tfrac{1}{6}$$

and all the non vanishing structure constants have the same modulus equal to $1/2\sqrt{3}$.

3. The Lie algebra has the dimension 35 and the Cartan subalgebra the dimension 5. We will use for this last subalgebra six generators H_j of sum zero:

$$H_1+H_2+H_3+H_4+H_5+H_6 = 0.$$

The commutation relations of the Lie algebra in its standard form are then given by:

$$[H_i, H_j] = 0 \qquad [E_{ij}, E_{ji}] = \frac{1}{2\sqrt{3}}(H_i - H_j)$$

$$[H_i, E_{ij}] = \frac{1}{2\sqrt{3}} E_{ij} \qquad [H_j, E_{ij}] = -\frac{1}{2\sqrt{3}} E_{ij}$$

$$[E_{ij}, E_{jk}] = \frac{1}{2\sqrt{3}} E_{ik} \qquad [E_{ji}, E_{kj}] = -\frac{1}{2\sqrt{3}} E_{ki}.$$

4. We can define 15 subalgebrae of the type E_α, $E_{-\alpha}$, (α, H), isomorphic to a Lie algebra A_1:

$$2\sqrt{3}E_{ij}, \qquad 2\sqrt{3}E_{ji}, \qquad \sqrt{3}(H_i - H_j).$$

For a practical manipulation it is more simple to use new generators X_{ij} normalized in the following way:

$$X_{ij} = 2\sqrt{3}E_{ij}, \qquad X_{jj} = 2\sqrt{3}H_j$$

and we have the zero trace condition $\sum_j X_{jj} = 0$.

5. The subgroup SO(6) of SU(6) has its Lie algebra defined by the linear combinations:

$$Z_{ij} = X_{ij} - X_{ji}$$

and, as expected, we have 15 such a generators.

8.2. Fundamental representations

1. We have five fundamental representations with the following highest weights:

$$\begin{aligned} L^1 &= \tfrac{1}{6}[5e_1 - e_2 - e_3 - e_4 - e_5 - e_6] \\ L^2 &= \tfrac{1}{3}[2(e_1 + e_2) - e_3 - e_4 - e_5 - e_6] \\ L^3 &= \tfrac{1}{2}[e_1 + e_2 + e_3 - e_4 - e_5 - e_6] \\ L^4 &= \tfrac{1}{3}[e_1 + e_2 + e_3 + e_4 - 2(e_5 + e_6)] \\ L^5 &= \tfrac{1}{6}[e_1 + e_2 + e_3 + e_4 + e_5 - 5e_6]. \end{aligned}$$

The two contragradient representations F^1 and F^5 are 6 dimensional; the two contragradient representations F^2 and F^4 are 15 dimensional; the self contragradient representation F^3 is 20 dimensional.

2. The matrix representation of the Lie algebra for the F^1 representation is easily computed, using the properties of the roots and of the weights as in the case of SU(3) studied in chapter I.

We introduce a basis of six orthonormalized vectors:

$$\langle 6, k | 6, j \rangle = \delta_{jk}$$

and we obtain the explicit forms of representation:

$$\begin{aligned} X_{kk} &= \tfrac{5}{6}|6, k\rangle\langle 6, k| - \tfrac{1}{6}\sum_{j \neq k} |6, j\rangle\langle 6, j| \\ X_{jk} &= |6, j\rangle\langle 6, k|. \end{aligned}$$

3. With a convenient choice of basis for the space of the contragradient representation, as explained in chapter I, the $\overline{6}$ representation of the Lie algebra is given by:

$$\begin{aligned} X_{kk} &= -\tfrac{5}{6}|\overline{6}, k\rangle\langle \overline{6}, k| + \tfrac{1}{6}\sum_{j \neq k} |\overline{6}, j\rangle\langle \overline{6}, j|, \\ X_{jk} &= -|\overline{6}, k\rangle\langle \overline{6}, j|. \end{aligned}$$

8.3. Adjoint representation

1. The adjoint representation is 35 dimensional and its weight diagram is the root diagram. The product of the two 6 dimensional contragradient fundamental representations:

$$D^{(6)}(10000) \otimes D^{(6)}(00001) = D^{(35)}(10001) \oplus D^{(1)}(00000)$$

gives the simplest way to construct the adjoint representation. The scalar representation is associated to the conserved hermitian form, by definition invariant under unitary transformations.

2. The vectors of the adjoint representation associated to a non zero root α_{ij} are immediately written as a tensor product:

$$|35, ij\rangle = |6, i\rangle \otimes |\bar{6}, j\rangle, \qquad i \neq j.$$

The scalar associated to the invariant representation of the tensor product is easily obtained, from the particular choice of basis in the 6 and $\bar{6}$ spaces, as:

$$|1\rangle = \frac{1}{\sqrt{6}} \sum_{j=1}^{6} |6, j\rangle \otimes |\bar{6}, j\rangle.$$

It follows that the five eigenvectors of the adjoint representation associated to the weight zero are characterized, as expected, by a zero trace condition:

$$|35, \rho^\alpha\rangle = \sum_{j=1}^{6} \rho_j^\alpha |6, j\rangle \otimes |\bar{6}, j\rangle$$

where the numbers ρ_j^α satisfy the restrictions:

$$\sum_j \rho_j^\alpha = 0 \qquad \sum_j (\rho_j^\alpha)^2 = 1.$$

3. The adjoint representation is self-contragradient and therefore it is possible to construct a bilinear symmetrical form in the adjoint representation space which is invariant under unitary transformations. The conserved form C has the following 35×35 matrix representation:

$$C = \sum_{i \neq j} |35, ij\rangle\langle 35, ji| + \sum_\alpha |35, \rho^\alpha\rangle\langle 35, \rho^\alpha|.$$

8.4. Topology

1. The universal covering group of the Lie algebra A_5 is the simply connected group SU(6). The center of SU(6) is isomorphic to Z_6 and can be represented, in the representation $D^6(10000)$, by the six matrices:

$$\{I, kI, k^2I, k^3I, k^4I, k^5I\} \qquad \text{with} \quad k = \exp(\tfrac{1}{3}i\pi).$$

The center is then generated by the element kI for the 6 fundamental representation, by k^2I for the 15 fundamental representation, by $k^3I = -I$ for the 20 self-contragradient representation.

For the irreductible representation $D^N(\lambda_1, \lambda_2, \lambda_3, \lambda_4, \lambda_5)$, the generating element of the center is represented by:

$$I_N \exp(\tfrac{1}{3}i\pi)[(\lambda_1-\lambda_5)+2(\lambda_2-\lambda_4)+3\lambda_3]$$

where now I_N is the $N \times N$ unit matrix.

2. The kernel of the homomorphism:

$$SU(6) \Rightarrow SU(6)/Z_6$$

must be represented by the unit matrix in all the representations of the factor group $SU(6)/Z_6$. The representations of the Lie algebra which are also representations of $SU(6)/Z_6$ are characterized by:

$$\lambda_1-\lambda_5+2(\lambda_2-\lambda_4)+3\lambda_3 \equiv 0 \quad (6).$$

The adjoint representation satisfies of course this condition and generates, by tensor product all the irreductible representations of the factor group $SU(6)/Z_6$.

3. The kernel of the homomorphism:

$$SU(6) \Rightarrow SU(6)/Z_3$$

is generated in the representation $D^N(\lambda_1, \lambda_2, \lambda_3, \lambda_4, \lambda_5)$ by the quantity:

$$I_N \exp(\tfrac{2}{3}i\pi)[\lambda_1-\lambda_5+2(\lambda_2-\lambda_4)+3\lambda_3]$$

and it must be represented by the unit matrix in all the representations of the factor group $SU(6)/Z_3$. The representations of the Lie algebra which are also representations of $SU(7)/Z_3$ are characterized by:

$$\lambda_1-\lambda_5+2(\lambda_2-\lambda_4)+3\lambda_3 \equiv 0 \quad (3).$$

The fundamental 20 dimensional representation satisfies this condition and generates by tensor product the group $SU(6)/Z_3$.

4. The kernel of the homomorphism:

$$SU(6) \Rightarrow SU(6)/Z_2$$

is generated, in the representation $D^N(\lambda_1, \lambda_2, \lambda_3, \lambda_4, \lambda_5)$ by the quantity:

$$I_N \exp(i\pi)[\lambda_1-\lambda_5+2(\lambda_2-\lambda_4)+3\lambda_3]$$

and it must be represented by the unit matrix in all the representations of the factor group $SU(6)/Z_2$. The representations of the Lie algebra which are also representations of $SU(6)/Z_2$ are characterized by:

$$\lambda_1-\lambda_2+2(\lambda_2-\lambda_4)+3\lambda_3 \equiv 0 \quad (2).$$

The fundamental 15 dimensional representation satisfies this condition and generates by tensor product the group $SU(6)/Z_2$.

5. The set of the irreducible representations $D^N(\lambda_1, \lambda_2, \lambda_3, \lambda_4, \lambda_5)$ can be written as the direct sum of six classes C_α where $\alpha(-3 < \alpha \leqq +3)$ is the integer defined by:

$$\lambda_1-\lambda_5+2(\lambda_2-\lambda_4)+3\lambda_3 \equiv \alpha \quad (6).$$

The class C_0 corresponds to the group $SU(6)/Z_6$.

The direct sum C_0+C_3 corresponds to the group $SU(6)/Z_3$.

The direct sum $C_0+C_2+C_{-2}$ corresponds to the group $SU(6)/Z_2$.

The set of these six classes is a finite group obviously isomorphic to Z_6.

8.5. Tensor algebra

1. The vectors of the fundamental representations $D^{(6)}(10000)$ can be associated to a first order contravariant tensor ξ_j:

$$\xi_j \Rightarrow |6, j\rangle.$$

The vectors of the fundamental representation $D^{(6)}(00001)$ can be associated to a first order covariant tensor ξ^k:

$$\xi^k \Rightarrow |\bar{6}, k\rangle.$$

2. The vectors of the fundamental representation $D^{(15)}(01000)$ can be associated to a second order skew symmetric contravariant tensor $\xi_{j,k}$ and for the contravariant representation $D^{(15)}(00010)$ we introduce a second order skew symmetric covariant tensor $\xi^{j,k}$.

For the self-contragradient representation $D^{(20)}(00100)$ we will use a third order completely skew symmetric tensor which can be either covariant or contravariant $\xi_{j,k,l}$ or $\xi^{m,n,p}$. The equivalence of these two descriptions is due to the invariant character, in the unimodular group SU(6), of the sixth order completely skew symmetric one component tensor ε_{jklmnp}.

3. The vectors of the adjoint representation $D^{(35)}(10001)$ are then associated to a second order mixed tensor ξ_j^k of trace zero. It is useful in many applications, to represent such a tensor by a 6×6 matrix of trace zero.

4. In the unimodular group, all the irreducible represention $D^N(\lambda_1, \lambda_2, \lambda_3, \lambda_4, \lambda_5)$ can be described by an irreducible purely contravariant tensor of order p:

$$p = \lambda_1 + 2\lambda_2 + 3\lambda_3 + 4\lambda_4 + 5\lambda_5 .$$

For the calculus with the Young diagrams it is convenient to use purely contravariant tensors.

5. We now give a very restrictive list of irreducible representations of SU(6). In each case we draw the corresponding contravariant Young diagram and we indicate the class of the representation. The smallest rank mixed tensor associated which the representation is also given. The dimension of the irreducible representation is calculated using the formula obtained in chapter XVI:

$$\begin{aligned} N(\lambda_1, \lambda_2, \lambda_3, \lambda_4, \lambda_5) = {} & (1+\lambda_1)(1+\lambda_2)(1+\lambda_3)(1+\lambda_4)(1+\lambda_5) \times \\ & \times (1+\tfrac{1}{2}(\lambda_1+\lambda_2))(1+\tfrac{1}{2}(\lambda_2+\lambda_3))(1+\tfrac{1}{2}(\lambda_3+\lambda_4))(1+\tfrac{1}{2}(\lambda_4+\lambda_5)) \times \\ & \times (1+\tfrac{1}{3}(\lambda_1+\lambda_2+\lambda_3))(1+\tfrac{1}{3}(\lambda_2+\lambda_3+\lambda_4))(1+\tfrac{1}{3}(\lambda_3+\lambda_4+\lambda_5)) \times \\ & \times (1+\tfrac{1}{4}(\lambda_1+\lambda_2+\lambda_3+\lambda_4))(1+\tfrac{1}{4}(\lambda_2+\lambda_3+\lambda_4+\lambda_5)) \times \\ & \times (1+\tfrac{1}{5}(\lambda_1+\lambda_2+\lambda_3+\lambda_4+\lambda_5)). \end{aligned}$$

TABLE 8.1

Rank	Irreducible representation	Class	Mixed tensor	Young diagram
	$D^{(6)}(10000) \simeq 6$	1	ξ_j	
1				
	$D^{(6)}(00001) \simeq \overline{6}$	−1	ξ^j	
	$D^{(21)}(20000) \simeq 21$	2	$\xi_{jk,}$	
2	$D^{(21)}(00002) \simeq \overline{21}$	−2	$\xi^{jk,}$	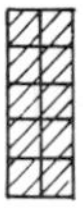
	$D^{(15)}(01000) \simeq 15$	2	$\xi_{j,k}$	

TABLE 8.1 (Continued)

Rank	Irreducible representation	Class	Mixed tensor	Young diagram
2	$D^{(15)}(00010) \simeq \overline{15}$	-2	$\xi^{j,k}$	
	$D^{(35)}(10001) \simeq 35$	0	ξ_j^k	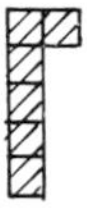
3	$D^{(56)}(30000) \simeq 56$	3	$\xi_{jkl,}$	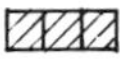
	$D^{(56)}(00003) \simeq \overline{56}$	3	$\xi^{jkl,}$	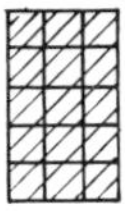
	$D^{(70)}(11000) \simeq 70$	3	$\xi_{jk,l}$	
	$D^{(70)}(00011) \simeq \overline{70}$	3	$\xi^{jk,l}$	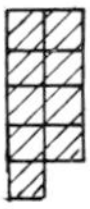
	$D^{(20)}(00100) \simeq 20$	3	$\xi_{j,k,l}$	
4	$D^{(405)}(20002) \simeq 405$	0	$\xi^{lm,}_{jk,}$	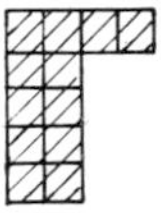
	$D^{(280)}(20010) \simeq 280$	0	$\xi^{l,m}_{jk,}$	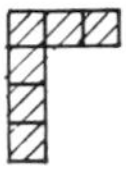
	$D^{(280)}(01002) \simeq \overline{280}$	0	$\xi^{lm,}_{j,k}$	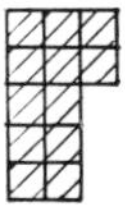
	$D^{(189)}(01010) \simeq 189$	0	$\xi^{l,m}_{j,k}$	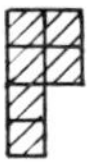

TABLE 8.1 (Continued)

Rank	Irreducible representation	Class	Mixed Tensor	Young diagram
	$D^{(700)}(40001) \simeq 700$	3	$\xi^{n}_{jklm,}$	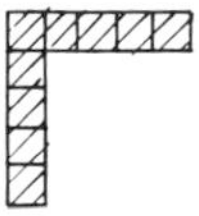
	$D^{(1134)}(21001) \simeq 1134$	3	$\xi^{n}_{jkl,\,m}$	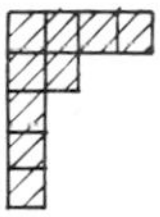
5	$D^{(560)}(02001) \simeq 560$	3	$\xi^{n}_{jk,\,lm}$	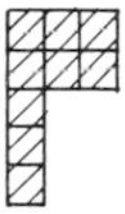
	$D^{(540)}(10101) \simeq 540$	3	$\xi^{n}_{jk,\,l,\,m}$	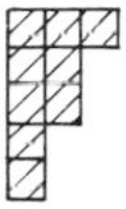
	$D^{(2695)}(30003) \simeq 2695$	0	$\xi^{mnp,}_{jkl,}$	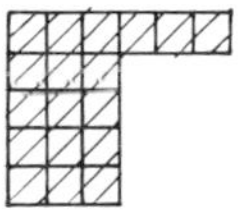
	$D^{(462)}(60000) \simeq 462$	0	$\xi_{ijklmn,}$	
	$D^{(1050)}(41000) \simeq 1050$	0	$\xi_{ijklm,\,n,}$	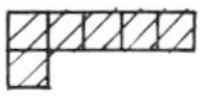
6	$D^{(1134)}(22000) \simeq 1134'$	0	$\xi_{ijkl,\,m,n}$	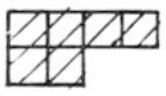
	$D^{(490)}(03000) \simeq 490$	0	$\xi_{ijklm,\,n,}$	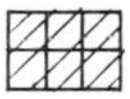
	$D^{(175)}(00200) \simeq 175$	0	$\xi_{ij,\,kl,\,mn}$	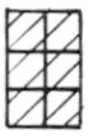
	$D^{(3675)}(11011) \simeq 3675$	0	$\xi^{lm,\,n}_{ij,\,k}$	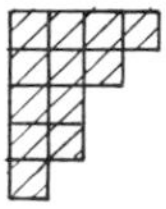

6. The reduction in its irreducible parts of a product of representations can be obtained by an algebraic analysis of the tensor algebra or by using the Littlewood method with the Young diagrams.

We give only a set of useful results:

$$\begin{aligned} 6 \otimes \overline{6} &= 35 \oplus 1 \\ 6 \otimes 6 &= 15 \oplus 21 \\ 15 \otimes 6 &= 20 \oplus 70 \\ 21 \otimes 6 &= 70 \oplus 56 \end{aligned}$$

$$6 \otimes 6 \otimes 6 = 56 \oplus 70 \oplus 70 \oplus 20$$

$$\begin{aligned} 15 \otimes \overline{15} &\Rightarrow 1 \oplus 35 \oplus 189 \\ 21 \otimes \overline{21} &= 1 \oplus 35 \oplus 405 \\ 21 \otimes \overline{15} &= 35 \oplus 280 \\ \overline{21} \otimes 15 &= 35 \oplus \overline{280} \end{aligned}$$

$$35 \otimes 35 = 1 \oplus 35_a \oplus 35_s \oplus 280 \oplus \overline{280} \oplus 189 \oplus 405$$

$$\begin{aligned} 20 \otimes 20 &= 1 \oplus 35 \oplus 189 \oplus 175 \\ 56 \otimes \overline{56} &= 1 \oplus 35 \oplus 405 \oplus 2695 \\ 56 \otimes 35 &= 56 \oplus 70 \oplus 700 \oplus 1134 \\ 70 \otimes 35 &= 20 \oplus 2(70) \oplus 56 \oplus 540 \oplus 560 \oplus 1134 \\ 56 \otimes 56 &= 462 \oplus 1050 \oplus 1134' \oplus 490 \\ 70 \otimes \overline{70} &= 1 \oplus 35 \oplus 35 \oplus 280 \oplus \overline{280} \oplus 189 \oplus 405 \oplus 3675. \end{aligned}$$

CHAPTER IX

THE SU(6) MODEL

9.1. Generalities

1. The supermultiplet model has been proposed by WIGNER [1937] and FEENBERG and WIGNER [1937] to classify the nuclear states. In the approximation where the nuclear forces can be assumed independent of the spin and of the isotopic spin the group $SU(2) \otimes SU(2)$ associated to these two spins can be enlarged to a group SU(4).

The nucleon has $S = \frac{1}{2}$ spin and $I = \frac{1}{2}$ isotopic spin. The four-nucleon states are then described by the fundamental 4-dimensional representation of SU(4). The nuclear states are then constructed by tensor product and the irreducible representations of SU(4) characterize a supermultiplet of nuclear levels.

The model appears to be satisfactory for the light nuclei. For the heavy nuclei, the SU(4) symmetry is disturbed by the Coulomb interaction and by the spin orbit forces. Nevertheless the total isotopic spin seems to be a good quantum number and the classification as given by the SU(4) symmetry appears to be useful.

A systematic study of the ground state of nuclei by FRANZINI and RADICATI [1963] shows a remarkable agreement with the Wigner theory up to $A = 140$.

2. The physical idea of the supermultiplet theory can be applied to elementary particles replacing the nucleons by the quarks. The isotopic spin symmetry SU(2) becomes the SU(3) symmetry. The $SU(2) \otimes SU(3)$ group of the spin S and the internal symmetry is enlarged to the SU(6) group. The SU(3) triplet of quarks with spin $J = \frac{1}{2}$ is classified in the fundamental 6-dimensional representation of SU(6). All the elementary particle states – bound states of resonances – are constructed from the quarks by tensor product and associated to irreducible representations of SU(6). The SU(6) model has been proposed by GÜRSEY and RADICATI [1964] and independently by SAKITA [1964b].

In the Gell-Mann theory of quarks the baryonic number is included in the form of a U(3) group and the present extension leads to a U(6) group. If now the eightfold way is used in its original version, without the reference to a fundamental triplet of quarks, the group of symmetry is simply:

$$(SU(6)/Z_3) \otimes T.$$

In both cases the physical consequences for all the known particles are identical. Nevertheless the first aspect is very attractive and useful even if the quarks do not exist as physical particles and represent only mathematical objects.

3. The Wigner supermultiplet theory is non relativistic but such a feature is perfectly acceptable for low energy nuclear physics. The situation is certainly different in elementary particle physics where the Lorentz and the Poincaré invariances play very important roles.

In the eightfold way model the internal symmetry is completely independent of the relativistic invariance. They are of different nature in that the SU(3) symmetry is an approximate symmetry for strong interactions whereas the relativistic invariance holds for all types of interactions. If the baryonic gauge group T_B and the leptonic gauge group T_L are added to the Poincaré group the physical extension of P is non trivial due to a relation between B, L and the spin J as shown by LURÇAT and MICHEL [1961]. The complete group takes then the form

$$(SU(3)/Z_3) \otimes (P \otimes T_B \otimes T_L)/Z_2.$$

The second problem we have to solve now is to define mathematically the relation between the spin S associated to the subgroup SU(2) of SU(6) and the Poincaré group. The little group of a time like energy momentum four vector is the rotation group SO(3) for which the universal covering group is SU(2). For a non zero mass particle at rest, the little group is simply the subgroup of space rotations. In many cases, S can be identified with the total angular momentum J at rest, in particular this result is certainly true for the basis quark particles. But in a composite model of quarks other forces, as for instance spin-orbit forces, can appear and the general situation is not yet well defined. We will come back to this point later.

We then have to extend the Poincaré group by an internal symmetry group and to look for non trivial extensions. Many authors have studied this problem from a mathematical point of view and have obtained very restrictive results. We do not discuss this question here because of its technical aspect and we refer the reader to some original papers: MCGLINN [1964], GREENBERG

[1964], MAYER et al. [1964], COESTER et al. [1964], OTTOSON et al. [1965], MICHEL [1965] and RAYFEARTAIGH [1965].

Actually two models of "relativistic extension" of the SU(6) symmetry emerge. The homogeneous and inhomogeneous SL(6, C) theory has been studied by SAKITA and WALI [1965] and extensively described by RÜHL [1965 a, b]. A second model based on the pseudounitary group SU(6, 6) has been proposed by SALAM, DELBOURGO and STRATHDEE [1965], SALAM, STRATHDEE, CHARAP and MATTHEWS [1965], DELBOURGO, RASHID and STRATHDEE [1965] and the Trieste group has produced a considerable lot of papers in this direction.

Nevertheless all the attempts made to define coherently a relativistic group including SU(3) and the Poincaré group in a way different from that of the direct product, encounter many difficulties. As pointed out by ALLES and AMATI [1965], one of the most crucial problems is the incompatibility of some models with the unitarity and the crossing.

It is perhaps not necessary to produce a covariant formulation of the SU(6) symmetry and the model can be physically useful and interesting if we restrict ourselves to problems strictly at rest as the classification of particles and the question of mass breaking.

9.2. Physical interpretation of the Lie algebra

1. In the eightfold way, it is useful to speak, at least formally, a quark language in order to derive rapidly the results about the tensor algebra of the representations.

The quarks correspond to an SU(3) triplet of spin $J = \frac{1}{2}$ and we then have six possible states. In an SU(6) framework, these six states play completely equivalent roles and the quarks are now described by the six dimensional fundamental representation 6 of SU(6) and consequently represented by a first order contravariant tensor q. We will use the following notations for the groups SU(6), SU(3) and SU(2).

TABLE 8.1

SU(6)	α	1	2	3	4	5	6
SU(3)	A	1	2	3	1	2	3
SU(2)	j	1	1	1	2	2	2

2. The adjoint representation can be associated to a mixed second order

tensor T_α^β of trace zero $T_\alpha^\alpha = 0$, following the relation

$$\overline{6} \otimes 6 = 35 \oplus 1.$$

This tensor is reducible with respect to the subgroup SU(2) ⊗ SU(3). We now use the notation T_{Aj}^{Bk} and the trace condition is written as

$$T_{Aj}^{Aj} = 0.$$

The partial trace T_{Aj}^{Bj} is an SU(2) singulet and an SU(3) octuplet.
The partial trace T_{Aj}^{Ak} is an SU(2) triplet and an SU(3) singulet.
The remaining part:

$$T_{Aj}^{Bk} - \tfrac{1}{2}\delta_j^k T_A^B - \tfrac{1}{3}\delta_A^B T_{Cj}^{Ck}$$

is transformed like an SU(2) triplet and an SU(3) octuplet.

We use the notation (N_2, N_3) for the irreducible representations of SU(2) ⊗ SU(3), where N_2 is the dimension of an irreducible representation of SU(2) and N_3 the dimension of an irreducible representation of SU(3). The previous decomposition can be symbolically written as:

$$35 = (1, 8) \oplus (3, 1) \oplus (3, 8).$$

3. This technique can be directly applied to the Lie algebra of SU(6) and we first separate the SU(3) part and the SU(2) part respectively associated, in the previous framework, to the representations (1, 8) and (3, 1).

a) The SU(3) subalgebra. From the partial trace condition we see that the SU(3) generators have the general form:

$$X_{AB} + X_{A+3\,B+3}.$$

More precisely for the I spin, the U spin, the V spin generators, we obtain

$$I \begin{cases} X_{12} + X_{45} \\ X_{21} + X_{54} \\ \tfrac{1}{2}(X_{11} + X_{44} - X_{22} - X_{55}) \end{cases} \qquad U \begin{cases} X_{32} + X_{65} \\ X_{23} + X_{56} \\ \tfrac{1}{2}(X_{33} + X_{66} - X_{22} - X_{55}) \end{cases}$$

$$V \begin{cases} X_{13} + X_{46} \\ X_{31} + X_{64} \\ \tfrac{1}{2}(X_{11} + X_{44} - X_{33} - X_{66}). \end{cases}$$

In particular the hypercharge and electric charge operators are defined by

$$Y = -(X_{33} + X_{66}) \qquad Q = X_{11} + X_{44}.$$

b) The SU(2) subalgebra: the second partial trace condition immediately gives the expression of the three S spin generators

$$\boldsymbol{S}\begin{cases}X_{14}+X_{25}+X_{36}\\X_{41}+X_{52}+X_{63}\\X_{11}+X_{22}+X_{33}\,.\end{cases}$$

Obviously the S spin generators commute with the eight SU(3) generators.

c) The last 24 generators are transformed like the product of the SU(2) generator by an SU(3) generator. The SU(6) generators of this part are characterized by:

$$\begin{gathered}X_{A\,B+3}-\tfrac{1}{3}\delta_{AB}(X_{14}+X_{25}+X_{36})\\X_{A+3\,B}-\tfrac{1}{3}\delta_{AB}(X_{41}+X_{52}+X_{63})\\\tfrac{1}{2}(X_{AB}-X_{A+3\,B+3})-\tfrac{1}{3}\delta_{AB}(X_{11}+X_{22}+X_{33}).\end{gathered}$$

For instance, the three operators $(\boldsymbol{S}, Q)$, which we will associate in the following to the magnetic moment, are given by:

$$(\boldsymbol{S}, Q)\begin{cases}\tfrac{1}{3}(2X_{14}-X_{25}-X_{36})\\\tfrac{1}{3}(2X_{41}-X_{52}-X_{63})\\\tfrac{1}{2}(X_{11}-X_{44})-\tfrac{1}{3}(X_{11}+X_{22}+X_{33}).\end{cases}$$

4. We have just seen how the direct product SU(2) ⊗ SU(3) is a subgroup of SU(6). It is interesting to know the decomposition of the irreducible representations of SU(6) with respect to this subgroup. To do this it is sufficient to start with the SU(3) ⊗ SU(3) content of the fundamental representation 6 of SU(6) and to proceed by tensor products to construct the irreducible representations of SU(6) and the irreducible representations of SU(2) ⊗ SU(3).

As previously, (N_2, N_3) denotes an irreducible representation of SU(2) ⊗ SU(3) and two contragradient representations of SU(3) will be differentiated as usual by a bar: N_3 and $\overline{N}_3$.

The fundamental representation 6 of SU(6) is a SU(3) triplet of spin $J = \frac{1}{2}$,

$$6 = (2, 3) \qquad \overline{6} = (2, \overline{3})$$

and the adjoint representation has been reduced in the previous paragraph

$$35 = (3, 1) \oplus (1, 8) \oplus (3, 8).$$

Using the products of representations as given in SU(6) we obtain, step by step, the following useful results:

$$21 = (3, 6) \oplus (1,\bar{3})$$
$$15 = (1, 6) \oplus (3,\bar{3})$$
$$56 = (4,10) \oplus (2,8)$$
$$20 = (2,8) \oplus (4,1)$$
$$70 = (2,10) \oplus (4,8) \oplus (2,8) \oplus (2,1)$$
$$189 = (1,27) \oplus (3,10) \oplus (3,\overline{10}) \oplus (5,8) \oplus 2(3,8) \oplus (1,8) \oplus (5,1) \oplus (1,1)$$
$$280 = (3,27) \oplus (5,10) \oplus (3,10) \oplus (1,10) \oplus (1,\overline{10}) \oplus (5,8) \oplus 2(3,8) \oplus (1,8) \oplus (1,1)$$
$$\overline{280} = (3,27) \oplus (5,\overline{10}) \oplus (3,\overline{10}) \oplus (1,10) \oplus (1,\overline{10}) \oplus (5,8) \oplus 2(3,8) \oplus (1,8) \oplus (1,1)$$
$$405 = (5,37) \oplus (3,27) \oplus (1,27) \oplus (3,10) \oplus (3,\overline{10}) \oplus (5,8) \oplus 2(3,8) \oplus (1,8) \oplus (5,1) \oplus (1,1)$$
$$2\,695 = (7,64) \oplus (5,64) \oplus (3,64) \oplus (1,64) \oplus (5,35) \oplus (5,\overline{35}) \oplus (3,35) \oplus (3,\overline{35}) \oplus (7,27) \oplus 2(5,27) \oplus 3(3,27) \oplus (1,27) \oplus (5,10) \oplus (5,\overline{10}) \oplus (3,10) \oplus (3,\overline{10}) \oplus (1,10) \oplus (1,\overline{10}) \oplus (7,8) \oplus 2(5,8) \oplus 2(3,8) \oplus (1,8) \oplus (7,1) \oplus (3,1)$$
$$490 = (1,28) \oplus (3,35) \oplus (5,27) \oplus (1,27) \oplus (7,\overline{10}) \oplus (3,10) \oplus (3,\overline{10}) \oplus (5,8) \oplus (3,8) \oplus (1,1)$$
$$1\,050 = (5,28) \oplus (7,35) \oplus (5,35) \oplus (3,35) \oplus (5,27) \oplus (3,27) \oplus (1,27) \oplus (5,10) \oplus (3,10) \oplus (3,\overline{10}) \oplus (3, 8) \oplus (1,8)$$
$$175 = (3,27) \oplus (1,10) \oplus (1,\overline{10}) \oplus (5,8) \oplus (3,8) \oplus (1,7) \oplus (1,3).$$

5. As an illustration of the connection between SU(6) and its physical subgroup SU(2) ⊗ SU(3) it is useful to study the reduction of the 56 dimensional representation in view of future applications.

The 56 dimensional representation is associated to a completely symmetric third order tensor corresponding to the Young diagram with one row and three columns

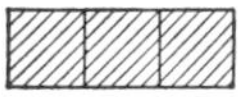
$\leftrightarrow T_{\alpha\beta\gamma}$.

This representation under SU(2) ⊗ SU(3) subgroup is reducible following

$$56 = (4,10) \oplus (2,8).$$

Such a result is easily obtained on the explicit form $T_{A_iB_jC_k}$. The complete symmetry between the three sets of indices A_i, B_j, C_k can be obtained in two independent ways:

a) complete symmetry in the spin indices and complete symmetry in the SU(3) indices: we have a decuplet of spin $\frac{3}{2}$;

b) antisymmetry in two spin indices and antisymmetry in the two corresponding SU(3) indices: we have an octuplet of spin $\frac{1}{2}$.

The tensor $T_{A_iB_jC_k}$ can then be conveniently written as:

$$T_{A_iB_jC_k} = t_{ijk,}\ d_{ABC,} + \frac{1}{3\sqrt{2}}[\varepsilon_{ij}\chi_k\varepsilon_{ABD}N^D_C+\varepsilon_{jk}\chi_i\varepsilon_{BCD}N^D_A+\varepsilon_{ki}\chi_j\varepsilon_{CAD}N^D_B]$$

where

$t_{ijk,}$ is a spin $J = \frac{3}{2}$ spinor
x_k is a spin $J = \frac{1}{2}$ spinor
$d_{ABC,}$ is an SU(3) decuplet
N^D_C is an SU(3) octuplet ($N^D_D = 0$).

We have also used, in the previous expansion, the second-order skew symmetric tensor ε_{ij} and the third order completely skew symmetric tensor ε_{ABC}. As a consequence of the Jacobi identity in SU(2) and SU(3) we have the following identities:

$$\varepsilon_{ij}\chi_k+\varepsilon_{jk}\chi_i+\varepsilon_{ki}\chi_j = 0$$

$$\varepsilon_{ABD}N^D_C+\varepsilon_{BCD}N^D_A+\varepsilon_{CAD}N^D_B = 0$$

and the (2,8) part of the previous expansion can take different equivalent forms. For instance, the bracket can also be written as:

$$= (2\varepsilon_{ij}\chi_k+\varepsilon_{ki}\chi_j)\varepsilon_{ABD}N^D_C+(2\varepsilon_{ki}\chi_j+\varepsilon_{ij}\chi_k)\varepsilon_{CAD}N^D_B.$$

6. For future applications, it is interesting to define, in SU(6), a new subgroup with an SU(4) ⊗ SU(2) ⊗ T structure, where T as usual is a one parameter gauge group.

a) SU(4) *algebra*. This subalgebra is associated with the indices of strangeness zero. The 15 generators are defined by:

$$X_{\alpha\beta}-\tfrac{1}{4}\delta_{\alpha\beta}(X_{11}+X_{22}+X_{44}+X_{55}) \qquad \text{with} \quad \alpha, \beta = 1, 2, 4, 5.$$

The group SU(4) admits an SU(2) ⊗ SU(2) subgroup and one of the two dimensional unitary groups is the isotopic spin group:

$$I\begin{cases} X_{12}+X_{45} \\ X_{21}-X_{54} \\ \frac{1}{2}(X_{11}-X_{22}+X_{44}-X_{55}) \end{cases} \qquad N\begin{cases} X_{14}+X_{25} \\ X_{41}+X_{52} \\ \frac{1}{2}(X_{11}+X_{22}-X_{44}-X_{55}). \end{cases}$$

b) SU(4) ⊗ SU(2) *subalgebra*. We now define a third SU(2) type subgroup commuting with the 15 generators of SU(4):

$$M\begin{cases} X_{36} \\ X_{63} \\ \frac{1}{2}(X_{33}-X_{66}) \end{cases}$$

and we have the obvious relation between the three operators S, N, M

$$\boldsymbol{S} = \boldsymbol{N}+\boldsymbol{M}.$$

c) The gauge group T is related to hypercharge Y which is an operator commuting with all the generators of the previous SU(4) ⊗ SU(2) subalgebra.

7. The decomposition of the SU(6) irreducible representations with respect to the SU(2) ⊗ SU(4) ⊗ T_Y subgroup is obtained by tensor product algebra, using the same method as explained in the previous section. The notation for the irreducible representations of SU(2) ⊗ SU(4) will be (N_2, N_4), where N_j corresponds, as previously, to the dimension of the irreducible representation of SU(j).

In this case, the fundamental six dimensional representation of SU(6) is reducible:

$$6 = (1,4) \oplus (2,1) \qquad \bar{6} = (1,\bar{4}) \oplus (2,1)$$

and we obtain the following results for some interesting representations:

$$\begin{aligned}
35 &= (1,15) \oplus (3,1) \oplus (2,4) \oplus (2,\bar{4}) \oplus (1,1) \\
21 &= (1,10) \oplus (2,4) \oplus (3,1) \\
15 &= (1,6) \oplus (2,4) \oplus (1,1) \\
56 &= (1,20) \oplus (2,10) \oplus (3,4) \oplus (4,1) \\
70 &= (1,20') \oplus (2,10) \oplus (2,6) \oplus (3,4) \oplus (1,4) \oplus (2,1) \\
20 &= (2,6) \oplus (1,4) \oplus (1,\bar{4}).
\end{aligned}$$

We recall the Young diagram description of the SU(4) irreducible representations involved in the previous formulae:

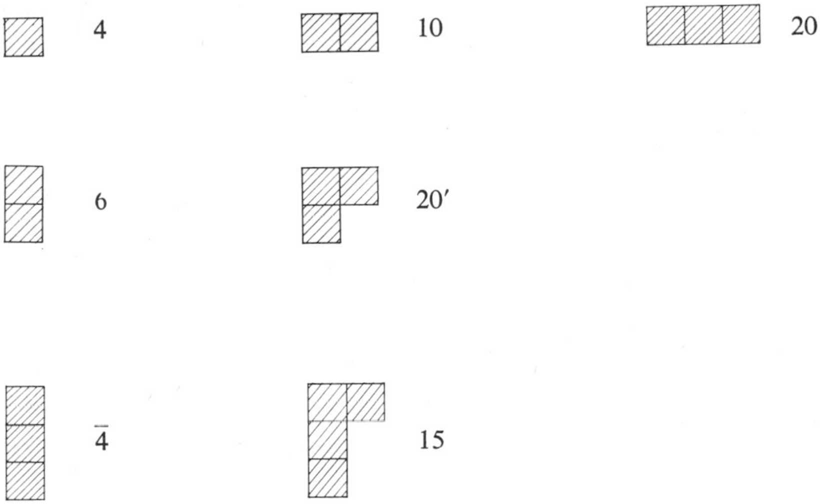

9.3. Classification of particles

1. The SU(3) triplet of quarks with spin $J = \frac{1}{2}$ is classified in the fundamental 6 dimensional representation of SU(6). As in the original Gell-Mann model, these quarks are assumed to have a baryonic number $B = \frac{1}{3}$ and the low lying states for baryons and mesons are constructed, respectively as three quarks systems and antiquark-quark system.

2. Let us consider first the case of low lying baryons. The product of three 6 dimensional representations can be reduced following:

$$6 \otimes 6 \otimes 6 = 56 \oplus 70 \oplus 70 \oplus 20.$$

The SU(2) ⊗ SU(3) decomposition of these representations has been given in the previous section

$$\begin{aligned} 56 &= (4,10) \oplus (2,8) \\ 70 &= (2,10) \oplus (4,8) \oplus (2,8) \oplus (2,1) \\ 20 &= (2,8) \oplus (4,1). \end{aligned}$$

The 56 dimensional representation is then particularly well adapted to accommodate the baryon octuplet and the excited baryon decuplet, both of positive parity (GÜRSEY and RADICATI [1964]). This result is also welcome from the point of view of mass breaking as it has been seen in chapter IV and fits experiment nicely.

3. The product of two contragradient 6 dimensional representations reduces to

$$\bar{6} \otimes 6 = 35 \oplus 1.$$

The adjoint representation has the following SU(2) ⊗ SU(3) content:

$$35 = (1,8) \oplus (3,8) \oplus (3,1)$$

and can accommodate the octuplet of pseudoscalar mesons and the nonet of vector mesons, both of negative parity (GÜRSEY and RADICATI [1964]). The singulet representation can then be associated to the X^0 resonance of mass 959 MeV. Such a description of the low lying meson states explains the strong ω-φ mixing and the small η^0-X^0 mixing as experimentally observed.

4. The physical significance of the S spin operators is not very clear. For the quarks, of course, S is simply the total angular momentum J at rest. The same situation holds also for the spin $J = \frac{1}{2}^+$ baryons, the spin $J = \frac{3}{2}^+$ excited baryons, the pseudoscalar and the vector mesons. The problem is not solved in general and we have two possible situations.

If, in all cases, S has to be identified with the operator J at rest, it will be necessary to introduce very high dimensionality supermultiplets to accommodate the particles with high values of the spin and we introduce in this way also high values of the isotopic spin and of the hypercharge. Such a feature is not very attractive and has no experimental support. If now S cannot be identified with J at rest, we can define a new operator $\mathscr{L}$ by

$$\mathscr{L} = \boldsymbol{J}_{\text{at rest}} - \boldsymbol{S}.$$

It is easy to check that the 3 components of $\mathscr{L}$ commute with the operators of the SU(6) Lie algebra and, in particular with the $\boldsymbol{S}$ spin operators and generate the Lie algebra of an SO(3) group:

$$\mathscr{L} \times \mathscr{L} = \mathrm{i}\mathscr{L}.$$

We then have the following relation to calculate the total angular momentum at rest

$$\boldsymbol{J}_{\text{at rest}} = \mathscr{L} + \boldsymbol{S}.$$

The new static group, used for the classification of particles at rest becomes SU(6) ⊗ SO(3) and the low lying baryons and mesons previously studied are characterized by $\mathscr{L} = 0$.

5. Recently BORCHI and GATTO [1965] have proposed to classify the excited meson states in a 35 representation of SU(6) with $\mathscr{L} = 1$. These

mesons can also be formally considered as bound states of a $\bar{q}q$ system in a P wave and the 105 states can be collected into three nonet sand one octuplet following the various $\bar{q}q$ states:

TABLE 9.2

Nonets	$J = 2^+ : {}^3P_2$	$C = +1$
	$J = 1^+ : {}^3P_1$	$C = +1$
	$J = 0^+ : {}^3P_0$	$C = +1$
Octuplet	$J = 1^+ : {}^1P_1$	$C = -1$

The value of C indicated on the previous table corresponds to the $I_Z = 0$, $Y = 0$ neutral states of the multiplets.

Such a distribution of SU(3) multiplets seems to fit experiment nicely.

9.4. Mass formulae

1. In the eightfold way symmetry the Gell-Mann-Okubo mass formula can be derived from simple assumptions and the agreement with experiment is impressive even if the basic arguments are not very well understood from a dynamical point of view.

We now try to derive, in the case of SU(6) symmetry, a mass formula of the same type. In other terms we want to associate the mass operator to some $I = S = Y = 0$ components of irreducible representations of SU(6).

2. The case of the spin $J = \frac{1}{2}^+$ and $J = \frac{3}{2}^+$ baryons associated to the 56 dimensional representation is extremely useful to construct the mass operator.

We first consider the product of representations

$$\overline{56} \otimes 56 = 1 \oplus 35 \oplus 405 \oplus 2695.$$

The 56 dimensional representation is reducible into eight multiplets with respect to the medium strong interactions subgroup:

$$SU(2)_J \otimes SU(2)_I \otimes T_Y$$

and the previous decomposition exhibits eight $I = S = Y = 0$ states which it is convenient to lable with their SU(6) and SU(3) indices. The more general effective mass operator for the baryons can then be written as:

$$M_{\text{Baryon}} =$$
$$= M_1^{(1)} + M_8^{(35)} + M_1^{(405)} + M_8^{(405)} + M_{27}^{(405)} + M_8^{(2695)} + M_{27}^{(2695)} + M_{64}^{(2695)}.$$

The isometry associated to the first non invariant term $M_8^{(35)}$ is simply the hypercharge operator Y. This type of symmetry breaking is obviously insufficient and we need at least isometries associated to the 405 representation. The simpler extension of the Gell-Mann-Okubo assumption does not work in the SU(6) symmetry and the transformation properties of the mass operator are not connected to the adjoint representation only (BÉG and SINGH [1964]).

3. On the basis of the SU(3) results it is rather reasonable to restrict oneself first to the singulet and octuplet SU(3) components of the isometries. We then have to calculate the two 405 interesting isometries. The 405 representation enters the symmetric part of the product of two adjoint representations:

$$35 \otimes 35 = [1 \oplus 35_s \oplus 189 \oplus 405] \oplus [35_a \oplus 280 \oplus \overline{280}]$$

and we consider the symmetric products of two operators of the Lie algebra; from the previous expansion, we will obtain the corresponding 180 and 35_s isometries simultaneously (BÉG and SINGH [1964]):

TABLE 9.3

$$\Omega_1^{(405)} = 2S^2 + C_2^3 - \tfrac{5}{7}C_2^6$$
$$\Omega_1^{(189)} = 2S^2 - C_2^3 + \tfrac{1}{5}C_2^6$$
$$\Omega_8^{(405)} = 2S^2 + C_2^3 - 3[2I^2 - \tfrac{1}{2}Y^2 + 2N^2 - 2M^2] - \tfrac{21}{8}[2M^2 - C_2^4 + \tfrac{1}{4}Y^2 + \tfrac{1}{3}C_2^6]$$
$$\Omega_8^{(189)} = 2S^2 - C_2^3 + 3[2I^2 - \tfrac{1}{2}Y^2 - 2N^2 + 2M^2] - \tfrac{3}{4}[2M^2 - C_2^4 + \tfrac{1}{4}Y^2 + \tfrac{1}{3}C_2^6]$$
$$\Omega^{(35s)} = 2M^2 - C_2^4 + \tfrac{1}{4}Y^2 + \tfrac{2}{3}C_2^6$$

The second order Casimir operators C_2^6, C_2^4 and C_2^3 are respectively associated to the group SU(6) and to the previously defined subgroups SU(4) and SU(3). In terms of the λ_j parameters defining the irreducible representations we have:

$$C_2^3 = \tfrac{2}{3}(\lambda_1^2 + \lambda_1\lambda_2 + \lambda_2^2) + 2(\lambda_1 + \lambda_2)$$
$$C_2^4 = \tfrac{3}{4}(\lambda_1^2 + \lambda_3^2) + \tfrac{1}{2}\lambda_1\lambda_3 + \lambda_2^2 + (\lambda_1 + \lambda_3)\lambda_2 + 3(\lambda_1 + \lambda_3) + 4\lambda_2 .$$

4. We go back to the baryon case. Obviously the two 189 isometries do not contribute and the 35_s isometry reduces to the 35_a isometry. It is easy to prove the following set of identities for the 56 dimensional representation (BÉG and SINGH [1964])

$$\begin{aligned} 2S^2 - C_2^3 + \tfrac{9}{2} &= 0 \\ 2M^2 - C_2^4 + \tfrac{1}{4}Y^2 + \tfrac{15}{2} &= -8Y \\ 2I^2 - \tfrac{1}{2}Y^2 - 2N^2 + 2M^2 &= -2Y + \tfrac{3}{2}. \end{aligned}$$

The SU(6) Casimir operator being $C_2^6 = \frac{45}{2}$ for the 56 representation, we immediately check that the 189 isometries vanish identically and the (35s) isometry reduces, as expected, to a linear function of the hypercharge. The two 405 isometries then take the form:

$$\begin{aligned} \Omega_1^{(405)} &\Rightarrow 4S(S+1) - \tfrac{81}{7} \\ \Omega_8^{(405)} &\Rightarrow 4S(S+1) + 15Y - 3[4I(I+1) - Y^2] + 9. \end{aligned}$$

The four first terms $M_1^1 + M_8^{35} + M_1^{405} + M_8^{405}$ collapse into an extremely simple expression:

$$m = m_0 + m_1 Y + m_2[4I(I+1) - Y^2] + m_3 S(S+1)$$

which gives the Gell-Mann-Okubo formula for the baryon octuplet and the equal spacing rule for the decuplet. The breaking of the SU(3) symmetry is independent of the spin S and as it has been seen in chapter III, this feature agrees quite well with experiment. The term M_8^{2695} which depends, in a multiplicative way on the spin, isospin, hypercharge operators can be neglected in the baryon mass analysis to a good approximation.

5. We now study the mass splitting problem for the pseudoscalar and vector mesons of the adjoint representation of SU(6). The general effective mass operator – as usual we use a mass squared operator – can be written as:

$$M_{\text{Meson}} = M_1^1 + M_8^{(35)} + M_1^{(189)} + M_8^{(189)} + M_{27}^{(189)} + M_1^{(405)} + M_8^{(405)} + M_{27}^{(405)}.$$

The meson super-multiplet contains particles and antiparticles and this property eliminates, in the previous expansion, the antisymmetric part of the product of two meson representations. As expected, we have an eight-parameter formula to describe seven multiplet masses and the ω-φ mixing parameter. As in the case of the baryon supermultiplet and on the same basis of SU(3) results, it is legitimate to drop the contributions due to the 27 SU(3) representation. We then use the explicit expression of the isometries given in the previous section to write the mass formula in an equivalent form (BÉG and SINGH [1964]):

$$\begin{aligned} m^2 = a + bC_2^3 + cS(S+1) + e[2M(M+1) - C_2^4 + \tfrac{1}{4}Y^2] &+ \\ + f[N(N+1) - M(M+1)] + g[I(I+1) - \tfrac{1}{4}Y^2]&. \end{aligned}$$

In this formula we have operators related to the SU(2) ⊗ SU(3) subgroup as S^2 and C_2^3 and simultaneously operators defined in the SU(2) ⊗ SU(4) subgroup as M^2, N^2 and C_2^4. The states π, K, η, ρ, K* are eigenstates in both the sequences of operators and the mass squared expression, for these states, is a linear function of the parameters a, b, c, e, f and g. The same simple situation does not occur for the ω and φ particles. The physical ω and φ states are obtained after diagonalization of a 2×2 mass matrix; only the sum $m_\omega^2 + m_\varphi^2$ is a linear function of the mass formula parameters. For such a reason, the mass relations involving ω and φ states must have a quadratic form.

From the previous general formula, we obtain the Gell-Mann-Okubo formula for the pseudoscalar mesons:

$$4m_{\mathrm{K}}^2 = 3m_\eta^2 + m_\pi^2$$

and the mixing parameter is given in terms of physical masses. Some additional relations can be obtained if and only if we make supplementary ad hoc assumptions. For instance, the restriction $f = g$, equivalent to neglecting the $M_8^{(189)}$ contribution, gives a quadratic relation involving pseudoscalar and vector mesons and which is very well satisfied by experiment (Bég and Singh [1964]):

$$m_\omega^2 m_\varphi^2 = \tfrac{1}{2}(m_{\mathrm{K}^*}^2 - m_{\mathrm{K}}^2 + m_\pi^2)(3m_{\mathrm{K}^*}^2 - m_\rho^2 + m_{\mathrm{K}}^2 - m_\pi^2) + \\ - \tfrac{1}{6}(4m_{\mathrm{K}^*}^2 - m_\rho^2)(5m_{\mathrm{K}^*}^2 - m_\rho^2 - 2m_\varphi^2 - 2m_\omega^2 - m_{\mathrm{K}}^2 + m_\pi^2).$$

On the other hand, it has been pointed out in chapter III that the SU(3) breaking parameter is essentially the same for the pseudoscalar mesons and for the vector mesons leading to the relation (Schwinger [1964]):

$$m_{\mathrm{K}^*}^2 - m_\rho^2 = m_{\mathrm{K}}^2 - m_\pi^2 .$$

In the present framework, such an equality corresponds to the constraint $f = 0$. If now $f = g = 0$ the previous first quadratic relation can be written in a simpler form where only vector mesons are involved (Schwinger [1964]):

$$(m_\varphi^2 - m_\rho^2)(m_\omega^2 - m_\rho^2) = \tfrac{4}{3}(m_{\mathrm{K}^*}^2 - m_\rho^2)(m_\varphi^2 + m_\omega^2 - 2m_{\mathrm{K}^*}^2).$$

As far as the mesons are concerned, the octuplet components of the 189 and 405 isometries can be discarded and the final meson effective mass formula reduces simply to

$$m^2 = a + bC_2^3 + cS(S+1) + e[2M(M+1) - C_2^4 + \tfrac{1}{4}Y^2].$$

The SU(3) breaking is only produced by the $M_8^{(35s)}$ term and such a result follows naturally in a quark model. The spin J breaking by the $M_1^{(189)}$ and $M_1^{(405)}$ contributions.

6. We now try to formulate in a unified presentation the results empirically obtained for the baryons and the mesons. Besides the 35 isometries, both the $\Omega_1^{(405)}$ and $\Omega_8^{(405)}$ isometries are needed for the baryons and both the $\Omega_1^{(405)}$ and $\Omega_1^{(189)}$ isometries are present for the mesons. It follows in particular that the 405 component of the symmetry breaking interaction is different for the baryons and for the mesons and we must use two irreducible SU(6) operators associated to this representations.

In summary, we must introduce two symmetry breaking terms:

$$M = M_1^{35 \otimes 35} \oplus M_8^{35 \otimes 35}.$$

The first one is a SU(3) scalar, the second one a SU(3) octuplet. Both are J spin, I spin scalars with hypercharge $Y = 0$ and are transformed, under SU(6) rotations, as the product of two adjoint representations.

CHAPTER X

LIE ALGEBRA OF CURRENTS

10.1. Quark currents

1. We consider, for simplicity, a quark model with three spin $\frac{1}{2}$ particles belonging to the three-dimensional representation [1, 0, 0] of U(3).

The vector part and the axial vector part of the quark current are defined, as usual, by:

$$J_{\rho,\mu}(x) = \mathrm{i}\bar{q}(x)\gamma_\mu X_\rho q(x)$$
$$J^5_{\rho,\mu}(x) = \mathrm{i}\bar{q}(x)\gamma_\mu\gamma_5 X_\rho q(x)$$

where $q(x)$ is the Dirac quark field and X_ρ's the nine infinitesimal generators of the u(3) Lie algebra.

2. We first introduce the space integral of the time component of the vector current densities:

$$F_\rho = \frac{1}{\mathrm{i}}\int J_{\rho,4}(x)\mathrm{d}\boldsymbol{r}.$$

For a conserved vector current, as the isotopic spin current, the space integral is time-independent and the F_ρ covariantly defined. In an exact unitary symmetry the nine vector currents are also conserved and the nine quantities F_ρ generate a Lie algebra isomorphic to the original Lie algebra of the X_ρ's:

$$[F_\sigma, F_\rho] = C^\tau_{\sigma\rho}F_\tau$$

where the $C^\tau_{\sigma\rho}$ are the structure constants of the u(3) algebra.

3. Let us now introduce the space integral of the time component of the axial vector current densities:

$$F^5_\rho(t) = \frac{1}{\mathrm{i}}\int J^5_{\rho,4}(x)\mathrm{d}\boldsymbol{r}.$$

The axial vector currents cannot be divergenceless and the operators $F^5_\rho(t)$ are time dependent.

New equal time commutation relations can be computed in the particular quark model. Using the explicit expressions given for the currents we immediately find

$$[F_\sigma(t), F_\rho^5(t)] = C_{\sigma\rho}^{\tau} F_\tau^5(t)$$
$$[F_\sigma^5(t), F_\rho^5(t)] = C_{\sigma\rho}^{\tau} F_\tau(t).$$

It is then convenient to define two new sets of operators:

$$F_\rho^{\pm}(t) = \tfrac{1}{2}[F_\rho(t) \pm F_\rho^5(t)]$$

and the previous commutation relations are written in an interesting form:

$$[F_\sigma^{\pm}(t), F_\rho^{\mp}(t)] = 0$$
$$[F_\sigma^{\pm}(t), F_\rho^{\pm}(t)] = C_{\sigma\rho}^{\tau} F_\tau^{\pm}(t).$$

The two sets of operators $F_\rho^+(t)$ and $F_\rho^-(t)$ generate two commuting Lie algebrac each of them being isomorphic to the original Lie algebra u(3).

It is obvious that such a result, independent of the particular properties of the u(3) Lie algebra, can be extended to different symmetries.

The two sets of operators $F_\rho^+(t)$ and $F_\rho^-(t)$ are connected by a space reflection operation P:

$$PF_\rho^{\pm}(t)P^{-1} = F_\rho^{\mp}(t).$$

4. The same type of considerations can be extended to the space components of the currents. The cqual time commutation relations of space and time components of the currents involve spatial δ function and also, in general, gradients of the δ function which vanish after space integration.

Let us first consider the space integrals of the space components of the axial vector current:

$$F_{\rho,j}^5(t) = \int J_{\rho,j}^5(x)\mathrm{d}\mathbf{r}.$$

The set of 36 generators F_ρ, $F_{\rho,j}^5(t)$ can also be written in the equivalent form:

$$G_{\rho,\mu}(t) = \int q^*(x)\sigma_\mu X_\rho q(x)\mathrm{d}\mathbf{r} \qquad \sigma_0 = 1$$

and it is now trivial to prove that the $G_{\rho,\mu}(t)$ operators have the commutation relations of a u(6) Lie algebra.

5. If we now consider the space integrals of the time and space components of the vector and axial vector currents we obtain 72 operators $G_{\rho,\mu}(t)$

and $G^5_{\rho,\mu}(t)$ which it is convenient to replace by the linear combinations:

$$G^{\pm}_{\rho,\mu}(t) = \tfrac{1}{2}\int q^*(x)\sigma_\mu(1\pm\gamma_5)X_\rho q(x)\mathrm{d}\boldsymbol{r}.$$

The two sets of operators $G^{+}_{\rho,\mu}(t)$ and $G^{-}_{\rho,\mu}(t)$ generate two commuting Lie algebrae, each of them being isomorphic to a Lie algebra u(6).

In this case also we have the parity exchange relation:

$$PG^{\pm}_{\rho,\mu}(t)P^{-1} = G^{\mp}_{\rho,\mu}(t).$$

6. The last generalization then consists in introducing all the possible densities constructed with the 16 elements Γ_j of the Dirac algebra:

$$D_{\rho,j}(x) = q^*(x)\Gamma_j X_\rho q(x).$$

The space integral of these densities:

$$A(\Gamma_j X_\rho) = \int D_{\rho,j}(x)\mathrm{d}\boldsymbol{r}$$

generates a 144-dimensional Lie algebra isomorphic to u(12).

The various cases considered in the previous sections correspond to some particular subalgebrae of u(12) and we have the following scheme:

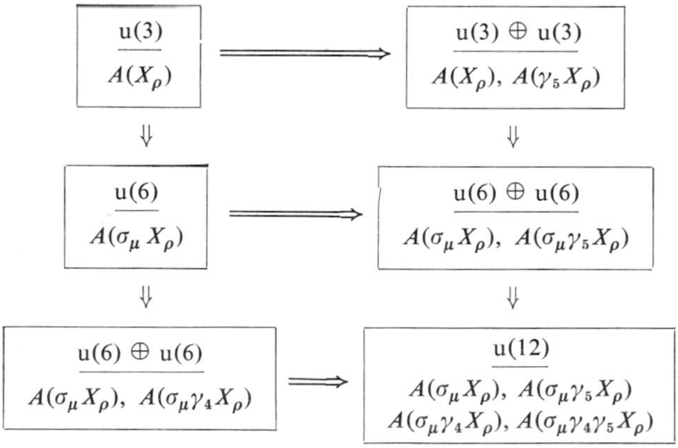

Lie algebrae of currents

7. Gell-Mann [1962, 1964a, b], Feynman et al. [1964], Zachariasen and Zweig [1965] and Dashen and Gell-Mann [1965a, b] have suggested that the equal time commutation rules of the space integrals of the physical densities are the same as calculated in the quark model. With such a strong assumption, the importance of the previous results becomes clear.

10.2. Renormalization and sum rules

1. FUBINI and FURLAN [1965] have proposed a very elegant and powerful method to get sum rules for the renormalization ratios between bare and dressed coupling constants using convenient commutation relations.

The method is quite general but we prefer to first consider, as an illustration, the problem of the renormalization of the vector coupling constant for neutron β decay when electromagnetic interactions are taken into account.

2. The isotopic spin current associated to the I_3 generator is conserved even in the presence of electromagnetic interactions where as the two other isotopic spin currents associated to the generators I^+ and I^- are not conserved.

Nevertheless we assume the commutation relations to be unmodified by the breaking of the symmetry

$$[I^+(t), I^-(t)] = 2I_3 .$$

Due to translational invariance we have, in the case of an exact isotopic spin symmetry:

$$\langle \mathrm{p}|I^+|\mathrm{n}\rangle = (2\pi)^3\delta_3(\boldsymbol{p}-\boldsymbol{n})\delta_{s_\mathrm{p}s_\mathrm{n}} .$$

When the symmetry is broken we introduce a renormalization factor:

$$\langle \mathrm{p}|I^+|\mathrm{n}\rangle = g(2\pi)^3\delta_3(\boldsymbol{p}-\boldsymbol{n})\delta_{s_\mathrm{p}s_\mathrm{n}} .$$

Let us now take the previous commutation relation between two one-proton states:

$$\langle \mathrm{p}'|[I^+, I^-]|\mathrm{p}\rangle = 2\langle \mathrm{p}'|I_3|\mathrm{p}\rangle.$$

Due to the conservation of I_3 the right-hand side is unrenormalized and we have simply:

$$2\langle \mathrm{p}'|I_3|\mathrm{p}\rangle = (2\pi)^3\delta_3(\boldsymbol{p}'-\boldsymbol{p})\delta_{s's} .$$

For the left-hand side we insert a complete set of intermediate states, the neutron state and a continuum of neutral states $|\alpha\rangle$ different from the neutron and of charge 2 states $|\beta\rangle$

$$\langle \mathrm{p}'|[I^+, I^-]|\mathrm{p}\rangle = \\ = g^2(2\pi)^3\delta_3(\boldsymbol{p}'-\boldsymbol{p})\delta_{s's} + \sum_{\alpha\neq \mathrm{n}}\langle \mathrm{p}'|I^+|\alpha\rangle\langle\alpha|I^-|\mathrm{p}\rangle - \sum_{\beta}\langle \mathrm{p}'|I^-|\beta\rangle\langle\beta|I^+|\mathrm{p}\rangle.$$

The sum rule is then simply written:

$$(1-g^2)(2\pi)^3\delta_3(\boldsymbol{p}'-\boldsymbol{p})\delta_{s's} = \sum_{\alpha\neq n} \langle p'|I^+|\alpha\rangle\langle\alpha|I^-|p\rangle - \sum_{\beta} \langle p'|I^-|\beta\rangle\langle\beta|I^+|p\rangle .$$

In an exact symmetry there is no transition between different isotopic spin multiplets, and the right-hand side of the previous sum rule being zero the renormalization is unity as expected.

When the symmetry is broken, the generators I^+ and I^- are time dependent and we can use the Heisenberg commutation relations:

$$\mathrm{i}\frac{\mathrm{d}}{\mathrm{d}t}I^{\pm}(t) = [I^{\pm}(t), H].$$

Between two physical eigenstates of H we obtain:

$$\langle f|[I^{\pm}(t), H]|i\rangle = (E_i - E_f)\langle f|I^{\pm}(t)|i\rangle.$$

The isotopic spin generators commute with the strong interactions hamiltonian and, neglecting the weak interactions, we retain only the electromagnetic hamiltonian in the Heisenberg relation:

$$\mathrm{i}\frac{\mathrm{d}}{\mathrm{d}t}I^{\pm}(t) = [I^{\pm}(t), H_{\mathrm{em}}].$$

The electromagnetic hamiltonian H_{em} can be written as:

$$H_{\mathrm{em}} = e\int J_{\mu}^{\mathrm{em}}(x)A^{\mu}(x)\mathrm{d}\boldsymbol{r}$$

where $A^{\mu}(x)$ is the electromagnetic field and e the electromagnetic coupling constant.

We now use the isotopic spin commutation relations:

$$[I^{\pm}(t), H_{\mathrm{em}}] = \mp H^{\pm}(t)$$

with

$$H^{\pm}(t) = e\int J_{\mu}^{\pm}(x)A^{\mu}(x)\mathrm{d}\boldsymbol{r}$$

and the sum rule takes the final form:

$$(1-g^2)(2\pi)^3\delta_3(\boldsymbol{p}'-\boldsymbol{p})\delta_{s's} =$$

$$= \sum_{\alpha\neq n} \frac{\langle p'|H^+|\alpha\rangle\langle\alpha|H^-|p\rangle}{(E_{p'}-E_{\alpha})(E_p-E_{\alpha})} - \sum_{\beta} \frac{\langle p'|H^-|\beta\rangle\langle\beta|H^+|p\rangle}{(E_{p'}-E_{\beta})(E_p-E_{\beta})}$$

which shows clearly that the renormalization occurs only at second order in e.

3. The Ademollo Gatto theorem can obviously be obtained in an identical way. The commutation relations of interest involve the V spin subgroup of SU(3),

$$[V^+(t), V^-(t)] = 2V_3$$

and the operator V_3 is a linear combination of more familiar conserved quantities

$$2V_3 = Q + Y.$$

We now take the matrix elements of the commutation relation between two one nucleon states. Let us first consider the case of two neutrons. As previously the right-hand side is unrenormalized and we have simply:

$$\langle \mathrm{n}'|2V_3|\mathrm{n}\rangle = (2\pi)^3\delta_3(\boldsymbol{n}'-\boldsymbol{n})\delta_{s's}.$$

The only possible one-particle state is a Σ^--hyperon and we introduce a renormalization factor f_1:

$$\langle \mathrm{n}'|V^+|\Sigma^-\rangle = -f_1(2\pi)^3\delta_3(\boldsymbol{n}'-\Sigma)\delta_{s's_\Sigma}.$$

The sum rule then takes the form:

$$(1-f_1^2)(2\pi)^3\delta_3(\boldsymbol{n}'-\boldsymbol{n})\delta_{s's} = \sum_{\alpha\neq\Sigma}\langle \mathrm{n}'|V^+|\alpha\rangle\langle\alpha|V^-|\mathrm{n}\rangle - \sum_{\beta}\langle \mathrm{n}'|V^-|\beta\rangle\langle\beta|V^+|\mathrm{n}\rangle.$$

The right-hand side is zero in exact unitary symmetry and is of second order in the SU(3) breaking interaction.

The case of two one-proton states is slightly more complicated because of the presence of two one-particle intermediate states, the Σ^0 and the Λ^0. For the unrenormalized matrix element we have as previously:

$$\langle \mathrm{p}'|2V_3|\mathrm{p}\rangle = 2(2\pi)^3\delta_3(\boldsymbol{p}'-\boldsymbol{p})\delta_{s's}.$$

We have to use two renormalization constants, f_1 for the Σ^0, the same as previously because of isotopic spin conservation, and f_2 for the Λ^0,

$$\langle \mathrm{p}'|V^+|\Sigma^0\rangle = \frac{f_1}{\sqrt{2}}(2\pi)^3\delta_3(\boldsymbol{p}'-\Sigma)\delta_{s's_\Sigma}$$

$$\langle \mathrm{p}'|V^+|\Lambda^0\rangle = \sqrt{\tfrac{3}{2}}f_2(2\pi)^3\delta_3(\boldsymbol{p}'-\Lambda)\delta_{s's_\Lambda}.$$

The sum rule is then written as:

$$(2-\tfrac{1}{2}f_1^2-\tfrac{3}{2}f_2^2)(2\pi)^3\delta_3(\boldsymbol{p}'-\boldsymbol{p})\delta_{s's} \simeq$$
$$\simeq \sum_{\alpha\neq\Sigma^0,\Lambda^0}\langle \mathrm{p}'|V^+|\alpha\rangle\langle\alpha|V^-|\mathrm{p}\rangle - \sum_{\beta}\langle \mathrm{p}'|V^-|\beta\rangle\langle\beta|V^+|\mathrm{p}\rangle$$

and the right-hand side is again of second order in the SU(3) breaking interaction.

4. The two previous examples of application of the Fubini and Furlan method were essentially of pedagogical interest but nothing new was emerging from the calculations.

We are now interested in the renormalization ratio G_A/G_V involved in neutron β decay. The problem was recently studied by the same technique, independently by WEISBERGER [1965] and by ADLER [1965].

Let us begin by defining the normalization for the vector and axial vector currents of neutron β decay (note the difference with the axial vector current used in chapter VI by a constant G_V/G). The current is written as:

$$J^{\alpha}_{\pm} = G_V[J^{V\alpha}_{\pm} + J^{A\alpha}_{\pm}].$$

In the limit of zero momentum transfer we have the two normalization conditions:

$$\langle p|J^{V\alpha}_{+}|n\rangle = i\bar{u}(p)\gamma^{\alpha}u(n)$$

$$\langle p|J^{A\alpha}_{+}|n\rangle = i\bar{u}(p)\gamma^{\alpha}\gamma_5 u(n)\left(-\frac{G_A}{G_V}\right).$$

The integral of the time-component of these currents are defined by:

$$V_{I_j}(t) = \int J^{Vo}_{j}(x)\mathrm{d}\boldsymbol{r}$$

$$A_{I_j}(t) = \int J^{Ao}_{j}(x)\mathrm{d}\boldsymbol{r}.$$

The assumptions are now the following:

a) The algebra of the isotopic spin group SU(2) can be extended to the algebra of the vector and axial vector isotopic spin operators of the chiral SU(2) ⊗ SU(2) group. More precisely the equal time commutation relation:

$$[A_{I^+}(t), A_{I^-}(t)] = 2V_{I_3}$$

will be used.

b) The partially conserved axial vector current hypothesis relates the divergence of the isotopic spin axial current to the renormalized π meson field operator $\phi_k(x)$ by:

$$\operatorname{div} J^{A}_{k}(x) = \left(-\frac{G_A}{G_V}\right) m_{\pi}^2 \frac{M}{gK(0)} \phi_k(x).$$

A more condensed expression of the propertionality constant can be written using the Goldberger-Treiman relation for the π decay coupling constant as introduced in chapter VI:

$$\text{div}\, J_k^{\mathrm{A}}(x) = f m_\pi^2 \phi_k(x).$$

The matrix elements of the equal time commutation relation are taken between two one-physical-proton states where p is the energy momentum and s the spin of the proton. Because of the normalization condition given above we obtain for the left-hand side:

$$\langle p', s'|2V_{I_3}|p, s\rangle = (2\pi)^3\delta_3(\boldsymbol{p}'-\boldsymbol{p})\delta_{s's}\,.$$

As usually we insert a complete set of physical states between the two operators of the commutator in the right-hand side. The contribution of the neutron is easily calculated from the normalization condition.

We find simply:

$$\frac{\boldsymbol{p}^2}{E^2}(2\pi)^3\delta_3(\boldsymbol{p}'-\boldsymbol{p})\delta_{s's}\left(\frac{G_\mathrm{A}}{G_\mathrm{V}}\right)^2,$$

where $E^2 = \boldsymbol{p}^2 + M^2$.

The sum rule is then written as:

$$(2\pi)^3\delta_3(\boldsymbol{p}'-\boldsymbol{p})\delta_{s's} = \left(1-\frac{M^2}{E^2}\right)(2\pi)^3\delta_3(\boldsymbol{p}'-\boldsymbol{p})\delta_{s's}\left(\frac{G_\mathrm{A}}{G_\mathrm{V}}\right)^2 +$$
$$+\sum_{\alpha\neq \mathrm{n}}\langle p', s'|A_{I^+}|\alpha\rangle\langle\alpha|A_{I^-}|p, s\rangle - \sum_{\beta}\langle p', s'|A_{I^-}|\beta\rangle\langle\beta|A_{I^+}|p, s\rangle.$$

In order to evaluate the contributions from $\sum_{\alpha\neq n}$ and $\sum_\beta$ we use the same technique as in section 10.2. We first deduce from the Heisenberg commutation relation:

$$\langle \mathrm{f}|A_\pm(t)|\mathrm{i}\rangle = \frac{1}{\mathrm{i}}\frac{1}{E_\mathrm{f}-E_\mathrm{i}+\mathrm{i}\varepsilon}\frac{\mathrm{d}}{\mathrm{d}t}\langle \mathrm{f}|A_\pm(t)|\mathrm{i}\rangle.$$

In the last factor of the left-hand side the time derivative $\partial J^{\mathrm{A}0}(x)/\partial t$ can be replaced by div $J^\mathrm{A}(x)$ because of the vanishing of the space integral of $\partial J_k^\mathrm{A}(x)/\partial x^k$. The P.C.A.C. hypothesis is then explicitly used:

$$\langle \mathrm{f}|A_\pm(t)|\mathrm{i}\rangle = \frac{1}{\mathrm{i}}\frac{1}{E_\mathrm{f}-E_\mathrm{i}-\mathrm{i}\varepsilon}(f m_\pi^2)\int\langle \mathrm{f}|\phi_\pm(x)|\mathrm{i}\rangle \mathrm{d}\boldsymbol{r}.$$

After space integration, the product of two such matrix elements takes the form:

$$\langle p', s'|A_{I^+}(t)|\alpha\rangle\langle\alpha|A_{I^-}(t)|p, s\rangle = (2\pi)^3\delta_3(\boldsymbol{p}'-\boldsymbol{p})(2\pi)^3\delta_3(\boldsymbol{p}'-\boldsymbol{p}_\alpha)\times$$
$$\times(fm_\pi^2)^2\int_{k_{0\,\mathrm{min}}}^{\infty}\frac{\mathrm{d}k_0}{k_0^2}\,\delta(E+k_0-E_\alpha)|\langle\alpha|\phi_-(0)|\mathrm{p}\rangle|^2$$

with $k_{0\,\mathrm{min}} = [(M+m_\pi)^2+\boldsymbol{p}^2]^{\frac{1}{2}}-E$ corresponding to a π-N state for α.

The next step is to relate the matrix elements:

$$\langle\alpha|\phi_-(0)|\mathrm{p}\rangle \quad\text{and}\quad \langle\beta|\phi_+(0)|\mathrm{p}\rangle$$

to the T matrix elements for the reactions:

$$\pi^-+\mathrm{p}\Rightarrow\alpha \quad\text{and}\quad \pi^++\mathrm{p}\Rightarrow\beta.$$

A detailed and rigourous analysis has been performed by Weisberger using the analyticity properties of the matrix elements and the technique of dispersion relations.

We only give the final covariant result which allows us to calculate the renormalization ratio $G_\mathrm{A}/G_\mathrm{V}$ in terms of π-meson nucleon total cross-sections for a π meson of zero mass:

$$\left(\frac{G_\mathrm{V}}{G_\mathrm{A}}\right)^2 = 1+\left(\frac{2M}{\sqrt{2}gK(0)}\right)^2\frac{1}{\pi}\int_0^\infty\frac{q\,\mathrm{d}\nu}{\nu^2}\,[\sigma_\mathrm{T}^-(\nu)-\sigma_\mathrm{T}^+(\nu)]$$

where ν is the meson energy and q the π-meson momentum in the laboratory system. The sign $\pm$ in σ_T refers to the incident π-meson charge.

The Adler-Weisberger sum rule can also be written in the equivalent simple form:

$$\left(\frac{G_\mathrm{A}}{G_\mathrm{V}}\right)^2 = 1+f^2\,\frac{1}{\pi}\int^\infty\frac{q\,\mathrm{d}\nu}{\nu^2}\,[\sigma_\mathrm{T}^+(\nu)-\sigma_\mathrm{T}^-(\nu)]$$

more convenient for generalizations and extensions.

The numerical evaluation of the integral is difficult because of the presence of extrapolated cross sections for a zero mass π meson. Using the experimental data and no extrapolation, Weisberger found:

$$\left|\frac{G_\mathrm{A}}{G_\mathrm{V}}\right| = 1.16.$$

Adler trying to take into account off mass shell corrections obtains the value:

$$\left|\frac{G_\mathrm{A}}{G_\mathrm{V}}\right| = 1.24.$$

Both results are in remarkable agreement with experiment.

5. Analogous expressions can be obtained for the renormalization of the hypercharge violating coupling constant in the framework of the unitary symmetry extended to the chiral SU(3) ⊗ SU(3) group.

In fact, the only useful equal time commutation relation involves V spin operators an in 3:

$$[A_{V^+}(t), A_{V^-}(t)] = 2V_{V_3}$$

and we recall the identity previously used in 3:

$$2V_3 = Q + Y.$$

The partially conserved axial current hypothesis is extended to the octuplet of currents following:

$$\operatorname{div} J^{\mathrm{A}}_{\rho}(x) = f m_{\rho}^2 \phi_{\rho}(x).$$

The index ρ corresponds to the weight of the octuplet and the coupling constant f is independent of such a weight by the generalized Goldberger-Treiman relation.

Using the results and the notations of chapter VI we have:

$$\left(\frac{G_{\mathrm{A}}}{G_{\mathrm{V}}}\right)^2_{\mathrm{np}} = (f_{\mathrm{a}}+f_{\mathrm{s}})^2$$

$$\left(\frac{G_{\mathrm{A}}}{G_{\mathrm{V}}}\right)^2_{\Sigma^-\mathrm{n}} = (f_{\mathrm{a}}-f_{\mathrm{s}})^2$$

$$\left(\frac{G_{\mathrm{A}}}{G_{\mathrm{V}}}\right)^2_{\Lambda\mathrm{p}} = \tfrac{3}{2}(f_{\mathrm{a}}+\tfrac{1}{3}f_{\mathrm{s}})^2$$

$$\left(\frac{G_{\mathrm{A}}}{G_{\mathrm{V}}}\right)^2_{\Sigma^0\mathrm{p}} = \tfrac{1}{2}(f_{\mathrm{a}}-f_{\mathrm{s}})^2.$$

We consider the equal time commutation relation between two one-nucleon states. In the case of two neutrons, the one-particle intermediate state is a Σ^- hyperon whereas in the case of two protons it can be a Λ^0 or a Σ^0 hyperon. We then obtain two new relations analogous to the Adler-Weisberger sum rules (AMATI et al. [1965] and LEVINSON and MUZINICH [1965])

$$(f_{\mathrm{a}}-f_{\mathrm{s}})^2 = 1+f^2\,\frac{1}{\pi}\int\frac{q\,\mathrm{d}\nu}{\nu^2}\,[\sigma_{\mathrm{T}}^{\mathrm{K^+n}}(\nu)-\sigma_{\mathrm{T}}^{\mathrm{K^-n}}(\nu)]$$

$$2(f_{\mathrm{a}}^2+\tfrac{1}{3}f_{\mathrm{s}}^2) = 2+f^2\,\frac{1}{\pi}\int\frac{q\,\mathrm{d}\nu}{\nu^2}\,[\sigma_{\mathrm{T}}^{\mathrm{K^+p}}(\nu)-\sigma_{\mathrm{T}}^{\mathrm{K^-p}}(\nu)].$$

Let us write the three sum rules in the symbolic form:

$$(f_a+f_s)^2 = 1+I_\pi$$
$$(f_a-f_s)^2 = 1+I_{K^0}$$
$$2(f_a^2+\tfrac{1}{3}f_s^2) = 2+I_{K^+}.$$

Using the solution obtained by Willis and collaborators from an analysis of baryon leptonic decays with the Cabibbo theory:

$$f_a = 0.437 \qquad f_s = 0.742$$

the expected values of the cross section integrals are given by:

$$I_\pi = 0.387$$
$$I_{K^0} = -0.907$$
$$I_{K^+} = -1.253.$$

The values of these integrals estimated by AMATI, BOUCHIAT and NUYTS [1965]:

$$I_\pi \simeq 0.4$$
$$I_{K^0} \simeq -0.7$$
$$I_K \simeq -1.15$$

agree very well, to within 20 %, with the previous ones.

The possibility to calculate the $\rho_W = f_s/f_a$ ratio from I_π, I_{K^0} and I_{K^+} seems more problematic to us. In fact the three sum rules are related by a consistency relation between the three integrals

$$(I_\pi - I_{K^0})^2 = 3(I_\pi + I_{K^0} - I_{K^+})(4+3I_{K^+} - I_\pi - I_{K^0})$$

and two equivalent expressions of ρ_W, involving the three integrals, are given by:

$$\rho_W = \frac{I_\pi - I_{K^0}}{4+3I_{K^+} - I_\pi - I_{K^0}} = \frac{3(I_\pi + I_{K^0} - I_{K^+})}{I_\pi - I_{K^0}}.$$

With the number given by AMATI, BOUCHIAT and NUYTS [1965] we find:

$$\rho_W \simeq 1.29 \simeq 2.32$$

and, taking into account only I_π and I_{K^0} these authors obtain:

$$\rho_W \simeq 2.7.$$

On the other hand, with I_π and I_{K^+} only we deduce $\rho_W = 1.2$ and with I_{K^0} and I_{K^+}, $\rho_W = 1.63$. The large variations of ρ_W due to small errors on the integrals make difficult a good estimate of ρ_W.

10.3. Lie algebra of currents and SU(6) symmetry

1. The SU(3) symmetry is generally understood as a good symmetry of strong interactions – Lie algebra commuting with the hamiltonian – broken in a precise manner by medium strong, electromagnetic and weak interactions.

It seems extremely hard to formulate the same assumption for the non relativistic SU(6) invariance. Perhaps this symmetry cannot be defined in a covariant scheme. Nevertheless some interesting results of SU(6) invariance have been derived in non-static situations. The algebra of current components can give a framework to understand these results.

2. Two assumptions are needed practically to obtain the SU(6) results. The first one, as pointed out in section 10.1, is the validity of equal time commutation relations between the space integrals of the current components. These relations are those calculated in the quark model and given in section 10.1. In other terms, the Lie algebra of the current components is isomorphic to the Lie algebra of the quark current components, at least, as far as the space integrals of the current components are concerned.

The second assumption is a saturation condition on the summation over intermediate states in the commutator. The exact significance of such an assumption will be clarified later in practical applications. We only remark that, if we abandon the saturation condition, we are able to calculate renormalization effect due to a breaking of the symmetry, as shown in section 10.2.

3. The Lie algebra of the U(6) type is defined by the space integrals of the time component of the vector currents and the space integrals of the spaces components of the axial vector currents. In the quark model as explained in section 10.1 the U(6) algebra is generated by:

$$F_\sigma(t) = \int q^*(x) X_\sigma q(x) \mathrm{d}\boldsymbol{r}$$

$$F^5_{\sigma,j}(t) = \int q^*(x)\sigma_j X_\sigma q(x)\mathrm{d}\boldsymbol{r} \qquad j = 1, 2, 3.$$

By convention the U(3) index $\sigma = 0$ is associated to the 3×3 unit matrix:

$$F_0 = \int q^*(x)q(x)\mathrm{d}\boldsymbol{r} \qquad F^5_{0,j}(t) = \int q^*(x)\sigma_j q(x)\mathrm{d}\boldsymbol{r}.$$

We will use the conventional notations for the physical currents and the isomorphism of Lie algebra assumed by Gell-Mann is simply:

$$F_\sigma(t) \Leftrightarrow V_\sigma(t)$$
$$F^5_{\sigma,j}(t) \Leftrightarrow A_{\sigma,j}(t).$$

Some useful subalgebrae are defined in the following way:

a) $V_\sigma(t)$ U(3) algebra,
b) $A_{0,j}(t)$ SU(2) algebra,
c) $V_\sigma(t)$ and $A_{\sigma,j}(t)$ for a given j: three chiral U(3) ⊗ U(3) Lie algebrae.

4. We now consider the particular equal time commutation relation (at $t = 0$):

$$[A_{I^+,j}, I_{I^-,k}] = 2\delta_{jk} V_{I_3} + \mathrm{i}\varepsilon_{jkl}(V_{Y,l} + \tfrac{2}{3}V_{0,l}).$$

Following LEE [1965] we take this equation between two $J = \frac{1}{2}^+$ baryon states at rest and for simplicity we drop the Dirac function obtained after space integration. The matrix elements of the operators V and A involve the two coupling constants f_a and f_s previously introduced:

$$\langle \mathrm{B}, \alpha | V_\rho | \mathrm{B}, \beta \rangle = \bar{u}(0)u(0)[\Omega_\rho^{(8a)}]_{\alpha\beta}$$
$$\langle \mathrm{B}, \alpha | A_{0,j} | \mathrm{B}, \beta \rangle = \bar{u}(0)\sigma_j u(0)\delta_{\alpha\beta}$$
$$\langle \mathrm{B}, \alpha | A_{\rho,j} | \mathrm{B}, \beta \rangle = \bar{u}(0)\sigma_j u(0)\left[f_a[\Omega_\rho^{(8a)}]_{\alpha\beta} + f_s[\Omega_\rho^{(8s)}]_{\alpha\beta}\right].$$

We insert a complete set of intermediate states between the two operators of the commutator. If we restrict the summation to $J = \frac{1}{2}^+$ baryon states, no solution for f_a and f_s can be obtained. If we include, in addition, contributions due to the $J = \frac{3}{2}^+$ excited baryon states, the system of matrix elements has now an unique solution.

The octuplet-decuplet transition coupling constant is defined by:

$$\langle \mathrm{B}^*, \alpha | A_{\rho,j} | \mathrm{B}, \beta \rangle = \bar{u}_j(0)u(0)f_{\mathrm{T}}[\Omega_\rho^8]_{\alpha\beta}$$

and the solution is:

$$f_a = \tfrac{2}{3}, \qquad f_s = 1, \qquad f_{\mathrm{T}}^2 = \tfrac{2}{3}.$$

We then immediately deduce the weak D/F ratio and the renormalization ratio $-G_A/G_V$ from neutron β decay:

$$\rho_W = \tfrac{3}{2}, \qquad -\frac{G_A}{G_V} = \tfrac{5}{3}.$$

5. As pointed out by I. S. GERNSTEIN [1965], the same result is obtained using only a chiral U(3) ⊗ U(3) group, the summation over intermediate states being always restricted to $J = \frac{1}{2}^+$ and $J = \frac{3}{2}^+$ baryon states. In the language of the Fubini Furlan method as explained in section 10.2, the present

calculation gives an estimate of the integrals I_π, I_{K^0} and I_{K^+}, taking into account only the contributions due to the decuplet resonances. More precisely, we have:

$$I_\pi \simeq \tfrac{8}{3} f_T^2, \qquad I_{K^0} = -\tfrac{4}{3} f_T^2, \qquad I_{K^+} = -\tfrac{2}{3} f_T^2$$

and with the numerical value $f_T^2 = \frac{2}{3}$ we deduce:

$$I_\pi \simeq 1.78, \qquad I_{K^0} \simeq -0.89, \qquad I_{K^+} \simeq -0.44.$$

Additionnal contributions are needed to obtain a value for $-G_A/G_V$ in better agreement with experiment.

6. With the same restriction concerning the intermediate states, we can study the complete systems of $J = \frac{1}{2}^+$ and $J = \frac{3}{2}^+$ baryons. New matrix elements are needed and we introducc a coupling constant f_{10} for the decuplet-decuplet axial vector transition:

$$\langle B_\alpha^* | V_\rho | B_\beta^* \rangle = \bar{u}_m(0) u_m(0) [\Omega_\rho^8]_{\alpha\beta}$$

$$\langle B_\alpha^* | A_{0,j} | B_\beta^* \rangle = \frac{3}{i} \varepsilon_{jmn} \bar{u}_m(0) u_n(0) \delta_{\alpha\beta}$$

$$\langle B_\alpha^* | A_{\rho,j} | B_\beta^* \rangle = \frac{1}{i} \varepsilon_{jmn} \bar{u}_m(0) u_n(0) f_{10} [\Omega_\rho^8]_{\alpha\beta}.$$

The solution is always unique and we obtain for f_{10}:

$$f_{10} = 1.$$

7. The case of mesons has been investigated by SCHNITZER [1965]. The saturation assumption is to retain only the pseudoscalar mesons and the vector mesons in the sum over the intermediate states. We have to use the following non vanishing matrix elements:

$$\langle M, \alpha | V_\rho | M, \beta \rangle = [\Omega^{(8a)}]_{\alpha\beta}$$

$$\langle V^8, \alpha | V_\rho | V^8, \beta \rangle = e_m^*(0) e_m(0) [\Omega^{(8a)}]_{\alpha\beta}$$

$$\langle V^8, \alpha | A_{0,j} | V^8, \beta \rangle = \frac{2}{i} \varepsilon_{jmn} e_m^*(0) e_n(0) \delta_{\alpha\beta}$$

$$\langle \omega^0 | A_{0,j} | \omega^0 \rangle = \frac{2}{i} \varepsilon_{jmn} e_m^*(0) e_n(0)$$

$$\langle V^8, \alpha | A_{\rho,j} | V^8, \beta \rangle = \frac{1}{i} \varepsilon_{jmn} e_m^*(0) e_n(0) f_{V_8} [\Omega_\rho^{(8s)}]_{\alpha\beta}$$

$$\langle V^8, \alpha | A_{\rho,j} | \omega^0 \rangle = \frac{1}{i} \varepsilon_{jmn} e_m^*(0) e_n(0) f_{V_1} \delta_{\alpha\beta}$$

$$\langle V^8, \alpha | A_{\rho,j} | M, \beta \rangle = e_j^*(0) f_M [\Omega_\rho^{(8a)}]_{\alpha\beta}.$$

We obtain also an unique solution for the coupling constants:

$$f_{V_8} = 1, \qquad f_{V_1} = \sqrt{\tfrac{2}{3}}, \qquad f_M^2 = 1.$$

8. In both cases we have reproduced the results of SU(6) invariance (GÜRSEY and RADICATTI [1964]) without assuming the invariance of the hamiltonian. The reason this fact is due to the form given to the saturation condition. The $J = \frac{1}{2}^+$ and $J = \frac{3}{2}^+$ baryons form an irreducible representation 56 of the Lie algebra U(6) generated by the operators V_ρ and $A_{\rho,j}$: in the same way, the $J = 0^-$ and $J = 1^-$ mesons form an irreducible representation 35 of the same Lie algebra. The saturation condition allows transitions between members of the same super multiplet only so that it is natural to reproduce the results of SU(6) invariance.

10.4. Algebra of the moments of the current components

1. It is interesting to consider, in addition to the operators $V_{\rho,\mu}(t)$ and $A_{\rho,\mu}(t)$ which are assumed to generate a chiral U(6) ⊗ U(6) algebra, other low order moments of the current densities.

The equal time commutation relations of these new operators generate higher and higher moments and we are finally working with an infinite dimensional algebra.

The commutator of two components of the currents involves delta functions and also possibly gradients of delta functions. In many cases, these gradients can play an important role, even after space integration of the new densities (SCHWINGER [1959]).

2. A beautiful illustration of this method has been given by LEE [1965] who considers the magnetic moment operators defined by:

$$m_{\rho,j} = \tfrac{1}{2}\varepsilon_{jkl} \int \sigma_k J^{V}_{\rho,l}(x) \mathrm{d}\boldsymbol{r}.$$

The equal time commutation relation of two magnetic moment operators is calculated, in the quark model, neglecting possible derivatives of delta functions in the equal time commutator of two current densities.

The commutator, corresponding to the case studied in section 10.3 is simply:

$$4[m_{I^+,j}, m_{I^-,k}] = 2\{\tfrac{2}{3}\delta_{jk} R_{I_3} - \tfrac{1}{3} Q_{jk,I_3}\} + i\varepsilon_{jkl}\{P_{Y,l} + \tfrac{2}{3} P_{0,l}\}.$$

The operators R, Q, P are associated to second order moment following:

$$R_\rho = \int r^2 J_\rho^{V_0}(x)\mathrm{d}\boldsymbol{r}$$

$$Q_{jk,\rho} = \int (3x_j x_k - r^2\delta_{jk}) J_\rho^{V_0}(x)\mathrm{d}\boldsymbol{r}$$

$$P_{\rho,l} = \int x_l x^m J_{\rho,m}^{A}(x)\mathrm{d}\boldsymbol{r}.$$

The equal time commutation relation is taken between two $J = \frac{1}{2}^+$ baryon states at rest and the set of intermediate states inserted between the two magnetic moment operators of the commutator is restricted, as previously to $J = \frac{1}{2}^+$ and $J = \frac{3}{2}^+$ baryon states.

We will use the following matrix elements:

$$\langle \mathrm{B}, \alpha|m_{\rho,j}|\mathrm{B}, \beta\rangle = \bar{u}(0)\sigma_j u(0)\{\mu_\mathrm{a}[\Omega_\rho^{(8\mathrm{a})}]_{\alpha\beta} + \mu_\mathrm{s}[\Omega_\rho^{(8\mathrm{s})}]_{\alpha\beta}\}$$

$$\langle \mathrm{B}^*, \alpha|m_{\rho,j}|\mathrm{B}, \beta\rangle = \bar{u}_j(0)u(0)\mu_\mathrm{T}[\Omega_\rho^{8}]_{\alpha\beta}$$

$$\langle \mathrm{B}, \alpha|R_\rho|\mathrm{B}, \beta\rangle = \bar{u}(0)u(0)\{\langle r_\mathrm{a}^2\rangle[\Omega_\rho^{(8\mathrm{a})}]_{\alpha\beta} + \langle r_\mathrm{s}^2\rangle[\Omega_\rho^{(8\mathrm{s})}]_{\alpha\beta}\}$$

$$\langle \mathrm{B}, \alpha|P_{0,l}|\mathrm{B}, \beta\rangle = \bar{u}(0)\sigma_l u(0)p_1\delta_{\alpha\beta}$$

$$\langle \mathrm{B}, \alpha|P_{\rho,l}|\mathrm{B}, \beta\rangle = \bar{u}(0)\sigma_l u(0)\{p_\mathrm{a}[\Omega_\rho^{(8\mathrm{a})}]_{\alpha\beta} + p_\mathrm{s}[\Omega_\mathrm{p}^{(8\mathrm{s})}]_{\alpha\beta}\}.$$

Of course, the matrix elements of the quadrupole operator Q_{jk} between two $J = \frac{1}{2}^+$ baryon states vanish identically.

The system of equations has not an unique solution. But the more interesting solution can be obtained by analogy between the present problem and that studied in the previous section. This solution is characterized by $\langle r_\mathrm{s}^2\rangle = 0$ and the scale is given by $\frac{3}{2}\langle r_\mathrm{a}^2\rangle$. We then obtain:

$$2\mu_\mathrm{a} = f_\mathrm{a}(\tfrac{2}{3}\langle r_\mathrm{a}^2\rangle)^{\frac{1}{2}}, \qquad 2\mu_\mathrm{s} = f_\mathrm{s}(\tfrac{2}{3}\langle r_\mathrm{a}^2\rangle)^{\frac{1}{2}}, \qquad 2\mu_\mathrm{T} = f_\mathrm{T}(\tfrac{2}{3}\langle r_\mathrm{a}^2\rangle)^{\frac{1}{2}}$$

$$p_\mathrm{a} = f_\mathrm{a}\tfrac{2}{3}\langle r_\mathrm{a}^2\rangle \qquad p_\mathrm{s} = f_\mathrm{s}\tfrac{2}{3}\langle r_\mathrm{a}^2\rangle \qquad p_1 = \tfrac{2}{3}\langle r_\mathrm{a}^2\rangle.$$

The magnetic moment and the root mean square radius of charge are defined using the SU(3) component Q of the current. For the proton and the neutron we obtain:

$$\langle r_\mathrm{p}^2\rangle = \langle r_\mathrm{a}^2\rangle + \tfrac{1}{3}\langle r_\mathrm{s}^2\rangle \qquad r_\mathrm{n}^2 = -\tfrac{2}{3}r_\mathrm{s}^2$$

$$\mu_\mathrm{p} = \mu_\mathrm{a} + \tfrac{1}{3}\mu_\mathrm{s} \qquad \mu_\mathrm{n} = -\tfrac{2}{3}\mu_\mathrm{s}.$$

Let us first consider the results related to the electromagnetic form factors. They can be written in the more familiar form:

$$\langle r_\mathrm{n}^2\rangle = 0 \qquad \langle r_\mathrm{p}^2\rangle = 6\mu_\mathrm{p}^2$$

$$\mu_\mathrm{n}/\mu_\mathrm{p} = -\tfrac{2}{3} \qquad \mu_\mathrm{T} = \sqrt{\tfrac{2}{3}}\mu_\mathrm{p}.$$

The three last relations involve p_a, p_s, p_1 and we relate these quantities to the axial form factors appearing for instance in neutrino induced elastic reactions. From the definition of $P_{\rho,l}$, we have:

$$\langle B, \alpha|P_{\rho,l}|B, \beta\rangle = -\left\{\frac{\partial^2}{\partial q_l \partial q_m}\int \mathrm{d}\boldsymbol{r}\langle B, \alpha|J^A_{\rho,m}(x)|B, \beta\rangle\right\}_{q^2=0}.$$

The matrix elements of the axial vector current between one neutron and one proton have been defined in chapter VI:

$$\langle p|J^A_{I^+,m}(x)|n\rangle = \frac{M}{(E_p E_n)^{\frac{1}{2}}}\, e^{iqx}\bar{u}(p)\left[i\gamma_m\gamma_5 F^A_1(q^2) + \frac{q_m}{2M}\gamma_5 F^A_2(q^2)\right] u(n)$$

where the transfer of energy momentum is $q = p - n$.

The actual normalization is defined referring to the vector coupling constant and its follows:

$$F^A_1(0) = -\frac{G_A}{G_V} = p_a + p_s.$$

A straight-forward calculation of the q's derivatives gives immediately:

$$\langle p|P_{I^+,l}|n\rangle = -2\bar{u}(0)\sigma_l u(0)\left\{\left(\frac{\mathrm{d}F^A_1(q^2)}{\mathrm{d}q^2}\right)_{q^2=0} - \frac{F^A_1(0)}{4M^2} - \frac{F^A_2(0)}{2M^2}\right\}$$

and we deduce the relation:

$$\frac{p_a + p_s}{f_a + f_s} = \tfrac{2}{3}\langle r_p^2\rangle = -2\left\{\frac{1}{F^A_1(0)}\left(\frac{\mathrm{d}F^A_1(q^2)}{\mathrm{d}q^2}\right)_{q^2=0} - \frac{1}{4M^2} - \frac{1}{2M^2}\frac{F^A_2(0)}{F^A_1(0)}\right\}.$$

The last term can be evaluated using the one pion pole model. With the results of chapter VI:

$$\frac{1}{2M^2}\frac{F^A_2(0)}{F^A_1(0)} \simeq \frac{2}{m_\pi^2},$$

we obtain a prediction for the slope of the axial vector form factor:

$$-\frac{1}{F^A_1(0)}\left(\frac{\mathrm{d}F^A_1(q^2)}{\mathrm{d}q^2}\right)_{q^2=0} = \tfrac{1}{3}\langle r_p^2\rangle - \frac{1}{4M^2} - \frac{2}{m_\pi^2}.$$

3. Two of these relations are obtained in the original framework of SU(6) invariance (Bég, Lee and Pais [1964]). The first one:

$$\mu_n/\mu_p = -\tfrac{2}{3}$$

agrees surprisingly well with experiment. The second relation can also be written as:

$$\langle \mathrm{p}|m_{Q,j}|\mathrm{N}^{*+}\rangle = \frac{2}{\sqrt{3}}\mu_{\mathrm{p}}\bar{u}u_j .$$

The phenomenological analysis of π-meson photoproduction with an isobaric model (GOURDIN and SALIN [1963a]) has given a value of the coupling constant, for the magnetic transition larger by a factor 1.6.

Let us now discuss the new relations obtained by the Lee technique. The value of $\langle r_{\mathrm{n}}^2\rangle$ due to neutron scattering on atomic electrons is:

$$\langle r_{\mathrm{n}}^2\rangle \simeq 0.12 f^2$$

and can be considered as small with respect to the corresponding proton value:

$$\langle r_{\mathrm{p}}^2\rangle \simeq 0.72 f^2.$$

The relation between the magnetic moment and the root mean square radius of charge for the proton is experimentally satisfied within 20 %.

The situation is not so favorable for the axial vector form factor $F_1^{\mathrm{A}}(q^2)$. Due to the small pion mass the slope is predicted to be positive in contradiction with all a priori estimates.

4. The complete octuplet-decuplet system can be simultaneously studied with an analogous method. Some of the results have been given by DASHEN and GELL-MANN [1965a, b].

The matrix elements of the magnetic moment operators between two one excited baryon states can be written as:

$$\langle \mathrm{B}^*, \alpha|m_{\rho,j}|\mathrm{B}^*, \beta\rangle = \frac{1}{i}\,\varepsilon_{jmn}\bar{u}_m(0)u_n(0)\mu_{10}[\Omega_\rho^8]_{\alpha\beta} .$$

The reduced matrix element μ_{10} is found to be:

$$\mu_{10} = \mu_{\mathrm{p}} .$$

The root mean square radius for the B* charge form factor is defined by:

$$\langle \mathrm{B}^*, \alpha|R_\rho|\mathrm{B}^*, \beta\rangle = \bar{u}_m(0)u_n(0)\delta_{mn}\langle r_{10}^2\rangle[\Omega_\rho^8]_{\alpha\beta}$$

and turns out to be equal to the proton root mean square radius:

$$\langle r_{10}^2\rangle = \langle r_{\mathrm{p}}^2\rangle.$$

In this very restrictive approximation where only $J = \frac{1}{2}^+$ and $J = \frac{3}{2}^+$ baryons are taken into account in the sum over intermediate states, all the quadrupole moments are identically zero. For instance, the Ω^- quadrupole moment and the N*-N quadrupole transition vanish. The last result agrees up to 5 % with photoproduction experiments (GOURDIN and SALIN [1963a]).

5. SCHNITZER [1965] takes the matrix element of the commutator of two magnetic moment operators between two one pseudoscalar meson states. The saturation condition is the same as previously and only $J = 0^-$ and $J = 1^-$ meson states are taken into account.

We define the following matrix elements:

$$\langle \mathrm{M}, \alpha | R_\rho | \mathrm{M}, \beta \rangle = \langle r_\mathrm{M}^2 \rangle [\Omega_\rho^{(8a)}]_{\alpha\beta}$$
$$\langle \mathrm{M}, \alpha | m_{\rho, j} | \mathrm{V}^8, \beta \rangle = e_j(0) f_8 [\Omega_\rho^{(8s)}]_{\alpha\beta}$$
$$\langle \mathrm{M}, \alpha | m_{\rho, j} | \omega^0 \rangle = e_j(0) f_1 \delta_{\alpha\rho}$$

and we obtain, for the system of equations the unique solution:

$$f_8^2 = \tfrac{1}{6} \langle r_\mathrm{M}^2 \rangle \qquad f_1^2 = \tfrac{1}{9} \langle r_\mathrm{M}^2 \rangle .$$

If we now consider the complete system of pseudoscalar and vector mesons, the X^0 meson must be included in the scheme to obtain an unique solution. The root mean square radius of charge for vector mesons, defined by:

$$\langle \mathrm{V}^8, \alpha | R_\rho | \mathrm{V}^8, \beta \rangle = e_m^*(0) e_n(0) \delta_{mn} \langle r_\mathrm{V}^2 \rangle [\Omega_\rho^{(8a)}]_{\alpha\beta}$$

is the same as for the pseudoscalar mesons:

$$\langle r_\mathrm{V}^2 \rangle = \langle r_\mathrm{M}^2 \rangle = \langle r^2 \rangle .$$

The quadrupole moment for vector mesons is identically zero:

$$Q_\mathrm{V} = 0$$

and the reduced matrix elements for magnetic transitions:

$$\langle \mathrm{V}^8, \alpha | m_{\rho, j} | \mathrm{V}^8, \beta \rangle = \frac{1}{\mathrm{i}} \varepsilon_{jmn} e_m^*(0) e_n(0) g_8 [\Omega_\rho^{8a}]_{\alpha\beta}$$
$$\langle \mathrm{X}^0 | m_{\rho, j} | \mathrm{V}^8, \beta \rangle = e_j(0) \bar{f}_1 \delta_{\beta\rho}$$

are given by:

$$g_8^2 = \tfrac{1}{6} \langle r^2 \rangle \qquad \bar{f}_1^2 = \tfrac{1}{9} \langle r^2 \rangle .$$

The matrix elements of the operators $P_{\rho, l}$, also completely determined by their physical interpretation, seem to be untimely.

6. In order to find a unique and non zero solution for the magnetic moment equations, we have been obliged to introduce:

a. the $J = \frac{1}{2}^+$ octuplet and the $J = \frac{3}{2}^+$ decuplet for baryons,

b. the $J = 0^-$ singulet and octuplet, the $J = 1$ singulet and octuplet for mesons.

Such a result suggests that the irreducible representations of the non chiral group $U(6) \otimes U(6)$ are involved in this problem rather than the irreducible representations of the group U(6) (see section 11.3).

For the transition matrix elements between different SU(3) multiplets, the reduced matrix elements involved correspond to form factors taken for a non vanishing value of the square of the energy momentum four vector. More precisely for two particles at rest:

$$q^2 = -q_0^2 = -(\Delta M)^2$$

where ΔM is the difference of mass between the particles of the initial and the final states.

For instance, in the case of nucleon-N* electromagnetic transition, the photon is time like whereas the coupling constants measured in photoproduction correspond to a real photon $q^2 = 0$ and the physical situation is then a N* at rest and a nucleon in motion. In fact, the comparison with experiment of μ_T involves electroproduction results, extrapolated in the time like region.

This difficulty has been pointed out by Schnitzer in the case of mesons where the mass differences between the π meson and the vector mesons are extremely large.

CHAPTER XI

PHYSICAL CONSEQUENCES OF SU(6) SYMMETRY

11.1. Generalities

1. This chapter is divided into two parts. The sections 11.2 and 11.3 present some of the results obtained from SU(6) invariance following the original approach as initiated by GÜRSEY and RADICATI [1964]. Section 11.3 tries to study the presentation due to DASHEN and GELL-MANN [1965b], its difficulties and some consequences of hybride symmetries.

2. An extremely large number of papers has been written on SU(6) invariance and its possible applications to strong, electromagnetic and weak interactions. We have restricted ourselves to a review of a small number of these papers and we apologize for those not quoted here. Our criterium was to retain only some typical results for which the comparison with experiment is significant and the theoretical basis relatively well defined. Nevertheless even in the last cases the understanding of the assumptions has never been perfectly clear for the author.

11.2. Current of baryons

1. We use the name baryons in its large SU(6) sense for the particles of the 56 dimensional representation associated to the third order contravariant tensor $\psi^{\alpha\beta\gamma,}$. With respect to the subgroup $SU(2) \otimes SU(3)$ we have the well known reduction:

$$56 \Rightarrow (2,8) \oplus (4.10)$$

and the tensor $\psi^{\alpha\beta\gamma,}$ can also be written, as shown in chapter IX, in the form:

$$\psi^{\alpha\beta\gamma,} \Rightarrow \psi^{AiBjCk} \equiv$$

$$\equiv t^{ijk,}\, d^{ABC,} + \frac{1}{3\sqrt{2}} \{(2\varepsilon^{ij}\chi^k + \varepsilon^{ki}\chi^j)\varepsilon^{ABC} N^C_D + (2\varepsilon^{ki}\chi^j + \varepsilon^{ij}\chi^k)\varepsilon^{CAD} N^B_D\}.$$

The $J = \frac{3}{2}^+$ excited baryons are described by the SU(3) decuplet d^{ABC}, and the spin $\frac{3}{2}$ spinor $t^{ijk,}$. The $\frac{1}{2}^+$ ordinary baryons are described by the SU(3) octuplet N^A_B and the spin $\frac{1}{2}$ spinor χ^j.

The product $\bar{\psi} \otimes \psi$ can be reduced following:

$$\overline{56} \otimes 56 = 1 \oplus 35 \oplus 405 \oplus 2695.$$

We now restrict ourselves to the 1 and 35 parts of the current respectively defined by:

$$[\bar{\psi} \otimes \psi_1] = \bar{\psi}_{\alpha\beta\gamma,}\psi^{\alpha\beta\gamma,}$$
$$[\bar{\psi} \otimes \psi_{35}]_{\gamma}^{\gamma'} = \bar{\psi}_{\alpha\beta\gamma,}\psi^{\alpha\beta\gamma',} - \tfrac{1}{6}\delta_{\gamma}^{\gamma'}[\bar{\psi} \otimes \psi_1].$$

The invariant is immediately obtained calculating the complete trace:

$$\bar{\psi} \otimes \psi_1 = (\bar{N}N_1)(\bar{\chi}\chi_1) + (\bar{d}d_1)(\bar{t}t_1),$$

where:

$$\bar{N}N_1 = \bar{N}_A^B N_B^A \qquad \bar{d}d_1 = \bar{d}_{ABC,}d^{ABC,}$$
$$\bar{\chi}\chi_1 = \bar{\chi}_i\chi^i \qquad \bar{t}t_1 = \bar{t}_{ijk,}t^{ijk,}.$$

It is convenient to split the current associated to the adjoint representation in its SU(2) ⊗ SU(3) parts. The result is the following:

(1,8)

$$\tfrac{1}{6}\delta_k^{k'}[(\bar{N}N_F)_C^{C'}(\bar{\chi}\chi_1) + (3\bar{d}d_8)_C^{C'}(\bar{t}t_1)]$$

(3,1)

$$\tfrac{1}{3}\delta_C^{C'}[\tfrac{1}{3}(\bar{N}N_1)(\bar{\chi}\chi_3)_k^{k'} + (\bar{d}d_1)(\bar{t}t_3)_k^{k'}]$$

(3,8)

$$\tfrac{1}{3}\{[(\bar{N}N_D)_C^{C'} + \tfrac{2}{3}(\bar{N}N_F)_C^{C'}](\bar{\chi}\chi_3)_k^{k'} + (3\bar{d}d_8)_C^{C'}(\bar{t}t_3)_k^{k'} +$$
$$+ \sqrt{2}[(\bar{N}d_8)_C^{C'}(\bar{\chi}t_3)_k^{k'} + (\bar{d}N_8)_C^{C'}(\bar{t}\chi_3)_k^{k'}]\}$$

where:

$$(\bar{N}N_F)_C^{C'} = \bar{N}_C^D N_D^{C'} - N_C^D \bar{N}_D^{C'}$$
$$(\bar{N}N_D)_C^{C'} = \bar{N}_C^D N_D^{C'} + N_C^D \bar{N}_D^{C'} - \tfrac{2}{3}\delta_C^{C'}(\bar{N}N_1)$$
$$(\bar{d}d_8)_C^{C'} = \bar{d}_{ABC}d^{ABC'} - \tfrac{1}{3}\delta_C^{C'}(\bar{d}d_1)$$
$$(\bar{d}N_8)_C^{C'} = \varepsilon^{C'AD}d_{ABC}\bar{N}_D^B$$
$$(\bar{N}d_8)_C^{C'} = \varepsilon_{CAD}N_B^D d^{ABC'}$$
$$(\bar{\chi}\chi_3)_k^{k'} = \bar{\chi}_k\chi^{k'} - \tfrac{1}{2}\delta_k^{k'}(\bar{\chi}\chi_1)$$
$$(\bar{t}t_3)_k^{k'} = \bar{t}_{ijk}t^{ijk'} - \tfrac{1}{2}\delta_k^{k'}(\bar{t}t_1)$$
$$(\bar{t}\chi_3)_k^{k'} = \varepsilon^{k'i}t_{ijk}\chi^j$$
$$(\bar{\chi}t_3)_k^{k'} = \varepsilon_{ki}\bar{\chi}_j t^{ijk'}.$$

2. The Yukawa type coupling between baryons and mesons of the adjoint representation is known using the previous results. The adjoint representation is obtained only once in the $\overline{56} \otimes 56$ product and we have only one coupling constant f_0. As a particular consequence, the SU(6) invariance determines the $\rho_S = D/F$ ratio for the coupling between the pseudoscalar mesons and the ordinary baryons.

We do not give the detailed derivation of the various results and we prefer to refer the reader to the original papers (GÜRSEY and RADICATI [1964], PAIS [1964] and GÜRSEY, PAIS and RADICATI [1964]):

a) The coupling between baryons and *vector mesons* is assumed of the form $\bar{\psi}\gamma_\mu \psi v^\mu$ and we use the (1,8) part of the current to show that this coupling is of the pure F type;

b) The coupling between baryons and *pseudoscalar mesons* is assumed of the form $\bar{\psi}\gamma_\mu \gamma_5 \psi \partial^\mu \phi$ and we now use the (3,8) part of the current to show that this coupling is the mixture $D + \frac{3}{2}F$. It follows immediately:

$$\rho_S = \tfrac{3}{2}.$$

c) The pseudoscalar π-meson-nucleon coupling constant g is related to the pseudovector coupling by:

$$g = \tfrac{5}{3}\left(\frac{2M}{m}\right)\frac{f_0}{6},$$

where M is the baryon mass and m the meson mass. On the other hand, the vector mesons are coupled to the conserved vector current and the coupling constant f_ρ responsible to $\rho \Rightarrow 2\pi$ decay can be related to f_0 by:

$$f_\rho = \tfrac{1}{3} f_0 .$$

Experimentally, we have:

$$\frac{g^2}{4\pi} \simeq 14.6 \qquad \frac{f_\rho^2}{4\pi} \simeq 2.4.$$

Using, with GÜRSEY, PAIS and RADICATI [1964], some central values for the SU(6) multiplet:

$$M \simeq 1100 \text{ MeV}, \qquad m \simeq 700 \text{ MeV},$$

the value $g^2/4\pi$ calculated from $f^2/4\pi$ is in good agreement with experiment:

$$\left(\frac{g^2}{4\pi}\right)_{\text{calc.}} \simeq 16.3.$$

3. Let us now consider the weak currents in the static limit. The vector

current is associated to the (1,8) part and the axial vector current to the (3,8) part. We then immediately deduce the two results (GÜRSEY, PAIS and RADICATI [1964]):

$$f_s = 1 \qquad f_a = \tfrac{2}{3}$$

equivalent to:

$$\rho_W = \frac{f_s}{f_a} = \tfrac{3}{2}$$

$$-\frac{G_A}{G_V} = f_a + f_s = \tfrac{5}{3}.$$

The equality $\rho_S = \rho_W$ allows to generalize the Goldberger-Treiman relation and to apply the partially conserved axial current hypothesis.

4. The electromagnetic current can also be studied using the same technics. Following BÉG, LEE and PAIS [1964] and SAKITA [1964a] we associate the electromagnetic current with some weights of the adjoint representation. The electric charge corresponds to the part (1, Q) and the magnetic moment to the (S, Q) part (GELL-MANN [1965]).

The most spectacular consequence is that, for the magnetic moment of baryons $J = \frac{1}{2}$, the D/F electromagnetic ratio has the value $\frac{3}{2}$ and we obtain the prediction:

$$\mu_n = -\tfrac{2}{3}\mu_p$$

in perfect agreement with experiment.

The magnetic moment for the excited baryons is also predicted of the form:

$$\mu_{10} = \mu_p Q$$

and the transition magnetic moment between B and B* states is also proportional to μ_p and we obtain as a particular result:

$$\langle p|m_j|N^{*+}\rangle = (\bar{u}u_j)\frac{2}{\sqrt{3}}\mu_p.$$

11.3. Johnson-Treiman relations

1. In section 11.2 we have used the non relativistic SU(6) invariance for three bodies static vertices. The applicability of SU(6) invariance to four bodies reactions seems to be more difficult because of the motion of the involved particles.

For such a reason we restrict ourselves to the case studied by JOHNSON and

TREIMAN [1965] of forward scattering amplitudes. In the laboratory system, the target and the recoil particle are both at rest and can be associated to an irreducible representation of SU(6).

2. The reaction of interest is the elastic meson-baryon scattering in the forward direction. Even for the mesons in motion we try to use the transformation properties associated to the adjoint representation.

The meson-baryon product of representation can be decomposed in its irreducible parts following:

$$56 \otimes 35 = 56 \oplus 70 \oplus 700 \oplus 1134.$$

We then have only four reduced amplitudes.

3. We now consider the physical case of a proton target, the incident meson being $\pi^+ \pi^- K^+ K^- K^0$ or $\overline{K}^0$. The six elastic amplitudes are then related by two relations:

$$\tfrac{1}{2}[A(K^+) - A(K^-)] = A(K^0) - A(\overline{K}^0) = A(\pi^+) - A(\pi^-)$$

where A(M) is the forward scattering amplitude of a meson M and protons.

Using now the optical theorem, we obtain the so called Johnson-Treiman relations between the total cross-sections.

$$\tfrac{1}{2}[\sigma_T(K^+) - \sigma_T(K^-)] = \sigma_T(K^0) - \sigma_T(\overline{K}^0) = \sigma_T(\pi^+) - \sigma_T(\pi^-).$$

4. It has been noted by SAWYER [1965] that the Johnson-Treiman relations can also be obtained from a vector exchange model, the vector meson-baryon coupling being of the pure F type. More precisely, in the framework of SU(3) symmetry as explained in chapter IV, the Johnson-Treiman relations imply the vanishing of some eigenamplitudes of the crossed channel, in the forward direction (see chapter IV):

$$\mathscr{A}_{8sa} = 0 \qquad \mathscr{A}_{10} = \mathscr{A}_{\overline{10}} = 0.$$

5. The comparison with experiment is satisfactory for momenta larger than 8 GeV/c for the first equality and larger than 10 GeV/c for the second equality. We remark that in this last case, due to the large π-K mass difference, phase space corrections can be important.

11.4. The Dashen Gell-Mann proposal

1. As it has been seen in the previous chapter, the equal time commutation relations of the space integrals of the current components are assumed to define a chain of Lie algebrae. The structure constants are those calculated

by the quark model and we have the isomorphism of Lie algebrae:

$$V_{\rho,\mu} \Leftrightarrow F_{\rho,\mu}$$
$$A_{\rho,\mu} \Leftrightarrow F^5_{\rho,\mu}.$$

It is convenient to write the operators F, in the quark model, in the form:

$$F(\Gamma) = \int q^*(x)\Gamma q(x)\mathrm{d}\boldsymbol{r}$$

and the operators associated to the true physical currents by $O(\Gamma)$. We then have:

$$V_\rho = O(X_\rho) \qquad A_\rho = O(\gamma_5 X_\rho)$$
$$V_{\rho,j} = O(\sigma_j \gamma_5 X_\rho) \qquad A_{\rho,j} = O(\sigma_j X_\rho).$$

2. The three operators V_{I^+}, V_{I^-}, V_{I_3} are time independent from the conserved vector current hypothesis and they generate the isotopic spin Lie algebra su(2). If we add the hypercharge operator V_Y we obtain a Lie algebra u(2), the C.V.C. hypothesis can be extended to the U(3) symmetry and the nine operators V_ρ generate a Lie algebra u(3). These generators are time independent only in the limit of an exact U(3) symmetry.

The set of 36 operators $O(\rho_\mu X_\rho)$ is assumed to have the equal time commutation relation of a Lie algebra u(6).

The last generalization is then to consider all the space integrals of the vector and axial vector current components $O(\sigma_\mu X_\rho)$ and $O(\sigma_\mu \gamma_5 X_\rho)$ which, in the quark model, as seen in the previous chapter, generate the Lie algebra of a chiral $U^+(6) \otimes U^-(6)$ group. The two $U^\pm(6)$ subgroups are associated to the operators:

$$O(\sigma_\mu \tfrac{1}{2}(1 \pm \gamma_5) X_\rho)$$

and the set of positive parity operators $O(\sigma_\mu X_\rho)$ corresponds to the subalgebra u(6).

3. Many difficulties appear in a formulation of the symmetry in the framework of quantum field theory with the introduction of creation and annihilation operators for the particles at rest and the particles in motion. As an example of such a complication we first give a theorem due to COLEMAN [1965a] and related to the behaviour of the vacuum:

THEOREM. If the vacuum is invariant under the transformations of an algebra of space integrals of current components then the generators are time independent and commute with the total hamiltonian.

It follows that the vacuum most have a very complicated structure and it is precisely the originality of the DASHEN and GELL-MANN [1965b] approach, also anticipated by LEE [1965], to work with equal time commutation relations of an algebra of operators without the explicit assumption of the commutation of this algebra with the total hamiltonian.

4. Let us consider the U(6) symmetry as a symmetry for particles at rest. If we go to a state moving in the z direction then the larger part of the U(6) symmetry we can retain is a U(3) ⊗ U(3) collinear symmetry associated to the operators $O(X_\rho)$ and $O(\sigma_z X_\rho)$. Of course, for coplanar processes where two independent momenta are involved the only remaining symmetry is the original U(3) symmetry corresponding to the operators $O(X_\rho)$.

We have the following sequence of hybride symmetries:

$$\underset{\text{at rest}}{\mathrm{U}(6)} \Rightarrow \underset{\text{collinear}}{\mathrm{U}(3) \otimes \mathrm{U}(3)} \Rightarrow \underset{\text{coplanar}}{\mathrm{U}(3)}.$$

5. In LEE [1965], the equal time commutation relations have been used between one particle states at rest and the saturation condition restricts the summation over the complete set of intermediate states to one particle states at rest.

In a more general situation where the particles are in motion in the z direction, one must be extremely careful because of a second theorem due also to COLEMAN [1965b].

THEOREM. If the hybride collinear group U(3) ⊗ U(3) transforms one particle states in motion in the z direction into one particle states in motion in the same direction, then the U(3)⊗U(3) infinitesimal generators commute with the hamiltonian.

Moreover, some complication in the application of hybride symmetries can appear because of the unitarity relations between T matrix elements. In particular in a situation where the initial and the final states are collinear the intermediate states involve momenta in various directions. Nevertheless, for the moment, no proof of the inconsistency of the present scheme with unitarity and crossing symmetry has been given (RUEGG and VOLKOV [1965]).

6. Some consequences of U(3) ⊗ U(3) collinear symmetry have been studied by VOLKOV [1965] and by RUEGG and VOLKOV [1965].

a) The coupling of the pseudoscalar mesons with the ordinary baryons has the D/F ratio $\rho_S = \frac{3}{2}$.

b) The axial vector baryonic current has the same D/F dependence as obtained with the P.C.A.C. hypothesis:

$$\rho_W = \tfrac{3}{2}$$

and the renormalization ratio is:

$$-G_A/G_V = \tfrac{5}{3}.$$

c) The electromagnetic D/F ratio for the magnetic current is also $\frac{3}{2}$ and we have the relation between the neutron and the proton magnetic form factors:

$$\frac{G_1^n(q^2)}{G_1^p(q^2)} = -\tfrac{2}{3}$$

which is in very good agreement with experiment.

d) We obtain only a linear combination of the two Johnson-Treiman relations:

$$\sigma_T(K^+)-\sigma_T(K^-) = \sigma_T(K^0)-\sigma_T(\overline{K}^0)+\sigma_T(\pi^+)-\sigma_T(\pi^-).$$

e) Some equalities can be proved for forward and backward amplitudes in meson-baryon scattering and transformed in relations between forward and backward cross-sections taking into account phase space corrections:

$$\tfrac{1}{4}\sigma(K^-p \Rightarrow K^+\Xi^-) = \sigma(K^-p \Rightarrow K^0\Xi^0) = \sigma(\pi^-p \Rightarrow K^+\Sigma^-)$$

and these equalities can be combined with the U spin relation:

$$\sigma(K^-p \Rightarrow K^0\Xi^0) = \sigma(K^-p \Rightarrow \pi^+\Sigma^-).$$

The agreement with experiment is better in the backward direction than in the forward direction.

7. It has also been suggested (DASHEN and GELL-MANN [1965b] and BARDAKCI et al. [1964, 1965]) that the non chiral group U(6) ⊗ U(6), associated to the operators:

$$O(\sigma_\mu \tfrac{1}{2}(1 \pm \gamma_4)X_\rho)$$

can be a useful symmetry for the particles at rest.

In such a model the quarks q are associated to a positive parity representation (6,1) and the antiquarks $\overline{q}$ to a negative parity representation $(1, \overline{6})$. The low lying baryon states composed of three quarks in a completely symmetric way are associated to the representation (56,10) and the low lying meson states constructed as $\overline{q}q$ bound states are described by the $(6,\overline{6})$ representation. The X^0 pseudoscalar meson is then naturally obtained in such a scheme together with the usual 35 states of the U(6) symmetry.

Now starting from a U(6) ⊗ U(6) symmetry at rest we can derive, as previously, a sequence of hybride symmetries:

$$\underset{\text{at rest}}{U(6) \otimes U(6)} \Rightarrow \underset{\text{collinear}}{U(6)} \Rightarrow \underset{\text{coplanar}}{U(3) \otimes U(3)} \Rightarrow \underset{\text{3 dimensional}}{U(3).}$$

The collinear U(6) group has been first considered by LIPKIN and MESHKOV [1965] and associated to what they call the W spin which is essentially related to the three operators $\sigma_x \gamma_4$, $\sigma_y \gamma_4$, σ_z.

Some consequences of the U(6) collinear symmetry have been investigated (LIPKIN and MESHKOV [1965], DIETZ and DRECHSLER [1965], CINI [1965], DOSCH and STECH [1965] and SCHÜLKE [1965]). It seems that the difficulties due to the unitarity relations and the crossing symmetry cannot be easily avoided.

CHAPTER XII

LIE GROUPS AND LIE ALGEBRA

12.1. Topological groups

1. *Group axioms.* A set G is a group if the composition law, defined in G, has the following properties:

a) Associativity: $a(bc) = (ab)c = abc \qquad a, b, c \in \mathrm{G}$
b) Identity: unit element $e \qquad ea = ae = a \qquad a \in \mathrm{G}$
c) Inverse $a^{-1}a = aa^{-1} = e \qquad a, a^{-1} \in \mathrm{G}$.

2. *Topological groups.* The mapping $(a, b) \to ab^{-1}$ of $\mathrm{G} \times \mathrm{G}$ into G is a continuous mapping. Such a condition is equivalent to the two following ones:

a) The mapping $a \Rightarrow a^{-1}$ of G into G is continuous;
b) The mapping $(a, b) \Rightarrow ab$ of $\mathrm{G} \times \mathrm{G}$ into G is continuous.

The mapping $a \Rightarrow a^{-1}$ of G into G coincides with its inverse because of the relation $(a^{-1})^{-1} = a$. Such a mapping, noted τ, is a homeomorphism of G.

3. *Translations.* The mapping $a \Rightarrow am$ of G into G is one to one and continuous.

This homeomorphism of G is called a right translation ρ_m.

The mapping $a \Rightarrow na$ of G into G is one to one and continuous.

This homeomorphism of G is called a left translation λ_n.

The right and left translations are related by:

$$\lambda_m \tau \rho_m = \tau.$$

4. *Theorem.* It is possible to show that the necessary and sufficient conditions for a group G to be a topological group can be given in the following form:

a) The translations ρ_m and λ_m are continuous $(m \in \mathrm{G})$;
b) The mapping $(a, b) \Rightarrow ab^{-1}$ of $\mathrm{G} \times \mathrm{G}$ into G is continuous at the point (e, e) of $\mathrm{G} \times \mathrm{G}$.

12.2. Lie groups

1. *Definition.* A group G is a Lie group if:

a) G is an analytic manifold;

b) The mapping $(a, b) \Rightarrow ab$ of $G \times G$ into G is an analytic mapping.

2. *Composition functions.* We choose a frame of reference at the point e of G and we denote the coordinates of an element $a \in G$ by a^σ. The composition law can be written as:

$$(ab)^\sigma = \phi^\sigma(a, b) \qquad a, b \in G.$$

The composition functions ϕ^σ are analytic functions of their arguments. We have the following evident properties:

$$\phi^\sigma(a, bc) = \phi^\sigma(ab, c)$$
$$\phi^\sigma(a, e) = \phi^\sigma(e, a) = a^\sigma$$
$$\phi^\sigma(a, a^{-1}) = \phi^\sigma(a^{-1}, a) = e^\sigma.$$

3. It can be easily shown that the mapping $a \Rightarrow a^{-1}$ of G is also an analytic mapping.

It follows that a Lie group is a topological group.

4. *Structure constants.* The identity transformation is described by the relation:

$$a^\sigma = \phi^\sigma(a, e)$$

and we now consider an infinitesimal transformation in the neighbourhood of the identity:

$$a^\sigma + \mathrm{d}a^\sigma = \phi^\sigma(a, e+\delta m) = \phi^\sigma(a, e) + \delta m^\rho \left[\frac{\partial}{\partial b^\rho} \phi^\sigma(a, b)\right]_{b=e}.$$

The velocity field is defined by:

$$\mu_\rho^\sigma(a) = \left[\frac{\partial}{\partial b^\rho} \phi^\sigma(a, b)\right]_{b=e}$$

and we obtain

$$\mathrm{d}a^\sigma = \mu_\rho^\sigma(a)\delta m^\rho.$$

It is convenient to use the inverse matrix $\check{\mu}(a)$:

$$\check{\mu}_\rho^\sigma(a)\mu_\tau^\rho(a) = \delta_\tau^\sigma.$$

The elimination of δm between the two relations:

$$\mathrm{d}a^\sigma = \mu_\rho^\sigma(a)\delta m^\rho \qquad \mathrm{d}b^\sigma = \mu_\rho^\sigma(b)\delta m^\rho$$

leads to the expression:

$$\frac{\partial a^\sigma}{\partial b^\tau} = \mu_\rho^\sigma(a)\check{\mu}_\tau^\rho(b).$$

We now introduce the continuity condition $\partial^2 a^\sigma/\partial b^\rho \partial b^\tau = \partial^2 a^\sigma/\partial b^\tau \partial b^\rho$. By using the previous expression for the first derivative, we obtain:

$$\frac{\partial^2 a^\sigma}{\partial b^\rho \partial b^\tau} = \frac{\partial \mu_\alpha^\sigma(a)}{\partial a^\lambda}\,\mu_\beta^\lambda(a)\check{\mu}_\rho^\beta(b)\check{\mu}_\tau^\alpha(b) + \mu_\gamma^\sigma(a)\,\frac{\partial \check{\mu}_\tau^\gamma(b)}{\partial b^\rho}$$

$$\frac{\partial^2 a^\sigma}{\partial b^\tau \partial b^\rho} = \frac{\partial \mu_\beta^\sigma(a)}{\partial a^\lambda}\,\mu_\alpha^\lambda(a)\check{\mu}_\tau^\alpha(b)\check{\mu}_\rho^\beta(b) + \mu_\gamma^\sigma(a)\,\frac{\partial \check{\mu}_\rho^\gamma(b)}{\partial b^\tau}.$$

Calculations are straightforward but tedious and we obtain the following equality:

$$\left[\frac{\partial \mu_\beta^\sigma(a)}{\partial a^\lambda}\,\mu_\alpha^\lambda(a) - \frac{\partial \mu_\alpha^\sigma(a)}{\partial a^\lambda}\,\mu_\beta^\lambda(a)\right]\check{\mu}_\sigma^\gamma(a) = \left[\frac{\partial \check{\mu}_\tau^\gamma(b)}{\partial b^\rho} - \frac{\partial \check{\mu}_\rho^\gamma(b)}{\partial b^\tau}\right]\mu_\alpha^\tau(b)\mu_\beta^\rho(b).$$

The left-hand side is a function of a only and the right-hand side is a function of b only. The two quantities a and b being independent variables, the two sides are constants. By definition, the structure constants $C_{\alpha\beta}^\gamma$ are given by the two equivalent expressions:

$$C_{\alpha\beta}^\gamma = \left[\frac{\partial \mu_\beta^\sigma(a)}{\partial a^\lambda}\,\mu_\alpha^\lambda(a) - \frac{\partial \mu_\alpha^\sigma(a)}{\partial a^\lambda}\,\mu_\beta^\lambda(a)\right]\check{\mu}_\sigma^\gamma(a)$$

$$C_{\alpha\beta}^\gamma = \left[\frac{\partial \check{\mu}_\tau^\gamma(a)}{\partial a^\rho} - \frac{\partial \check{\mu}_\rho^\gamma(a)}{\partial a^\tau}\right]\mu_\alpha^\tau(a)\mu_\beta^\rho(a).$$

An immediate property is:

$$C_{\alpha\beta}^\gamma + C_{\beta\alpha}^\gamma = 0.$$

12.3. Lie algebra

1. *Infinitesimal transformations.* We are first working in an analytic manifold $\mathscr{E}$ of elements $a \in \mathscr{E}$. The set of the analytic functions f in $\mathscr{E}$ is denoted by $\mathscr{F}$ and the space of analytical infinitesimal transformations X by τ.

The elements X of τ can be used to define the linear mappings:

$$f \Rightarrow Xf$$

of $\mathscr{F}$ into $\mathscr{F}$. The quantities XY and YX allow also to define linear mappings of $\mathscr{F}$ into itself but, in general, XY and YX do not belong to the space τ.

Let us introduce a coordinate system:

$$X = \lambda^i \frac{\partial}{\partial a^i} \qquad Y = \nu^j \frac{\partial}{\partial a^j}.$$

We have successively:

$$XYf = \lambda^i \frac{\partial}{\partial a^i} \nu^j \frac{\partial}{\partial a^j} f = \lambda^i \frac{\partial \nu^j}{\partial a^i} \frac{\partial f}{\partial a^j} + \lambda^i \nu^j \frac{\partial^2 f}{\partial a^i \partial a^j}$$

$$YXf = \nu^j \frac{\partial}{\partial a^j} \lambda^i \frac{\partial}{\partial a^i} f = \nu^j \frac{\partial \lambda^i}{\partial a^j} \frac{\partial f}{\partial a^i} + \nu^j \lambda^i \frac{\partial^2 f}{\partial a^j \partial a^i}.$$

The continuity condition $\partial^2 f/\partial a^i \partial a^j = \partial^2 f/\partial a^j \partial a^i$ allows us to write:

$$[X, Y]f = \left(\lambda^i \frac{\partial \nu^j}{\partial a^i} - \gamma^i \frac{\partial \lambda^j}{\partial a^i}\right) \frac{\partial f}{\partial a^j}$$

and it follows that the commutator $[X, Y]$ is also an element of τ which can be represented by:

$$[X, Y] = \left(\lambda^i \frac{\partial \nu^j}{\partial a^i} - \nu^i \frac{\partial \lambda^j}{\partial a^i}\right) \frac{\partial}{\partial a^j}.$$

2. *Lie algebra.* The Lie product of two operators X and Y is the commutator $[X, Y]$. The space τ can be considered as a linear algebra on the field K where $\mathscr{E}$ is defined and we have the following properties

a) Linear algebra:

$$[\alpha X + \beta Y, Z] = \alpha[X, Z] + \beta[Y, Z]$$
$$[X, \alpha Y + \beta Z] = \alpha[X, Y] + \beta[X, Z]$$

for all α, $\beta \in$ K and $X, Y, Z \in \tau$.

b) Antisymmetry:

$$[X, X] = 0.$$

c) Jacobi identity:

$$[X, [Y, Z]] + [Y, [Z, X]] + [Z, [X, Y]] = 0.$$

A Lie algebra is a linear algebra which satisfies the antisymmetry property and the Jacobi identity.

3. *Lie algebra of a Lie group* G. A Lie group G is an analytic manifold and we consider the set $\mathscr{F}$(G) of the analytic functions in G.

The right translations define completely the group G:

$$a \Rightarrow am \qquad a, m \in \mathrm{G}$$

and induce in $\mathscr{F}(\mathrm{G})$ a continuous mapping:

$$f \Rightarrow fm \qquad f, fm \in \mathscr{F}(\mathrm{G})$$

where:

$$fm(a) = f(am).$$

We now introduce a tangent vector L at the unit element e of G. The infinitesimal right translations are defined by:

$$X(a)f(a) = [L(m)f_m(a)]_{m=e}.$$

Let us precise these definitions with a coordinate system:

$$L(m) = \lambda^\sigma \frac{\partial}{\partial m^\sigma} \qquad X(a) = \lambda^\sigma X_\sigma(a)$$

$$X_\sigma(a)f(a) = \left[\frac{\partial}{\partial m^\sigma} f_m(a)\right]_{m=e}.$$

The right-hand side can be evaluated using the relation given in a previous section:

$$\frac{\partial b^\rho}{\partial m^\sigma} = \mu^\rho_\tau(b)\check{\mu}^\tau_\sigma(m)$$

and we obtain:

$$\frac{\partial}{\partial m^\sigma} f_m(a) = \left[\frac{\partial}{\partial b^\rho} f(b)\mu^\rho_\tau(b)\check{\mu}^\tau_\sigma(m)\right]_{b=am}.$$

In the limit $m = e$, we have $\check{\mu}^\tau_\sigma(e) = \delta^\tau_\sigma$ and the infinitesimal generators $X_\sigma(a)$ can be represented in terms of differential operators by:

$$X_\sigma(a) = \mu^\rho_\sigma(a) \frac{\partial}{\partial a^\rho}.$$

The Lie algebra of the generators $X_\sigma(a)$ is known from the Lie product of two operators as calculated in 1:

$$[X_\rho, X_\sigma] = \left[\mu^\alpha_\rho(a) \frac{\partial \mu^\beta_\sigma(a)}{\partial a^\alpha} - \mu^\alpha_\sigma(a) \frac{\partial \mu^\beta_\rho(a)}{\partial a^\alpha}\right] \frac{\partial}{\partial a^\beta}.$$

This expression can be simplified by using the structure constants introduced in section 12.2:

$$\mu_\rho^\alpha(a)\frac{\partial\mu_\sigma^\beta(a)}{\partial a^\alpha} - \mu_\sigma^\alpha(a)\frac{\partial\mu_\rho^\beta(a)}{\partial a^\alpha} = C_{\rho\sigma}^\tau\ \mu_\tau^\beta(a)$$

and we finally obtain the fundamental relation of a Lie algebra:

$$[X_\rho, X_\sigma] = C_{\rho\sigma}^\tau\ X_\tau.$$

The antisymmetry property of the Lie algebra is contained in the antisymmetry character of the structure constants. The infinitesimal generators satisfy the Jacobi identity and for the structure constants follows the relation:

$$C_{\rho\sigma}^\alpha\ C_{\alpha\tau}^\beta + C_{\sigma\tau}^\alpha\ C_{\alpha\rho}^\beta + C_{\tau\rho}^\alpha\ C_{\alpha\sigma}^\beta = 0.$$

12.4. Simple and semi-simple Lie algebrae

1. *Definitions.* We first give some classical definitions for the groups

a) In an abelian group the multiplication law is commutative.

b) A subgroup is a set of elements of a group which satisfies the group axioms. A trivial subgroup is the identity element itself.

c) An invariant subgroup H of a group G is a subgroup of G such that:

$$axa^{-1} \in \mathrm{H} \text{ for all } x \in \mathrm{H} \text{ and } a \in \mathrm{G}.$$

If we now consider the particular case of interest of Lie groups, it is easy to translate these properties in terms of Lie algebrae.

a) All the infinitesimal generators of the Lie algebra of an abelian group commute and all the structure constants are zero.

b) The Lie algebra h of an analytic subgroup H of a Lie group G is a subalgebra of the Lie algebra g of G and the structure constants satisfy the relation:

$$C_{jk}^\alpha = 0 \quad \text{for all } X_j, X_k \in \mathrm{h} \text{ if } X_\alpha \in \mathrm{g} \text{ is not in h}.$$

c) If now H is an invariant subgroup of G, the structure constants verify the condition:

$$C_{j\alpha}^\beta = 0 \text{ for all } X_j \in \mathrm{h},\ X_\alpha, X_\beta \in \mathrm{g} \text{ if } X_\beta \text{ is not in h}.$$

2. *Simple group and simple algebra.* A simple group has no invariant subgroups besides itself, the identity and perhaps discrete subgroups.

A simple algebra has no invariant subalgebra.

The Lie algebra of a simple Lie group is a simple algebra.

3. *Semi-simple group and semi-simple algebra.* A semi-simple group has no abelian invariant subgroup, besides itself, the identity and perhaps discrete subgroups.

A semi-simple algebra has no abelian invariant subalgebra.

The Lie algebra of a semi-simple Lie group is a semi-simple algebra.

4. *Cartan criterion for semi-simple algebra.* We define the symmetrical Cartan tensor

$$g_{\rho\sigma} = C^{\beta}_{\rho\alpha}\ C^{\alpha}_{\sigma\beta}.$$

The Cartan criterion is the following: a necessary and sufficient condition for a Lie algebra to be semi-simple is:

$$\det (g_{\rho\sigma}) \neq 0.$$

For a semi-simple algebra, the matrix $g_{\rho\sigma}$ is a regular matrix.

This condition is obviously a necessary condition. If we suppose that the Lie algebra possesses an abelian invariant subalgebra h, all the structure constants $C^{\beta}_{j\alpha}$ where $X_j \in$ h vanish and it follows that all elements $g_{j\gamma}$ of the row j of the Cartan tensor also vanish and $\det (g_{\rho\sigma}) = 0$.

Cartan has proved that if $\det(g_{\rho\sigma}) \neq 0$ the Lie algebra is semi-simple.

5. Let us consider a semi-simple Lie algebra. The Cartan tensor $g_{\sigma\rho}$ allows to define a symmetrical linear connection in the Lie algebra. In particular, this tensor can be used to lower the indices. As an example, we have:

$$C_{\rho\sigma\tau} = C^{\alpha}_{\rho\sigma}\ g_{\alpha\tau}\,.$$

We replace $g_{\alpha\tau}$ by its definition and we apply the Jacobi identiy:

$$C_{\rho\sigma\tau} = C^{\alpha}_{\beta\rho}\ C^{\gamma}_{\alpha\sigma}\ C^{\beta}_{\gamma\tau} - C^{\alpha}_{\beta\sigma}\ C^{\gamma}_{\alpha\rho}\ C^{\beta}_{\gamma\tau}.$$

The tensor $C_{\rho\sigma\tau}$ is invariant under a cyclic permutation of the indices and completely antisymmetric.

6. All the semi-simple Lie algebrae can be written as a direct sum of simple Lie algebrae.

CHAPTER XIII

LIE GROUPS OF TRANSFORMATIONS

13.1. Generalities

1. *Definition.* G is a Lie group of transformations of an analytic manifold† $\mathcal{M}$ if for each $x \in \mathcal{M}$ and $a \in G$, one can find a $y \in \mathcal{M}$, denoted $y = xa$ such that:

a) The mapping $(x, a) \Rightarrow y$ of $\mathcal{M} \times G$ into $\mathcal{M}$ is analytic.

b) $xe = x$ for each $x \in \mathcal{M}$.

c) Associativity $(xa)b = x(ab)$ for each $x \in \mathcal{M}$ and $a, b \in G$.

If the unit element e of G is the only one element satisfying the condition b, the group is called an effective group.

2. *Lie algebra.* Let us define a chart in $\mathcal{M}$ and a chart in G and we use greek indices in G and latin indices in $\mathcal{M}$. The mapping $xa \Rightarrow y$ is written as:

$$y^j = f^j(x, a)$$

where the composition functions f^j are analytic functions of their arguments. The velocity field is defined by:

$$U^j_\sigma(x) = \left[\frac{\partial}{\partial a^\sigma} f^j(x, a)\right]_{a=e}$$

and the infinitesimal generators of the Lie algebra are given by:

$$X_\sigma(x) = U^j_\sigma(x) \frac{\partial}{\partial x^j}.$$

For an effective group, the generators $X_\sigma(x)$ defined in this way are linearly independent and constitute a basis of the Lie algebra.

13.2. Group of linear transformations of a vector space on the field of real numbers

We are first working with a n-dimensional vector space on the field R of the

† In an analytic manifold, at each point there is a chart and any two charts are analytically related.

real numbers, as an analytic manifold R^n. We define, in R^n, a symmetrical bilinear† connection, with a regular matrix g which allows us to introduce, in R_n, a scalar product.

13.2.1. General linear group GL(n, R)

1. The regular $n \times n$ matrices with real coefficients generate a multiplicative group which is called the general linear group GL(n, R).
2. Any arbitrary $n \times n$ matrix with real coefficients defines in R_n a linear transformation by

$$y^j = x^k S_k^j(a).$$

The linear transformation is regular if and only if the matrix $S(a)$ is regular.

The group of regular linear transformations in R^n is isomorphic to GL(n,R) and can also be considered as the definition of the general linear group.

3. We consider the set $\mathcal{M}(n, \mathrm{R})$ of all $n \times n$ matrices with real coefficients. The general linear group is a subset of $\mathcal{M}(n, \mathrm{R})$. Let us define, in $\mathcal{M}(n,\mathrm{R})$, a basis E_{ij} by the matrix elements

$$[E_{ij}]_{kl} = g_{ki} g_{lj}.$$

Such a basis is complete because of the regular character of g.

We now expand the matrix $S(a)$ on this basis following

$$S(a) = E_{ij} a^{ij}.$$

The velocity field $U_\sigma^j(x)$ can then be written as

$$U_{[rs]}^j(x) = \frac{\partial}{\partial a^{rs}} [x^k S_k^j(a)]_{a=e} = x_r \delta_s^j$$

and the infinitesimal generators $X(x)$ have a representation as differential operators given by:

$$X_{rs}(x) = x_r \frac{\partial}{\partial x^s}.$$

This explicit expression enables us to deduce the commutation rules of the Lie algebra gl(n, R) of the general linear group:

$$[X_{rs}, X_{tu}] = g_{st} X_{ru} - g_{ur} X_{ts}.$$

† A bilinair form $G(x, y)$ satisfies:

$$G(\alpha x, y) = \alpha G(x, y)$$
$$G(x, \alpha y) = \alpha G(x, y),$$

where α is any complex number.

The group GL(n, R) depends on n^2 real parameters.

4. The product of two matrices E_{ij} is given, by definition, by:

$$E_{ij}E_{kl} = g_{jk}E_{il}.$$

The commutator of two such matrices takes then the form:

$$[E_{ij}, E_{kl}] = g_{jk}E_{il} - g_{li}E_{kj}.$$

The Lie algebra of all real $n \times n$ matrices, the operation being the Lie product defined by the commutator, is isomorphic to the Lie algebra of the general linear group. By extension we shall call also gl(n, R) this Lie algebra.

13.2.2. Special linear group

1. The particular operator $X = g^{sr}X_{rs}$ commutes, in an evident way, with the n^2 infinitesimal generators X_{tu}. The transformation generated by X is given by:

$$\mathrm{d}x^k = \varepsilon X x^k = \varepsilon g^{sr} x_r \frac{\partial}{\partial x^s} x^k = \varepsilon x^k$$

and is simply a real dilatation from the center of the origin.

2. The group generated by X is an one-parameter abelian group, invariant subgroup of GL(n, R) and isomorphic to the additive group of real numbers R.

The factor group GL(n, R)/R is the special linear group SL(n, R). It can be defined as the set of unimodular linear transformation in R^n, or, in an equivalent way, as that set of $n \times n$ unimodular matrices with real coefficients. The group SL(n, R) depends on $n^2 - 1$ real parameters.

The Lie algebra sl(n, R) is the Lie algebra of the $n \times n$ real matrices of trace zero. The infinitesimal generators are immediately deduced from the X_{rs} by the zero trace condition:

$$X'_{rs} = X_{rs} - \frac{1}{n} g_{rs} X.$$

Obviously, the commutation laws are unchanged.

13.2.3. Pseudo-orthogonal groups O($n-s$, s)

1. The scalar product in R^n is defined with the symmetrical linear connection g

$$(x, y) = g(x, y) = x^k g_{kl} y^l = (y, x).$$

Let us call A as an arbitrary linear transformation in R^n. The conservation of the scalar product under the transformation A is simply $(Ax, Ay) = (x, y)$.

This equality must be satisfied for all vectors $\boldsymbol{x}$ and $\boldsymbol{y}$ of R^n. The invariance property takes then the simple form

$$A^T g A = g.$$

A matrix which verifies the previous relation is called an orthogonal matrix with respect to the connection g. The orthogonal matrices generate a subgroup of GL(n, R), the pseudo-orthogonal group.

2. The connection g is a symmetrical bilinear regular form and can be diagonalized in the following way: $g_{ij} = \pm\delta_{ij}$. We choose now in R^n an orthogonal basis such that:

$$g_{ij} = \delta_{ij} \qquad i = 1, 2, \ldots, n-s$$
$$g_{ij} = -\delta_{ij} \qquad i = n-s+1, \ldots, n.$$

The number s of time like vectors is called the signature of the pseudo-euclidian space. The pseudo-orthogonal groups are characterized by the signature s and will be noted $O(n-s, s)$. The two pseudo-orthogonal groups $O(n-s, s)$ and $O(s, n-s)$ are isomorphic.

In the particular case $s = 0$ (or $s = n$), the vector space is an euclidian space and the connection g can always be choosen as the unit matrix I. The orthogonal group $O(n)$ is the set of orthogonal matrices satisfying $A^T A = I$.

3. The pseudo-orthogonal groups are analytic subgroups of GL(n, R). The Lie algebra of the pseudo-orthogonal group is a subalgebra of gl(n, R). The infinitesimal generator Z_{ij} can be written as a linear combination of the X_{mn}'s, previously defined, with real coefficients:

$$Z_{ij} = \lambda_{ij}^{mn} \; X_{mn}.$$

It is sufficient to impose the invariance of the norm of all vectors:

$$Z_{ij}(x, x) = 0 \text{ for all } x \in R^n.$$

This condition can easily be transformed into:

$$\lambda_{ij}^{mn} \; x_m x_n = 0.$$

The matrices λ_{ij} must be antisymmetrical:

$$\lambda_{ij}^{mn} + \lambda_{ij}^{nm} = 0,$$

and it is convenient to choose:

$$\lambda_{ij} = E_{ij} - E_{ji},$$

which gives, for the Z_{ij}'s, the explicit and simple form:

$$Z_{ij} = X_{ij} - X_{ji}.$$

It is possible to construct $\frac{1}{2}n(n-1)$ linearly independent $n \times n$ skew symmetric real matrices. The pseudo-orthogonal groups $O(n-s, s)$ depend of $\frac{1}{2}n(n-1)$ real parameters. The Lie algebra $O(n-s, s)$ is spanned by $\frac{1}{2}n(n-1)$ infinitesimal generators Z_{ij} with the commutation relations given by:

$$[Z_{ij}, Z_{kl}] = g_{jk} Z_{il} - g_{ik} Z_{jl} + g_{il} Z_{jk} - g_{jl} Z_{ik}.$$

From the previous results, it follows that $O(n, s)$ is the subalgebra of $\mathscr{M}(n, R)$ characterized by the following structure:

$$\begin{vmatrix} X_1 & X_2 \\ X_2^T & X_3 \end{vmatrix}$$

where X_1, X_2, X_3 are three real matrices with:

X_1 skew symmetric of order $n-s$
X_3 skew symmetric of order s.

The Lie algebra $o(n)$ of the orthogonal group is then isomorphic to the Lie algebra of all skew symmetric $n \times n$ real matrices.

For a given value of n, there exist $[\frac{1}{2}n]+1$ non equivalent pseudo-orthogonal groups.

Two interesting subgroups of $O(n, s)$ are the orthogonal groups $O(s)$ and $O(n-s)$ and their direct product:

$$O(s) \otimes O(n-s) \subset O(n-s, s).$$

13.2.4. Special pseudo-orthogonal groups $SO(n-s, s)$

1. As a consequence of the relation $A^T g A = g$ we obtain

$$(\det A)^2 = I.$$

It is then possible to define in $O(n-s, s)$ an equivalence with respect to the sign of det A. Only the coset det $A = +1$ is a subgroup called the special pseudo-orthogonal group $SO(n-s, s)$.

The equivalence is associated to the discrete group Z_2 of two elements $\{I, -I\}$ and we have the relation

$$O(n-s, s)/Z_2 \simeq SO(n-s, s).$$

2. The special orthogonal groups are also analytic subgroups for the special linear group SL(n, R). More precisely

$$SO(n-s, s) \simeq O(n-s, s) \cap SL(n, R).$$

3. In an euclidian space where $g \simeq I$, the group of unimodular orthogonal matrices is the special orthogonal group SO(n).

4. The two groups O($n-s$, s) and SO($n-s$, s) have the same Lie algebra but they are not isomorphic groups.

13.2.5. Applications

1. The signature of a 3-dimensional vector space can be $s = 0$ (or $s = 3$) and $s = 1$ (or $s = 2$). We will have only two pseudo-orthogonal groups O(3) and O(2, 1).

The infinitesimal generators can be represented as

$$Z_{12} = x_1 \frac{\partial}{\partial x^2} - x_2 \frac{\partial}{\partial x^1}$$

$$Z_{23} = x_2 \frac{\partial}{\partial x^3} - x_3 \frac{\partial}{\partial x^2}$$

$$Z_{31} = x_3 \frac{\partial}{\partial x^1} - x_1 \frac{\partial}{\partial x^3}.$$

In the case of an euclidian space, the connection g can be taken as:

$$g = \begin{vmatrix} 1 & 0 & 0 \\ 0 & 1 & 0 \\ 0 & 0 & 1 \end{vmatrix}$$

and the commutation rules are given by:

$$[Z_{23}, Z_{31}] = -Z_{12} \qquad [Z_{31}, Z_{12}] = -Z_{23} \qquad [Z_{12}, Z_{23}] = -Z_{31}.$$

In the case of a pseudo-euclidian space, the connection g can be choosen so that:

$$g = \begin{vmatrix} 1 & 0 & 0 \\ 0 & 1 & 0 \\ 0 & 0 & -1 \end{vmatrix}$$

and the commutation rules become:

$$[Z_{23}, Z_{31}] = Z_{12} \qquad [Z_{31}, Z_{12}] = -Z_{23} \qquad [Z_{12}, Z_{23}] = -Z_{31}$$

Usually, the hermitic infinitesimal generators of the orthogonal group O(3) are defined following:

$$Z_{jk} = \mathrm{i}\varepsilon_{jkl} J_l$$

and the commutation rules take the familiar form

$$\boldsymbol{J} \times \boldsymbol{J} = \mathrm{i}\boldsymbol{J}.$$

2. Let us now consider a 2-dimensional vector space. The linear connection g is defined by $g_{11} = 1$, $g_{22} = \varepsilon$ with $\varepsilon = \pm 1$. The general linear group GL(2, R) is a 4-parameter group and the Lie algebra gl(2, R) is known from the commutation relations:

$$[X_{11}, X_{12}] = X_{12} \qquad [X_{11}, X_{21}] = -X_{21} \qquad [X_{11}, X_{22}] = 0$$
$$[X_{22}, X_{12}] = -\varepsilon X_{12} \qquad [X_{22}, X_{21}] = \varepsilon X_{21} \qquad [X_{12}, X_{21}] = \varepsilon X_{11} - X_{22}.$$

The generator $X = X_{11} + \varepsilon X_{22}$ commutes with the four X_{jk}'s. The Lie algebra sl(2, R) can be conveniently defined by the following infinitesimal generators:

$$X^0 = \tfrac{1}{2}(X_{11} - \varepsilon X_{22}) \qquad X^{\pm} = \tfrac{1}{2}(X_{12} \pm \varepsilon X_{21}),$$

which satisfy the commutation relations

$$[X^0, X^+] = X^-, \qquad [X^+, X^-] = -X^0, \qquad [X^-, X^0] = -X^+.$$

If we compare these results with those obtained in the previous section, we immediately prove the isomorphism of the Lie algebrae of the special linear group SL(2, R) and of the pseudo-orthogonal group O(3,1):

$$\mathrm{sl}(2, \mathrm{R}) \simeq \mathrm{so}(3,1).$$

Of course, this result cannot be extended to the two groups itself.

3. The Lie algebra of the orthogonal group O(4) in an euclidian space is defined by the six infinitesimal generators and the metric tensor in its diagonal form is simply the unit matrix $g_{11} = g_{22} = g_{33} = g_{44} = +1$.

Let us define two sets of three generators by the linear combinations with real coefficients

$$Z_1^{\pm} = \tfrac{1}{2}(Z_{23} \pm Z_{14}), \qquad Z_2^{\pm} = \tfrac{1}{2}(Z_{31} \pm Z_{24}), \qquad Z_3^{\pm} = \tfrac{1}{2}(Z_{12} \pm Z_{34}).$$

The following relations can be immediately verified

$$[Z_j^{\pm}, Z_k^{\mp}] = 0$$
$$[Z_j^{\pm}, Z_k^{\pm}] = -\varepsilon_{jkl} Z_l^{\pm}.$$

The Lie algebra so(4) can be written as the direct sum of two Lie algebrae, each of them being isomorphic to a Lie algebra so(3)

$$\mathrm{so}(4) \simeq \mathrm{so}(3) \oplus \mathrm{so}(3).$$

4. A result of the same type can be obtained for the pseudo-orthogonal group O(2, 2). By using the metric tensor $g_{11} = g_{22} = 1, g_{33} = g_{44} = -1$, we can define two sets of three infinitesimal generators by the linear combinations with real coefficients:

$$Z_1^{\pm} = \tfrac{1}{2}(Z_{23} \pm Z_{14}), \qquad Z_2^{\pm} = \tfrac{1}{2}(Z_{31} \pm Z_{24}), \qquad Z_3^{\pm} = \tfrac{1}{2}(Z_{12} \mp Z_{34}).$$

The following relations can be easily obtained

$$[Z_j^{\pm}, Z_k^{\mp}] = 0$$

$$[Z_1^{\pm}, Z_2^{\pm}] = Z_3^{\pm} \qquad [Z_2^{\pm}, Z_3^{\pm}] = -Z_1^{\pm} \qquad [Z_3^{\pm}, Z_1^{\pm}] = -Z_2^{\pm}.$$

The Lie algebra so(2,2) can be written as the direct sum of two Lie algebrae, each of them being isomorphic to a Lie algebra so(2,1)

$$\mathrm{so}(2,2) \simeq \mathrm{so}(2,1) \oplus \mathrm{so}(2,1).$$

13.3. Group of linear transformations of a vector space on the field of complex numbers

We introduce a n-dimensional vector space on the field C of complex numbers as an analytic manifold C^n. We define in C^n a sesquilinear† connection with a regular hermitian matrix g which allows us to introduce, in C^n, an hermitian product.

Let us consider a Lie algebra $\Lambda = \{X_\sigma\}$ defined on the field of real numbers R with the commutation rules

$$[X_\sigma, X_\tau] = C^\rho_{\sigma\tau} X_\rho.$$

The complex extension Λ^* can be regarded either as the same Lie algebra defined on the field of complex numbers C or as a new Lie algebra $\{X_\sigma, Y_\sigma\}$ on R with the commutation rules

$$[X_\sigma, X_\tau] = C^\rho_{\sigma\tau} X_\rho \qquad [X_\sigma, Y_\tau] = C^\rho_{\sigma\tau} Y_\rho \qquad [Y_\sigma, Y_\tau] = -C^\rho_{\sigma\tau} X_\rho.$$

The complex extension of Λ^* can be written as a direct sum of two Lie algebrae, isomorphic to Λ^*:

$$(\Lambda^*)^* \simeq \Lambda^* \oplus \Lambda^*.$$

† A sesquilinear form $G(x, y)$ satisfies:

$$G(\alpha x, y) = \bar{\alpha}\, G(x, y)$$
$$G(x, \alpha y) = \alpha\, G(x, y)$$

where α is any complex number.

The Lie algebra $(\Lambda^*)^*$ defined on R, is a set of generators X_σ, Y_σ, Z_σ, T_σ with the following commutation rules:

$$[X_\sigma, X_\tau] = C^\rho_{\sigma\tau}\, X_\rho \qquad [X_\sigma, Y_\tau] = C^\rho_{\sigma\tau}\, Y_\rho \qquad [Y_\sigma, Y_\tau] = -C^\rho_{\sigma\tau}\, X_\rho$$
$$[X_\sigma, Z_\tau] = C^\rho_{\sigma\tau}\, Z_\rho \qquad [Y_\sigma, Z_\tau] = C^\rho_{\sigma\tau}\, T_\rho \qquad [Z_\sigma, Z_\tau] = -C^\rho_{\sigma\tau}\, X_\rho$$
$$[X_\sigma, T_\tau] = C^\rho_{\sigma\tau}\, T_\rho \qquad [Y_\sigma, T_\tau] = -C^\rho_{\sigma\tau}\, Z_\rho \qquad [T_\sigma, T_\tau] = C^\rho_{\sigma\tau}\, X_\rho$$
$$[Z_\sigma, T_\tau] = -C^\rho_{\sigma\tau}\, Y_\rho .$$

It is convenient to write these relations in the form:

$$[X_\sigma \pm T_\sigma, X_\tau \pm T_\tau] = 2C^\rho_{\sigma\tau}\,(X_\rho \pm T_\rho) \qquad [X_\sigma \pm T_\sigma, X_\tau \mp T_\tau] = 0$$
$$[X_\sigma \pm T_\sigma, Y_\tau \mp Z_\tau] = 2C^\rho_{\sigma\tau}\,(Y_\rho \rightarrow Z_\rho) \qquad [X_\sigma \pm T_\sigma, Y_\tau \pm Z_\tau] = 0$$
$$[Y_\sigma \mp Z_\sigma, Y_\tau \mp Z_\tau] = -2C^\rho_{\sigma\tau}\,(X_\rho \pm T_\rho) \qquad [Y_\sigma \mp Z_\sigma, Y_\tau \pm Z_\tau] = 0$$

which exhibits the previous result.

13.3.1. General linear group

1. The regular $n \times n$ complex matrices generate the general linear group GL(n, C).

The group of regular linear transformations in $\mathbf{C}^n$ is isomorphic to GL(n, C).

2. The Lie algebra gl(n, C) of the general linear group GL(n, C) is the complex extension of the Lie algebra gl(n, R). We consider gl(n, C) as a Lie algebra on R with the infinitesimal generators X_{rs} and Y_{rs} satisfying the following commutation rules

$$[X_{rs}, X_{tu}] = g_{st} X_{ru} - g_{ur} X_{ts}$$
$$[X_{rs}, Y_{tu}] = g_{st} Y_{ru} - g_{ur} Y_{ts}$$
$$[Y_{rs}, Y_{tu}] = -g_{st} X_{ru} + g_{ur} X_{ts} .$$

The Lie algebra gl(n, C) can be identified with the Lie algebra of the $n \times n$ complex matrices $\mathscr{M}(n, \mathrm{C})$, the operation being the Lie product.

A direct proof of such a result can be obtained, as in the real case, by using a convenient complete basis defined by

$$[E_{kl}]_{mn} = g_{mk} g_{ln} \qquad [E^I_{kl}]_{mn} = \mathrm{i} g_{mk} g_{ln} .$$

13.3.2. Special linear group

1. The two operators $X = g^{rs} X_{sr}$ and $Y = g^{rs} Y_{sr}$ commute with all the

generators of the linear group GL(n, C). They generate a two parameter abelian group corresponding to complex dilatations from the center of the origin. This invariant subgroup of GL(n, C) is isomorphic to the additive group C of the complex numbers.

The factor group GL(n, C)/C is the special linear group SL(n, C). It can be defined as the set of unimodular linear transformations in C^n or, equivalently, as the set of the $n \times n$ unimodular complex matrices.

The group SL(n, C) depends of $2n^2-2$ real parameters.

The Lie algebra sl(n, C) is the Lie algebra of the $n \times n$ complex matrices of trace zero. The infinitesimal generators are immediately deduced from the X_{rs} and Y_{rs} by the zero trace condition:

$$X'_{rs} = X_{rs} - \frac{1}{n} g_{rs} X \qquad Y'_{rs} = Y_{rs} - \frac{1}{n} g_{rs} Y.$$

Obviously the commutation laws are unchanged.

13.3.3. Pseudo unitary groups U($n-s$, s)

1. The hermitian product in C^n is given by the regular sesquilinear form g:

$$(x, y) = g(x, y) = \bar{x}^k g_{kl} y^l = \overline{(y, x)}.$$

Let us call as A an arbitrary linear transformation in C^n. The conservation of the hermitian product under the transformation A is simply

$$(Ax, Ay) = (x, y).$$

This equality must be satisfied for all vectors in C^n. The invariance property takes then the simple form

$$A^* g A = g.$$

A matrix which satisfies the previous equality is called an unitary matrix with respect to the connection g. The unitary matrices generate a subgroup of GL(n, C), the pseudo-unitary group.

2. The connection g is an hermitian sesquilinear regular form and it can be diagonalized in the following way $g_{ij} = \pm\delta_{ij}$. We will choose in C^n, an orthonormalized basis such that

$$g_{ij} = \delta_{ij} \qquad i = 1, 2, \ldots, n-s$$
$$g_{ij} = -\delta_{ij} \qquad i = n-s+1, \ldots, n.$$

The pseudo-unitary groups are characterized by the signature s and noted $U(n-s, s)$.

In the particular case $s = 0$ (or $s = n$) the vector space is an hermitian space and the connection g can always be choosen as the unit matrix I. The unitary group $U(n)$ is the set of unitary matrices satisfying $A^*A = I$.

3. The pseudo-unitary groups are analytic subgroups of $GL(n, C)$. The Lie algebra of the pseudo-unitary group is a subalgebra of $gl(n, C)$. The infinitesimal generators Z_{ij} can be written as a linear combination of the X_{mn}'s previously defined with complex coefficients

$$Z_{ij} = \lambda_{ij}^{mn} \; X_{mn}.$$

It is sufficient to impose the invariance of the norm of all vectors:

$$Z_{ij}(x, x) = 0 \qquad \text{for all } x \in C^n.$$

The matrices λ_{ij} turn out to be skew hermitian:

$$\lambda_{ij}^{mn} + \overline{\lambda_{ij}^{nm}} = 0.$$

It is possible to construct, in C^n, n^2 linearly independent $n \times n$ skew hermitian matrices. The pseudo-unitary groups $U(n-s, s)$ depend on n^2 real parameters. The Lie algebra $u(n-s, s)$ is spanned by n^2 infinitesimal generators and it is convenient to choose the skew hermitian matrices λ_{ij} so that:

$$\alpha) \quad \tfrac{1}{2}n(n-1) \quad \text{matrices} \quad E_{ij}+E_{ji}$$
$$\beta) \quad \tfrac{1}{2}n(n+1) \quad \text{matrices} \quad E^I_{ij}+E^I_{ji}$$

and we obtain, for the Z_{ij}'s the explicit and simple form:

$$Z_{ij} = -Z_{ji} = X_{ij} - X_{ji}$$
$$Z^I_{ij} = Z^I_{ji} = Y_{ij} + Y_{ji}.$$

The commutation relations are the following:

$$[Z_{ij}, Z_{kl}] = g_{jk}Z_{il} - g_{ik}Z_{jl} - g_{jl}Z_{ik} + g_{il}Z_{jk}$$
$$[Z_{ij}, Z^I_{kl}] = g_{jk}Z^I_{il} - g_{ik}Z^I_{jl} + g_{jl}Z^I_{ik} - g_{il}Z^I_{jk}$$
$$[Z^I_{ij}, Z^I_{kl}] = -g_{jk}Z_{il} - g_{ik}Z_{jl} - g_{jl}Z_{ik} - g_{il}Z_{jk}.$$

From the previous results it follows that $u(n-s, s)$ is the subalgebra of $\mathcal{M}(n, C)$ characterized by the following structure:

$$\begin{vmatrix} X_1 & X_2 \\ X_2^* & X_3 \end{vmatrix}$$

where X_1, X_2, X_3 are three complex matrices with:

X_1 skew hermitian of order $n-s$
X_3 skew hermitian of order s.

The Lie algebra u(n) of the unitary group is then isomorphic to the Lie algebra of all skew hermitian $n \times n$ complex matrices.

For a given value of n, there exist $[\frac{1}{2}n]+1$ non equivalent pseudo-unitary groups.

Two interesting subgroups of U($n-s$, s) are the unitary groups U(s) and U($n-s$) and their direct product

$$\mathrm{U}(s) \otimes \mathrm{U}(n-s) \subset \mathrm{U}(n-s, s).$$

From the commutation rules, the generators Z_{ij} span a Lie subalgebra isomorphic to the Lie algebra o($n-s$, s) of the pseudo-orthogonal group.

5. The Lie algebrae gl(n, R) and o($n-s$, s) have all the same complex extension which is simply gl(n, C).

13.3.4. Special pseudo-unitary groups SU($n-s$)

1. The operator $Z = g^{ij}Z^I_{ji}$ commutes with the n^2 infinitesimal generators Z_{ij} and Z^I_{ij}. The transformation in $\mathbf{C}^n$ generated by Z is given by:

$$\mathrm{d}x^k = \varepsilon Z x^k = \mathrm{i}\varepsilon x^k$$

and is simply a phase multiplication of each component of a vector.

2. The group generated by Z is a one-parameter abelian group, invariant subgroup of U($n-s$, s) and isomorphic to the multiplicative group T of complex numbers of modulus 1.

The factor group U($n-s$, s)/T is, up to a discrete subgroup, the special pseudo-unitary group SU($n-s$, s). It can be defined as the set of unimodular $n \times n$ pseudo-unitary matrices.

The special pseudo-unitary groups are also analytic subgroups of the special linear group SL(n, C). More precisely:

$$\mathrm{SU}(n-s, s) \simeq \mathrm{U}(n-s, s) \cap \mathrm{SL}(n, \mathrm{C}).$$

The group SU($n-s$, s) depends on n^2-1 real parameters.

3. In an hermitian space where $g \simeq I$, the group of unimodular unitary matrices is the special unitary group SU(n).

The Lie algebra su(n, s) of the pseudo-unitary group is defined by n^2-1 infinitesimal generators

$$Z'_{ij} = Z_{ij} \qquad Z'^I_{ij} = Z_{ij} - \frac{1}{n} g_{ij} Z$$

and the commutation laws are unchanged.

The Lie algebra su$(n-s, s)$ is the subalgebra of u$(n-s, s)$ which satisfies the zero trace condition: with the notations of the previous section, we have Tr X_1+Tr $X_3 = 0$. In particular the Lie algebra su(n) is the Lie algebra of the skew hermitian matrices of trace zero.

5. An inclusion which is a consequence of the explicit form given for the Lie algebrae is the following:

$$\mathrm{SO}(n-s, s) \subset \mathrm{SU}(n-s, s).$$

6. The Lie algebrae sl(n, R) and su$(n-s, s)$ have all the same complex extension which is simply sl(n, C).

13.3.5. Complex orthogonal group O(n, C)

1. The pseudo-orthogonal group O$(n-s, s)$ is the group of linear transformations in R^n which leaves invariant the symmetrical bilinear form g.

In the complex vector space C^n, the scalar product becomes a complex number explicitly given by

$$(x_1+\mathrm{i}x_2, y_1+\mathrm{i}y_2) = (x_1, y_1)-(x_2, y_2)+\mathrm{i}(x_1, y_2)+\mathrm{i}(x_2, y_1)$$

where each term is defined in R^n.

The group of linear transformations in C^n which leaves invariant the scalar product g is the complex orthogonal group O(n, C).

2. The group O(n, C) can be considered as the complex extension of the pseudo-orthogonal group O$(n-s, s)$. But, with a convenient change of basis in C^n, it is always possible, for our problem, to choose g as the unit matrix. It follows that all the pseudo-orthogonal groups O$(n-s, s)$ have the same complex extension O(n, C).

3. The orthogonality condition can always be written as $A^{\mathrm{T}}A = I$ and the infinitesimal generators of the Lie algebra are given by

$$Z_{ij} = X_{ij}-X_{ji} \qquad Z^I_{ij} = Y_{ij}-Y_{ji}.$$

The complex orthogonal group depends on $n(n-1)$ real parameters.

4. The Lie algebra O(n, C) of the complex orthogonal group, is isomorphic to the subalgebra of $\mathscr{M}(n, \mathrm{C})$ of all skew symmetric $n \times n$ complex matrices.

The condition $(\det A)^2 = I$ remains always true and we can define, in O(n, C) two cosets with respect to the value of det A.

The coset det $A = +1$ is the group of $n \times n$ complex unimodular orthogonal matrices and we have the two isomorphisms:

$$\mathrm{SO}(n, \mathrm{C}) \simeq \mathrm{O}(n, \mathrm{C})/\mathrm{Z}_2$$
$$\mathrm{SO}(n, \mathrm{C}) \simeq \mathrm{O}(n, \mathrm{C}) \cap \mathrm{SL}(n, \mathrm{C}).$$

Of course, the groups O(n, C) and SO(n, C) have the same Lie algebrae.

13.3.6. Applications

1. We consider a two dimensional vector space C^2. The connection g is defined by $g_{11} = 1$, $g_{22} = \varepsilon$ with $\varepsilon = \pm 1$. We have only two pseudo-unitary groups, U(2) and U(1,1).

The infinitesimal generators, Z_{12}, Z^I_{12}, Z^I_{11} and Z^I_{22}, verify the following commutation rules:

$$[Z_{12}, Z^I_{11}] = -2Z^I_{12} \qquad [Z_{12}, Z^I_{22}] = 2\varepsilon Z^I_{12}$$
$$[Z^I_{12}, Z^I_{11}] = 2Z_{12} \qquad [Z^I_{12}, Z^I_{22}] = -2\varepsilon Z_{12}$$
$$[Z^I_{12}, Z_{12}] = Z^I_{22} - \varepsilon Z^I_{11} \qquad [Z^I_{11}, Z^I_{22}] = 0.$$

The linear combination $Z = Z^I_{11} + \varepsilon Z^I_{22}$ commutes with all the generators and is associated to a gauge group T.

The Lie algebrae su(2) and su(1,1) having therefore only three infinitesimal generators it is convenient to write in the form:

$$M_1 = \tfrac{1}{2}Z^I_{12} \qquad M_2 = \tfrac{1}{2}Z_{12} \qquad M_3 = \tfrac{1}{4}(Z^I_{11} - \varepsilon Z^I_{22}).$$

From the commutation relations given above, it is easy to deduce:

$$[M_1, M_2] = -\varepsilon M_3 \qquad [M_2, M_3] = -M_1 \qquad [M_3, M_1] = -M_2$$

and after comparison with the results of the previous section for the orthogonal three dimensional groups, we obtain the following isomorphisms between the Lie algebrae:

$$\mathrm{su}(2) \simeq \mathrm{so}(3)$$
$$\mathrm{su}(1,1) \simeq \mathrm{so}(2,1) \simeq \mathrm{sl}(2, R).$$

2. The homogeneous Lorentz group is the pseudo-orthogonal group in a 4-dimensional vector space of signature $s = 1$ on the real numbers. The connection g is chosen so that $g_{11} = g_{22} = g_{33} = +1$ and $g_{00} = -1$.

The Lie algebra so(3,1) is defined by the following commutation rules:

$$[Z_{12}, Z_{23}] = -Z_{31} \qquad [Z_{23}, Z_{31}] = -Z_{12} \qquad [Z_{31}, Z_{12}] = -Z_{23}$$
$$[Z_{12}, Z_{01}] = -Z_{02} \qquad [Z_{23}, Z_{02}] = -Z_{03} \qquad [Z_{31}, Z_{03}] = -Z_{01}$$
$$[Z_{03}, Z_{23}] = -Z_{02} \qquad [Z_{01}, Z_{31}] = -Z_{03} \qquad [Z_{02}, Z_{12}] = -Z_{01}$$
$$[Z_{03}, Z_{01}] = Z_{31} \qquad [Z_{01}, Z_{02}] = Z_{12} \qquad [Z_{02}, Z_{03}] = Z_{23}.$$

Some particular subalgebrae are evident from the previous equations and correspond to particular invariances

a) Z_{12}, Z_{23}, Z_{31} generate a subalgebra so(3).

b) Three isomorphic so(2,1) subalgebrae are generated by

$$-Z_{12}, Z_{01}, Z_{02}$$
$$-Z_{23}, Z_{02}, Z_{03}$$
$$-Z_{31}, Z_{03}, Z_{01}.$$

The previous commutation relations show clearly that the Lie algebra of the Lorentz group can be regarded as the complex extension of its subalgebra so(3) and we have

$$\mathrm{so}(3,1) \simeq \mathrm{so}(3, \mathrm{C}).$$

We now extend the results of section 13.2 in a complex space and it follows:

$$\mathrm{so}(3,1) \simeq \mathrm{so}(3, \mathrm{C}) \simeq \mathrm{sl}(2, \mathrm{C}).$$

The Lie algebra of the complex Lorentz group is the complex extension of a complex extension. Consequently, so(4, C) can be written as a direct sum of two Lie algebrae, each of them being isomorphic to the Lie algebra of the real Lorentz group

$$\mathrm{so}(4, \mathrm{C}) \simeq \mathrm{so}(3,1) \oplus \mathrm{so}(3,1).$$

Such a result can also be considered as the complex extension of the isomorphism obtained in section 13.2

$$\mathrm{so}(4) \simeq \mathrm{so}(3) \oplus \mathrm{so}(3).$$

3. Another interesting sequence of isomorphisms is the following:

$$\mathrm{so}(6) \simeq \mathrm{su}(4)$$
$$\mathrm{so}(4,2) \simeq \mathrm{su}(2,2).$$

In the real space R^6 we consider the pseudo-orthogonal group which leaves invariant the metric tensor g defined by

$$g_{11} = g_{22} = g_{44} = g_{55} = 1$$
$$g_{33} = g_{66} = \varepsilon.$$

In the complex space C^4 we consider the pseudo-unitary groups which leave invariant the hermitian product h defined by

$$h_{11} = h_{22} = 1$$
$$h_{33} = h_{44} = \varepsilon,$$

where $\varepsilon = \pm 1$ is the same in both cases.

The infinitesimal generators of the special pseudo-unitary groups are noted Z_{ij}, Z^I_{ij} as usual with $i, j = 1, 2, 3, 4$ and we have the trace condition $Z^I_{11}+Z^I_{22}+\varepsilon Z^I_{33}+\varepsilon Z^I_{44} = 0$.

The infinitesimal generators of the pseudo-orthogonal groups are noted T_{rs} with $r, s = 1, 2, 3, 4, 5, 6$.

The two isomorphisms can be proved simultaneously by using the one to one correspondance between the two Lie algebrae given in the following table:

$$\begin{aligned}
T_{12} &= \tfrac{1}{2}(Z_{12}+\varepsilon Z_{34}) & T_{45} &= \tfrac{1}{2}(Z_{12}-\varepsilon Z_{34})\\
T_{23} &= \tfrac{1}{2}(Z_{23}+Z_{14}) & T_{56} &= \tfrac{1}{2}(Z_{23}-Z_{14})\\
T_{31} &= \tfrac{1}{2}(Z_{31}+Z_{24}) & T_{64} &= \tfrac{1}{2}(Z_{31}-Z_{42})\\
T_{51} &= \tfrac{1}{2}(Z^I_{12}+\varepsilon Z^I_{34}) & T_{42} &= \tfrac{1}{2}(Z^I_{12}-\varepsilon Z^I_{34})\\
T_{62} &= \tfrac{1}{2}(Z^I_{23}+Z^I_{14}) & T_{53} &= \tfrac{1}{2}(Z^I_{23}-Z^I_{14})\\
T_{43} &= \tfrac{1}{2}(Z^I_{31}+Z^I_{24}) & T_{61} &= \tfrac{1}{2}(Z^I_{31}-Z^I_{24})
\end{aligned}$$

$$\begin{aligned}
T_{14} &= \tfrac{1}{2}(Z^I_{22}+\varepsilon Z^I_{33}) = -\tfrac{1}{2}(Z^I_{11}+\varepsilon Z^I_{44})\\
T_{25} &= \tfrac{1}{2}(Z^I_{11}+\varepsilon Z^I_{33}) = -\tfrac{1}{2}(Z^I_{22}+\varepsilon Z^I_{44})\\
T_{36} &= \tfrac{1}{2}\varepsilon(Z^I_{11}+Z^I_{22}) = -\tfrac{1}{2}(Z^I_{33}+Z^I_{44}).
\end{aligned}$$

As a remark, the Lie algebrae of the generators Z_{kl} is isomorphic to the Lie algebra of the six generators T_{12}, T_{23}, T_{31}; T_{45}, T_{56}, T_{64} and this result has been proved in a previous section:

$$\mathrm{so}(4) \simeq \mathrm{so}(3) \oplus \mathrm{so}(3) \qquad \mathrm{so}(3,1) \simeq \mathrm{so}(2,1) \oplus \mathrm{so}(2,1).$$

If $\{Z_{kl}, Z^I_{kl}\}$ is a Lie algebra su(n), it is obvious that the Lie algebra $\{Z_{kl}, \overline{Z}^I_{kl}\}$, where $\overline{Z}^I_{kl}$ is the complex extension of Z_{kl}, is isomorphic to sl(n, r).

On the other hand, it is easy to verify that the Lie algebra:

$$\{T_{12}, T_{23}, T_{31}; T_{45}, T_{56}, T_{64}; T_{14}, T_{25}, T_{36}; T_{51}, T_{62}, T_{43}; T_{42}, T_{53}, T_{61}\}$$

is isomorphic to a Lie algebra so(3,3) corresponding to the metric tensor:

$$g_{11} = g_{22} = g_{33} = +1 \qquad g_{44} = g_{55} = g_{66} = -1$$

and we obtain a new isomorphism of Lie algebrae:

$$\mathrm{sl}(4, \mathrm{R}) \simeq \mathrm{so}(3,3).$$

13.4. Group of linear transformations of a vector space on the field of quaternions

We now introduce an n-dimensional space on the field of quaternions Q as an analytic manifold Q^n. We define, in Q^n, a connection with a regular matrix g. The matrix g can be diagonalized into the form $g_{ij} = \pm\delta_{ij}$. We will use also, in the following, a $2n$-dimensional space R^{2n} and a complex space C^{2n} with the connection $G = \begin{vmatrix} g & 0 \\ 0 & g \end{vmatrix}$.

The quaternionic extension Λ^Q of a Lie algebra $\Lambda = [X_\sigma]$ defined on the real numbers can be also considered as a Lie algebra on the real numbers with the infinitesimal generators X_σ, $Y_\sigma^{(1)}$, $Y_\sigma^{(2)}$, $Y_\sigma^{(3)}$, where $Y_\sigma^{(\alpha)} \simeq i\sigma_\alpha X_\sigma$. Of course, the three complex extensions $\Lambda^* = [X_\sigma, Y_\sigma^{(\alpha)}]$ are isomorphic.

13.4.1. Quaternions

1. The complex numbers C can be considered as a 2-dimensional algebra on the field of real numbers R with the commutative multiplication law:

$$(a, b)(c, d) = (ac-bd, ad+bc).$$

The quaternions Q can be defined as a 4-dimensional algebra on the field of real numbers R with the non commutative multiplication law:

$$(a_0, \boldsymbol{a})(b_0, \boldsymbol{b}) = (a_0 b_0 - \boldsymbol{a} \cdot \boldsymbol{b}, a_0 \boldsymbol{b} + b_0 \boldsymbol{a} - \boldsymbol{a} \times \boldsymbol{b}).$$

A simple matrix representation of a quaternion $(a_0, \boldsymbol{a})$ can be realized with the help of the Pauli matrices:

$$(a_0, \boldsymbol{a}) \Rightarrow a_0 - \boldsymbol{\sigma} \cdot \boldsymbol{a}.$$

The quaternions Q can also be considered as a 2-dimensional algebra on the field of complex numbers C with the multiplication law:

$$(x, y)(z, t) = (xz - \bar{y}t, \bar{x}t + yz).$$

A useful matrix representation of the quaternion (x, y) is then

$$(x, y) \Rightarrow \begin{vmatrix} x & \bar{y} \\ -y & \bar{x} \end{vmatrix}.$$

2. In order to define the norm of a complex number, we first consider the complex conjugate:

$$(a, b)^* = (a, -b)$$

and the norm is given by

$$N^2(a, b) = (a, b)^*(a, b) = (a^2+b^2, 0).$$

For the quaternions we proceed in the same way by introducing the quaternion hermitic conjugate:

$$(a_0, \boldsymbol{a})^* = (a_0, -\boldsymbol{a})$$

and the norm is given by:

$$N^2(a_0, \boldsymbol{a}) = (a_0, \boldsymbol{a})^*(a_0, \boldsymbol{a}) = (a_0^2+\boldsymbol{a}^2, 0).$$

If now we use the language of the complex numbers, we have:

$$(x, y)^* = (\bar{x}, -y)$$

and the norm takes the simple form:

$$N^2(x, y) = (x, y)^*(x, y) = (x\bar{x}+y\bar{y}, 0).$$

3. The hermitic product of two complex numbers is defined as the complex number $z_{12} = z_1^* z_2$ and we obtain

$$(a, b)^*(c, d) = (ac+bd, ad-bc).$$

The quaternionic product of two quaternions q_1 and q_2 will be defined by the quaternion $q_{12} = q_1^* q_2 = q_{21}^*$. By using the previous forms for the quaternions, we find:

$$(a_0, \boldsymbol{a})^*(b_0, \boldsymbol{b}) = (a_0 b_0 + \boldsymbol{a}\cdot\boldsymbol{b}, a_0 \boldsymbol{b} - b_0 \boldsymbol{a} + \boldsymbol{a}\times\boldsymbol{b})$$
$$(x, y)^*(z, t) = (\bar{x}z+\bar{y}t, xt-yz).$$

4. The transposed quaternion q^{T} is defined by

$$(x, y)^{\mathrm{T}} = (x, -\bar{y}).$$

The scalar product of two quaternions q_1 and q_2 is the quaternion $q_{12}^{\mathrm{S}} = q_1^{\mathrm{T}} q_2 = q_{21}^{\mathrm{ST}}$. By using the previous form, we find

$$(x, y)^{\mathrm{T}}(z, t) = (xz+yt, \bar{x}t-\bar{y}z).$$

13.4.2. General and special linear groups

1. The regular $n\times n$ matrices with quaternion coefficients generate the general linear group GL(n, Q).

The group of regular linear transformations in Q^n is isomorphic to GL(n, Q).

2. The Lie algebra gl(n, Q) of the general linear group is the quaternionic extension of gl(n, R). We then have $4n^2$ infinitesimal generators $[X, Y^{(1)}, Y^{(2)}, Y^{(3)}]$ with the following commutation relations

$$[X_{jk}, X_{lm}] = g_{kl} X_{jm} + g_{mj} X_{lk}$$
$$[X_{jk}, Y_{lm}^{(\alpha)}] = g_{kl} Y_{jm}^{(\alpha)} - g_{mj} Y_{lk}^{(\alpha)}$$
$$[Y_{jk}^{(\alpha)}, Y_{lm}^{(\alpha)}] = -g_{kl} X_{jm} + g_{mj} X_{lk}$$
$$[Y_{jk}^{(\alpha)}, Y_{lm}^{(\beta)}] = -\varepsilon_{\alpha\beta\gamma}(g_{kl} Y_{jm}^{(\gamma)} + g_{mj} Y_{lk}^{(\gamma)}).$$

The Lie algebra gl(n, Q) is isomorphic to the Lie algebra $\mathcal{M}(n, \mathrm{Q})$ of the $n \times n$ matrices with quaternion coefficients.

3. The operator $X = g^{rz} X_{sr}$ commutes with all the generators of gl(n, Q). It generates a one dimensional Lie algebra isomorphic to R and corresponds to real dilatations in Q^n. If now we exclude these transformations we obtain the special linear group SL(n, Q). Its Lie algebra sl(n, Q) has $4n^2-1$ dimensions and is spanned by the infinitesimal generators X', $Y^{(1)}$, $Y^{(2)}$, $Y^{(3)}$ with, as previously

$$X'_{ij} = X_{ij} - \frac{1}{n} g_{ij} X.$$

4. The complex extension of the real Lie algebra gl(n, Q) is a real Lie algebra isomorphic to gl($2n$, C). In order to obtain this result, we first consider the Lie algebra gl($2n$, R) defined by the four sets of n^2 infinitesimal generators X_{ij}, $X_{i,n-j}$, $X_{n-i,j}$, $X_{n+i,n+j}$ where $i, j = 1, 2, \ldots, n$. The commutations relations are given by:

$$\begin{aligned}
[X_{ij}, X_{kl}] &= g_{jk} X_{il} - g_{li} X_{kj} \\
[X_{ij}, X_{n+k,l}] &= -g_{li} X_{n+k,j} \\
[X_{ij}, X_{k,n+l}] &= g_{jk} X_{i,n+l} \\
[X_{i,n+j}, X_{k,n+l}] &= 0 \\
[X_{ij}, X_{n+k,n+l}] &= 0 \\
[X_{n+i,n+j}, X_{n+k,n+l}] &= g_{jk} X_{n+i,n+l} - g_{li} X_{n+k,n+j} \\
[X_{n+i,n+j}, X_{k,n+l}] &= -g_{li} X_{k,n+j} \\
[X_{n+i,n+j}, X_{n+k,l}] &= g_{jk} X_{n+i,l} \\
[X_{n+i,j}, X_{n+k,l}] &= 0 \\
[X_{i,n+j}, X_{n+k,l}] &= g_{jk} X_{il} - g_{li} X_{n+k,n+i}.
\end{aligned}$$

It is then convenient to define the linear combinations:

$$\begin{aligned}
A_{ij} &= X_{ij} + X_{n+i,n+j} & A^{(1)}_{ij} &= X_{i,n+j} - X_{n+i,j} \\
A^{(2)}_{ij} &= X_{ij} - X_{n+i,n+j} & A^{(3)}_{ij} &= X_{i,n+j} + X_{n+i,j}
\end{aligned}$$

and the commutation relations for A, $A^{(1)}$, $A^{(2)}$, $A^{(3)}$ are written as

$$\begin{aligned}
[A_{ij}, A_{kl}] &= g_{jk} A_{il} - g_{li} A_{ki} \\
[A_{ij}, A^{(\alpha)}_{kl}] &= g_{jk} A^{(\alpha)}_{il} - g_{li} A^{(\alpha)}_{ki} \\
[A^{(\alpha)}_{ij}, A^{(\alpha)}_{kl}] &= -\varepsilon(\alpha)[g_{jk} A_{il} - g_{li} A_{kj}] \\
[A^{(\alpha)}_{ij}, A^{(\beta)}_{kl}] &= \varepsilon(\gamma)\varepsilon_{\alpha\beta\gamma}[g_{jk} A^{(\gamma)}_{il} + g_{li} A^{(\gamma)}_{kj}]
\end{aligned}$$

with $\varepsilon(1) = 1, \varepsilon(2) = \varepsilon(3) = -1$ and where $\varepsilon_{\alpha\beta\gamma}$ is the completely antisymmetrical third order tensor.

The Lie algebra gl($2n$, C) is the complex extension of gl($2n$, R). It is defined by the $8n^2$ generators $A, A^{(1)}, A^{(2)}, A^{(3)}, \bar{A}, \bar{A}^{(1)}, \bar{A}^{(2)}, \bar{A}^{(3)}$. The set of infinitesimal generators $A, A^{(1)}, \bar{A}^{(2)}, \bar{A}^{(3)}$ defines a Lie subalgebra; by putting

$$B = A \qquad B^{(1)} = A^{(1)} \qquad B^{(2)} = \bar{A}^{(2)} \qquad B^{(3)} = \bar{A}^{(3)}$$

the $4n^2$ dimensional Lie algebra $B, B^{(1)}, B^{(2)}, B^{(3)}$ is a real Lie algebra with the commutation relations

$$\begin{aligned} [B_{ij}, B_{kl}] &= g_{jk} B_{il} - g_{li} B_{kj} \\ [B_{ij}, B^{(\alpha)}_{kl}] &= g_{jk} B^{(\alpha)}_{il} - g_{li} B^{(\alpha)}_{kj} \\ [B^{(\alpha)}_{ij}, B^{(\alpha)}_{kl}] &= -g_{jk} B_{il} + g_{li} B_{kj} \\ [B^{(\alpha)}_{ij}, B^{(\beta)}_{kl}] &= -\varepsilon_{\alpha\beta\gamma}(g_{jk} B^{(\gamma)}_{il} + g_{li} B^{(\gamma)}_{kj}) \end{aligned}$$

and therefore is isomorphic to gl(n, Q).

In the same way it is easy to prove that the complex extension of sl(n, Q) is isomorphic to sl($2n$, C).

The Lie algebrae gl(n, Q) and sl(n, Q) can be considered as two Lie subalgebrae of $\mathscr{M}(2n, \mathrm{C})$ with the quaternionic structure:

$$\begin{vmatrix} P & \bar{Q} \\ -Q & \bar{P} \end{vmatrix}$$

where P and Q are two $n \times n$ complex matrices.

For sl(n, Q) we have, in addition, the zero trace condition

$$\mathrm{Tr}\, P + \mathrm{Tr}\, \bar{P} = 0$$

corresponding to the unimodular character of the transformation.

13.4.3. Pseudo-symplectic groups Sp($n-s$, s)

1. The quaternionic product of two vectors in Q^n is the quaternion given by the connection g:

$$(u, v) = g(u, v) = u^{*k} g_{kl} v^l = (v, u)^*.$$

Let us call as A an arbitrary linear transformation in Q^n. The conservation of the quaternionic product under the transformation A is simply:

$$(Au, Av) = (u, v).$$

This equality must be satisfied by all the vectors in Q^n and the invariance property takes the simple form:

$$\tilde{A} g A = g.$$

The matrix $\tilde{A}$ is defined from A by $[\tilde{A}]_{ij} = [A_{ji}]^*$.

The matrices A which satisfy the previous equality are called symplectic matrices with respect to the connection g. They generate a subgroup of $GL(n, Q)$, the pseudo-symplectic group.

2. As previously we introduce the signature s of the vector space Q^n and the pseudo-symplectic group will be noted $Sp(n-s, s)$.

3. The Lie algebra $sp(n-s, s)$ is a subalgebra of $Gl(n, Q)$. The infinitesimal generators Z_{ij} can be written as linear combinations, with quaternion coefficients of the X_{ij}'s defined in section 13.2:

$$Z_{ij} = \lambda_{ij}{}^{mn} X_{mn}.$$

It is sufficient to impose the invariance of the norm of all vectors and the matrix elements $\lambda_{ij}{}^{mn}$ must satisfy the requirement

$$\lambda_{ij}{}^{mn} + \lambda_{ij}{}^{nm*} = 0.$$

The infinitesimal generators can then be written as

$$\begin{aligned} Z_{ij} &= X_{ij} - X_{ji} = -Z_{ji} \\ Z_{ij}^{(\alpha)} &= Y_{ij}^{(\alpha)} + Y_{ji}^{(\alpha)} = Z_{ji}^{(\alpha)}. \end{aligned}$$

The dimension of $sp(n-s, s)$ is then $n(2n+1)$ and the commutation laws can easily be written in the following form:

$$\begin{aligned} [Z_{ij}, Z_{kl}] &= g_{jk} Z_{il} - g_{ik} Z_{jl} - g_{jl} Z_{ik} + g_{il} Z_{jk} \\ [Z_{ij}, Z_{kl}^{(\alpha)}] &= g_{jk} Z_{il}^{(\alpha)} - g_{ik} Z_{jl}^{(\alpha)} + g_{jl} Z_{ik}^{(\alpha)} - g_{il} Z_{jk}^{(\alpha)} \\ [Z_{ij}^{(\alpha)}, Z_{kl}^{(\alpha)}] &= -g_{jk} Z_{il} - g_{ik} Z_{jl} - g_{jl} Z_{ik} - g_{il} Z_{jk} \\ [Z_{ij}^{(\alpha)}, Z_{kl}^{(\beta)}] &= -\varepsilon_{\alpha\beta\gamma}(g_{jk} Z_{il}^{(\gamma)} + g_{ik} Z_{jl}^{(\gamma)} + g_{jl} Z_{ik}^{(\gamma)} + g_{il} Z_{jk}^{(\gamma)}). \end{aligned}$$

As a trivial consequence, the Z_{ij}'s generate a Lie algebra isomorphic to $so(n-s, s)$ and the three Lie algebrae $[Z_{ij}, Z_{ij}^{(\alpha)}]$ are isomorphic to a Lie algebra $u(n-s, s)$.

The Lie algebra $sp(n-s, s)$ can also be considered as a Lie subalgebra of $gl(2n, C)$. Using the results of the previous section we obtain the following expressions:

$$\begin{aligned} Z_{ij} &= A_{ij} - A_{ji} &&= X_{ij} + X_{n+i, n+j} - X_{ji} - X_{n+j, n+i} \\ Z_{ij}^{(1)} &= A_{ij}^{(1)} + A_{ji}^{(1)} &&= X_{i, n+j} - X_{n+i, j} + X_{j, n+i} - X_{n+j, i} \\ Z_{ij}^{(2)} &= \bar{A}_{ij}^{(2)} + \bar{A}_{ji}^{(2)} &&= Y_{ij} - Y_{n+i, n+j} + Y_{ji} - Y_{n+j, n+i} \\ Z_{ij}^{(3)} &= \bar{A}_{ij}^{(3)} + \bar{A}_{ji}^{(3)} &&= Y_{i, n+j} + Y_{n+i, j} + Y_{j, n+i} + Y_{n+j, i}. \end{aligned}$$

4. It is also possible to define the pseudo-symplectic group as the intersection of the general linear group $GL(n, Q)$ with the pseudo-unitary group

U$(2(n-s), 2s)$. The proof is extremely simple and we first consider the Lie algebra gl$(2n, \mathrm{C})$ with the infinitesimal generators:

$$\{A_{ij}, A_{ij}^{(1)}, A_{ij}^{(2)}, A_{ij}^{(3)}, \bar{A}_{ij}, \bar{A}_{ij}^{(1)}, \bar{A}_{ij}^{(2)}, \bar{A}_{ij}^{(3)}\}.$$

The Lie algebra u$(2n-2s, 2s)$ is the subset given by the linear combinations:

$$\{A_{ij}-A_{ji}, A_{ij}^{(1)}+A_{ji}^{(1)}, A_{ij}^{(2)}-A_{ji}^{(2)}, A_{ij}^{(3)}-A_{ji}^{(3)}, \bar{A}_{ij}+\bar{A}_{ji},$$
$$\bar{A}_{ij}^{(1)}-\bar{A}_{ji}^{(1)}, \bar{A}_{ij}^{(2)}+\bar{A}_{ji}^{(2)}, \bar{A}_{ij}^{(3)}+\bar{A}_{ji}^{(3)}\}$$

and the Lie algebra gl(n, Q) is the subset:

$$\{A_{ij}, A_{ij}^{(1)}, \bar{A}_{ij}^{(2)}, \bar{A}_{ij}^{(3)}\}.$$

The intersection is obviously the subset:

$$\{A_{ij}-A_{ji}, A_{ij}^{(1)}+A_{ji}^{(1)}, \bar{A}_{ij}^{(2)}+\bar{A}_{ji}^{(2)}, \bar{A}_{ij}^{(3)}+\bar{A}_{ji}^{(3)}\}$$

and we obtain

$$\mathrm{SL}(n, \mathrm{Q}) \cap \mathrm{U}(2n-2s, 2s) \simeq \mathrm{Sp}(n-s, s).$$

5. The quaternion q can be represented by a set of two complex numbers (x, y). The components q^j of a vector $\boldsymbol{q}$ of Q^n can be considered as the components (x^j, y^j) of a vector $\boldsymbol{X}$ of C^{2n} defined as:

$$X^j = x^j \qquad X^{n+j} = y^j \qquad j = 1, 2, \ldots, n.$$

Let us now consider two vectors $\boldsymbol{u}$ and $\boldsymbol{v}$ of Q^n. They can be associated to two vectors $\boldsymbol{X}$ and $\boldsymbol{Y}$ of C^{2n} by:

$$u^j = (X^j, X^{n+j}) \qquad v^k = (Y^k, Y^{n+k}).$$

The quaternionic product $g(u, v)$ can be written, in terms of X and Y, in the form:

$$g(u, v) = g_{jk}(\bar{X}^j Y^k + \bar{X}^{n+j} Y^{n+k}, X^j Y^{n+k} - X^{n+j} Y^k).$$

We introduce in C^{2n} two connections G and J related to g by:

$$G = \begin{vmatrix} g & 0 \\ 0 & g \end{vmatrix} \qquad J = \begin{vmatrix} 0 & g \\ -g & 0 \end{vmatrix}.$$

We now use G as a sesquilinear hermitian form and J as a bilinear antisymmetrical form and the quaternion $g(u, v)$ can then be written as:

$$g(u, v) = (G(X, Y), J(X, Y)).$$

The invariance of the quaternionic product in Q^n is equivalent, in C^{2n}, to the invariance of the two connections G and J. In other terms the pseudo-symplectic group $\mathrm{Sp}(n-s, s)$ is the subgroup of the pseudo-unitary group $\mathrm{U}(2n-2s, 2s)$ which leaves invariant the antisymmetrical linear connection J.

13.4.4. Quaternionic orthogonal group $\mathrm{O}(n, \mathrm{Q})$

1. The group of linear transformations in Q^n which leaves invariant the scalar product g^{S} is the quaternionic orthogonal group $\mathrm{O}(n, \mathrm{Q})$.

The scalar product of two vectors $\boldsymbol{u}$ and $\boldsymbol{v}$ of Q^n is given by the quaternion:

$$g^{\mathrm{S}}(u, v) = u^{k\mathrm{T}} g_{kl} V^l = [g^{\mathrm{S}}(v, u)]^{\mathrm{T}}.$$

The invariance of the scalar product under a linear transformation A takes the simple form:

$$A^{\mathrm{T}} g A = g.$$

The matrix A^{T} is defined, from A by $[A^{\mathrm{T}}]_{ij} = [A_{ji}]^{\mathrm{T}}$.

As in the complex vector space C^n, it is always possible, with a convenient change of basis, to choose g as the unit matrix, and the orthogonality condition can always be written as $A^{\mathrm{T}} A = I$. The set of $n \times n$ matrices with quaternion coefficients which satisfy the previous relations generates the quaternionic orthogonal group $\mathrm{O}(n, \mathrm{Q})$.

2. The Lie algebra $\mathrm{O}(n, \mathrm{Q})$ is a subalgebra of $\mathrm{gl}(n, \mathrm{Q})$ and the infinitesimal generators are given by:

$$Z_{ij} = X_{ij} - X_{ji}, \quad Z_{ij}^{(1)} = Y_{ij}^{(1)} + Y_{ji}^{(1)}, \quad Z_{ij}^{(2)} = Y_{ij}^{(2)} - Y_{ji}^{(2)}, \quad Z_{ij}^{(3)} = Y_{ij}^{(3)} - Y_{ji}^{(3)},$$

where we have taken into account the symmetry properties of the Pauli matrices.

The dimension of $\mathrm{O}(n, \mathrm{Q})$ is then $n(2n-1)$ and the commutation relations are given by:

$$\begin{aligned}
[Z_{ij}, Z_{kl}] &= g_{jk} Z_{il} - g_{ik} Z_{jl} - g_{jl} Z_{ik} + g_{il} Z_{jk} \\
[Z_{ij}, Z_{kl}^{(1)}] &= g_{kj} Z_{il}^{(1)} - g_{ik} Z_{jl}^{(1)} + g_{jl} Z_{ik}^{(1)} - g_{il} Z_{jk}^{(1)} \\
[Z_{ij}, Z_{kl}^{(\beta)}] &= g_{jk} Z_{il}^{(\beta)} - g_{ik} Z_{jl}^{(\beta)} - g_{jl} Z_{ik}^{(\beta)} + g_{il} Z_{jk}^{(\beta)} \qquad \beta = 2, 3 \\
[Z_{ij}^{(1)}, Z_{kl}^{(1)}] &= -g_{jk} Z_{il} - g_{ik} Z_{jl} - g_{jl} Z_{ik} - g_{il} Z_{jk} \\
[Z_{ij}^{(\beta)}, Z_{kl}^{(\beta)}] &= -g_{jk} Z_{il} + g_{ik} Z_{jl} + g_{jl} Z_{ik} - g_{il} Z_{jk} \qquad \beta = 2, 3 \\
[Z_{ij}^{(1)}, Z_{kl}^{(2)}] &= -g_{jk} Z_{il}^{(3)} - g_{ik} Z_{jl}^{(3)} + g_{jl} Z_{ik}^{(3)} + g_{il} Z_{jk}^{(3)} \\
[Z_{ij}^{(2)}, Z_{kl}^{(3)}] &= -g_{jk} Z_{il}^{(1)} + g_{ik} Z_{jl}^{(1)} + g_{jl} Z_{ik}^{(1)} - g_{il} Z_{jk}^{(1)} \\
[Z_{ij}^{(3)}, Z_{kl}^{(1)}] &= -g_{jk} Z_{il}^{(2)} + g_{ik} Z_{jl}^{(2)} - g_{jl} Z_{ik}^{(2)} + g_{il} Z_{jk}^{(2)}.
\end{aligned}$$

The condition $(\det A)^2 = I$ is always valid. The coset $\det A = I$ is the group of $n \times n$ unimodular orthogonal matrices with quaternion coefficients and will be noted SO(n, Q)

$$SO(n, Q) \simeq O(n, Q) \cap SL(n, Q) \simeq O(n, Q)/Z_2.$$

4. The Lie algebra sO(n, Q) can also be considered as a Lie subalgebra of gl($2n$, C). Using the results of the previous sections we obtain the following expressions:

$$\begin{aligned}
Z_{ij} &= A_{ij} - A_{ji} &&= X_{ij} + X_{n+i,n+j} - X_{ji} - X_{n+j,n+i}\\
Z_{ij}^{(1)} &= A_{ij}^{(1)} + A_{ji}^{(1)} &&= X_{i,n+j} - X_{n+i,j} + X_{j,n+i} - X_{n+j,i}\\
Z_{ij}^{(2)} &= \bar{A}_{ij}^{(2)} - \bar{A}_{ji}^{(2)} &&= Y_{ij} - Y_{n+i,n+j} - Y_{ji} + Y_{n+j,n+i}\\
Z_{ij}^{(3)} &= \bar{A}_{ij}^{(3)} - \bar{A}_{ji}^{(3)} &&= Y_{i,n+j} + Y_{n+i,j} - Y_{j,n+i} - Y_{n+j,i}.
\end{aligned}$$

5. It is also possible to define the quaternionic orthogonal group as the intersection of the general linear group GL(n, Q) with the complex orthogonal group O($2n$, C).

The Lie algebra sO($2n$, C) is the subset of gl($2n$, C) given by the linear combinations:

$$\{A_{ij} - A_{ji},\ A_{ij}^{(1)} + A_{ji}^{(1)},\ A_{ij}^{(2)} - A_{ji}^{(2)},\ A_{ij}^{(3)} - A_{ji}^{(3)},\ \bar{A}_{ij} - \bar{A}_{ji},$$
$$\bar{A}_{ij}^{(1)} + \bar{A}_{ji}^{(1)},\ \bar{A}_{ij}^{(2)} - \bar{A}_{ji}^{(2)},\ \bar{A}_{ij}^{(3)} - \bar{A}_{ji}^{(3)}\}.$$

The Lie algebra gl(n, Q) is the subset $[A_{ij},\ A_{ij}^{(1)},\ \bar{A}_{ij}^{(2)},\ \bar{A}_{ij}^{(3)}]$ and the intersection is defined by:

$$\{A_{ij} - A_{ji},\ A_{ij}^{(1)} + A_{ji}^{(1)},\ \bar{A}_{ij}^{(2)} - \bar{A}_{ji}^{(2)},\ \bar{A}_{ij}^{(3)} - \bar{A}_{ji}^{(3)}\}$$

and we obtain:

$$SL(n, Q) \cap O(2n, C) \simeq SO(n, Q).$$

6. The Lie algebra sO(n, Q) is a subalgebra of both sl(n, Q) and sO($2n$, C). The general structure is then given by

$$\begin{vmatrix} P & \bar{Q} \\ -Q & \bar{P} \end{vmatrix}$$

where P and Q are two $n \times n$ complex matrices with the restrictions of antisymmetry:

α) P is skew symmetric

β) Q is hermitian.

7. The complex extension of the Lie algebra sO(n, Q) is obviously the algebra of the complex $2n$-dimensional orthogonal group, sO($2n$, C).

8. Let us now consider two vectors u and v of Q^n; they are associated to two vectors X and Y of C^{2n} as explained in section C. The scalar product $g^S(u, v)$ can be written in terms of X and Y and we obtain a quaternion of the form:

$$g^S(u, v) = g_{jk}(X^j Y^k + X^{n+j} Y^{n+k}, \overline{X}^j Y^{n+k} - \overline{X}^{n+j} Y^k).$$

We now use G as a bilinear symmetrical form and J as a sesquilinear skew hermitian form. The quaternion $g^S(u, v)$ can be written as:

$$g^S(u, v) = (G(X, Y), J(X, Y)).$$

The invariance of the scalar product in Q^n is equivalent, in C^{2n}, to the invariance of the two connections G and J. In other terms the quaternionic orthogonal group $O(n, Q)$ is the subgroup of the complex orthogonal group $O(n, C)$ which leaves invariant the skew hermitian sesquilinear connection J.

13.4.5. Real and complex pseudo-symplectic groups

1. We consider the real vector space R^{2n} and the two connexions G and J. A vector $X \in R^{2n}$ has $2n$ real components; it is convenient to write

$$X_j = x_j \qquad X_{n+j} = y_j \qquad j = 1, 2, \ldots, n.$$

The general linear group $GL(2n, R)$ depends on $4n^2$ real parameters and its Lie algebra $gl(2n, R)$ has been studied in section 13.4.2. The subgroup of $GL(2n, R)$ which leaves invariant the symmetrical linear connexion G is the pseudo-orthogonal group $O(2n\text{–}2s, 2s)$ depending on $n(2n-1)$ real parameters:

$$A^T G A = G.$$

2. The subgroup of $GL(2n, R)$ which leaves invariant the antisymmetrical form J is, by definition, the real symplectic group $Sp(n, R)$,

$$A^T J A = J.$$

It is obvious that, after a convenient change of basis, J can always be written as:

$$J = \begin{vmatrix} 0 & I_n \\ -I_n & 0 \end{vmatrix}$$

where I_n is the $n \times n$ unit matrix.

The infinitesimal generators of the symplectic group are then defined by:

$$R_{ij} = X_{ij} - X_{n+j,\,n+i}$$
$$S_{ij} = X_{i,\,n+j} + X_{j,\,n+i} = S_{ji}$$
$$T_{ij} = X_{n+i,\,j} + X_{n+j,\,i} = T_{ji}$$

and the commutations relations are given by:

$$[R_{ij}, R_{kl}] = \delta_{jk} R_{il} - \delta_{li} R_{kj}$$
$$[S_{ij}, S_{kl}] = 0 = [T_{ij}, T_{kl}]$$
$$[R_{ij}, S_{kl}] = \delta_{jk} S_{il} + \delta_{jl} S_{ik}$$
$$[R_{ij}, T_{kl}] = -\delta_{ik} T_{jl} - \delta_{il} T_{jk}$$
$$[S_{ij}, T_{kl}] = \delta_{jk} R_{il} + \delta_{ik} R_{jl} + \delta_{jl} R_{ik} + \delta_{il} R_{jk}\,.$$

The n^2 generators R_{ij} define a Lie subalgebra isomorphic to gl(n, R). The $\frac{1}{2}n(n+1)$ generators S_{ij} and the $\frac{1}{2}n(n+1)$ generators T_{ij} define two abelian Lie subalgebrae.

The real symplectic group SP(n, R) depends on $n(2n+1)$ real parameters.

From the previous results, it follows that the Lie algebra sp(n, R) is the subalgebra of $\mathscr{M}(2n, \mathrm{R})$ characterized by the following structure:

$$\begin{vmatrix} X_1 & X_2 \\ X_3 & -X_1^{\mathrm{T}} \end{vmatrix}$$

where X_1, X_2, X_3 are three $n \times n$ real matrices, X_2 and X_3 being symmetric.

3. The subgroup of GL($2n$, R) which leaves invariant the two connections G and J is the intersection of the groups O($2n-2s$, $2s$) and Sp(n, R). For the orthogonal group:

$$g(x_1, x_2) + g(y_1, y_2)$$

is invariant and for the symplectic group:

$$g(x_1, y_2) - g(x_2, y_1)$$

is invariant. Let us introduce a vector space C^n with the sesquilinear form g. The vector $z = x + \mathrm{i}y$ is an element of C^n and the hermitian product of z_1 and z_2 is defined by:

$$g(z_1, z_2) = [g(x_1, x_2) + g(y_1, y_2)] + \mathrm{i}[g(x_1, y_2) - g(x_2, y_1)].$$

From the previous results, this product is invariant for a transformation which belongs to O($2n-2s$, $2s$) and to Sp($n-s$, s; R). It follows immediately that:

$$\mathrm{O}(2n-2s, 2s) \cap \mathrm{Sp}(n-s, s; \mathrm{R}) \simeq \mathrm{U}(n-s, s).$$

The infinitesimal generators are immediately known by using the anti-symmetry condition:

$$\tfrac{1}{2}n(n-1) \quad \text{generators} \quad Z_{ij} = R_{ij} - R_{ji}$$
$$\tfrac{1}{2}n(n+1) \quad \text{generators} \quad Z_{ij}^{(1)} = S_{ij} - T_{ij}.$$

It is easy to explicit these linear combinations in terms of the generators of the general linear group GL($2n$, R) previously introduced:

$$Z_{ij} = A_{ij} - A_{ji}$$
$$Z_{ij}^{(1)} = A_{ij}^{(1)} + A_{ji}^{(1)}.$$

From these expressions or from a direct calculation, it follows that the Lie algebra $\{Z_{ij}, Z_{ij}^{(1)}\}$ is isomorphic to u($n-s$, s).

4. We now introduce a $2n$-dimensional complex vector space C^{2n} and we will use again the two connections G symmetric and J antisymmetric.

The general linear group GL($2n$, C) depends on $8n^2$ real parameters. The Lie algebra gl($2n$, C) is the complex extension $[X, \bar{X}]$ of the Lie algebra gl($2n$, R) studied in the previous section.

The subgroup of GL($2n$, C) which leaves invariant the sesquilinear form G is the pseudo-unitary group U($2n-2s$, $2s$) which depends on $4n^2$ parameters:

$$A^*GA = G.$$

The subgroup of GL($2n$, C) which leaves invariant the linear form J is the complex symplectic group Sp(n, C) which depends on $2n(2n+1)$ parameters

$$A^{\mathrm{T}}JA = J.$$

The Lie algebra sp(n, C) is the complex extension of the Lie algebra sp(n, R) defined in the previous section. The infinitesimal generators is the set $\{R, S, T, \bar{R}, \bar{S}, \bar{T}\}$. This Lie algebra is the subalgebra of $\mathscr{M}(2n, \mathrm{C})$ characterized by the following structure

$$\begin{vmatrix} X_1 & X_2 \\ X_3 & -X_1^{\mathrm{T}} \end{vmatrix}$$

where X_1, X_2, X_3 are three $n \times n$ complex matrices, X_2 and X_3 being symmetric.

5. The subgroup of GL($2n$, C) which leaves invariant both the sesquilinear form G and the linear form J is the intersection of the two spaces U($2n-2s$, $2s$) and Sp(n, C). By definition this group is called the pseudo-symplectic group Sp($n-s$, s),

$$\mathrm{Sp}(n-s, s) \simeq \mathrm{U}(2n+2s, 2s) \cap \mathrm{Sp}(n, \mathrm{C}).$$

The infinitesimal generators are immediately known by using the anti-hermiticity condition

$$Z_{ij} = R_{ij} - R_{ji} \qquad Z^{(1)}_{ij} = S_{ij} - T_{ij}$$
$$Z^{(2)}_{ij} = \bar{R}_{ij} + \bar{R}_{ji} \qquad Z^{(3)}_{ij} = \bar{S}_{ij} + \bar{T}_{ij}.$$

In terms of the infinitesimal generators of GL($2n$, C) we obtain

$$Z_{ij} = A_{ij} - A_{ji} \qquad Z^{(1)}_{ij} = A^{(1)}_{ij} + A^{(1)}_{ji}$$
$$Z^{(2)}_{ij} = \bar{A}^{(2)}_{ij} + \bar{A}^{(2)}_{ji} \qquad Z^{(3)}_{ij} = \bar{A}^{(3)}_{ij} + \bar{A}^{(3)}_{ji}$$

and this identification proves that the Lie algebra $\{Z_{ij}, Z^{(1)}_{ij}, Z^{(2)}_{ij}, Z^{(3)}_{ij}\}$ is isomorphic to sp(n, s) as defined in section 13.4.3.

The generators $\{Z_{ij}, Z^{(\alpha)}_{ij}\}$ define three subalgebrae of the type u(n, s). This property, directly shown in the previous section for $\alpha = 1$ has two interesting consequences:

$$\mathrm{O}(2n-2s, 2s) \cap \mathrm{Sp}(n-s, s) \simeq \mathrm{U}(n-s, s)$$
$$\mathrm{U}(2n-2s, 2s) \cap \mathrm{Sp}(n, \mathrm{R}) \simeq \mathrm{U}(n-s, s).$$

The Lie algebra sp($n-s$, s) is a subalgebra of both u($2n-2s$, $2s$) and sp(n,C). By using the results previously given on these Lie algebrae, the general structure of sp($n-s$, s) is given by

$$\begin{vmatrix} X_{11} & X_{12} & X_{13} & X_{14} \\ X^*_{12} & X_{22} & X^*_{14} & X_{24} \\ -\bar{X}_{13} & \bar{X}_{14} & \bar{X}_{11} & -\bar{X}_{12} \\ X^*_{14} & -\bar{X}_{24} & -X^{\mathrm{T}}_{12} & \bar{X}_{22} \end{vmatrix}$$

where the X_{ij}'s are complex matrices with the properties:

X_{11} of order $(n-s)$	skew hermitian
X_{22} of order s	skew hermitian
X_{13} or order $(n-s)$	symmetric
X_{24} of order s	symmetric.

By using this explicit form for the matrices of sp(n, s) it is easy to prove the relation:

$$\mathrm{Sp}(n-s, s) \cap \mathrm{U}(2n) \simeq \mathrm{Sp}(n-s) \otimes \mathrm{Sp}(s).$$

In fact, the condition for the matrices of sp($n-s$, s) to be skew hermitian implies the relations:

$$X_{12} = 0, \qquad X_{14} = 0.$$

The matrices are then reducible into the form:

$$\left|\begin{array}{cc:cc} X_{11} & X_{13} & \multicolumn{2}{c}{\multirow{2}{*}{0}} \\ -\overline{X}_{13} & \overline{X}_{11} & & \\ \hdashline \multicolumn{2}{c:}{\multirow{2}{*}{0}} & X_{22} & X_{24} \\ & & -\overline{X}_{24} & \overline{X}_{22} \end{array}\right|$$

which proves the above relation.

6. We now are interested in the quaternionic orthogonal group and, as explained previously, in this case, G is used as a linear symmetrical connection and J as a sesquilinear skew hermitian connection.

The subgroup of GL($2n$, C) which leaves invariant the linear form G is the complex orthogonal group O($2n$, C) which depends on $2n(2n-1)$ real parameters

$$A^{\mathrm{T}}GA = G.$$

The subgroup of GL($2n$, C) which leaves invariant the sesquilinear form J is a $4n^2$ dimensional group isomorphic to GL(n, Q)

$$A^*JA = J.$$

The subgroup of GL($2n$, C) which leaves invariant both the linear form G and the sesquilinear form J is the intersection of the two spaces O($2n$, C) and GL(n, Q). As it has been proved in section 13.4.4, this group is isomorphic to the quaternionic orthogonal group O(n, Q).

13.4.6. Applications

1. We first consider the case $n = 1$. The Lie algebra sp(1) is isomorphic to the Lie algebra Q. Due to the properties of the quaternionic previously given, it is obvious that:

$$\mathrm{sp}(1) \simeq \mathrm{su}(2).$$

Let us now consider the real symplectic group Sp(1, R). The three infinitesimal generators R_{11}, S_{11}, T_{11} are defined from the generators X_{ij} of GL(2, R) by:

$$R_{11} = X_{11}-X_{22} \qquad S_{11} = 2X_{12} \qquad T_{11} = 2X_{21}$$

and we obtain the following isomorphisms:

$$\mathrm{sp}(1, \mathrm{R}) \simeq \mathrm{sl}(2, \mathrm{R}) \simeq \mathrm{so}(2, 1)$$
$$\mathrm{sp}(1, \mathrm{C}) \simeq \mathrm{so}(3, 1).$$

The one dimensional complex symplectic Lie algebra is isomorphic to the Lie algebra of the Lorentz group.

2. In the case $n = 2$ we can obtain three interesting isomorphisms between pseudo-symplectic and pseudo-orthogonal groups. Let us first study the real symplectic group Sp(2, R). The ten infinitesimal generators are noted R_{ij}, S_{ij}, T_{ij} as previously explained. If we consider the following linear combinations:

$$Z_{12} = \tfrac{1}{2}(R_{12}+R_{21}) \qquad Z_{23} = \tfrac{1}{2}(R_{12}-R_{21}) \qquad Z_{31} = \tfrac{1}{2}(R_{11}-R_{22})$$
$$Z_{14} = \tfrac{1}{4}(S_{11}+S_{22}+T_{11}+T_{22}) \qquad Z_{15} = \tfrac{1}{4}(S_{11}+S_{22}-T_{11}-T_{22})$$
$$Z_{43} = \tfrac{1}{4}(S_{11}-S_{22}-T_{11}+T_{22}) \qquad Z_{53} = \tfrac{1}{4}(S_{11}-S_{22}+T_{11}-T_{22})$$
$$Z_{24} = \tfrac{1}{2}(S_{12}-T_{12}) \qquad Z_{25} = \tfrac{1}{2}(S_{12}+T_{12}) \qquad Z_{54} = \tfrac{1}{2}(R_{11}+R_{22})$$

the infinitesimal generators $Z_{\mu\nu}$ span a Lie algebra isomorphic to so(3, 2) associated to the metric tensor:

$$g_{22} = g_{33} = g_{44} = 1 \qquad g_{11} = g_{55} = -1$$
$$\text{sp}(2, \text{R}) \simeq \text{so}(5, 2).$$

We now define the Lie algebra of the symplectic group Sp(2) with the infinitesimal generators R, S, T and their complex extension. In terms of $Z_{\mu\nu}$ and $\bar{Z}_{\mu\nu}$, the Lie algebra sp(2) is spanned by

$$\{Z_{23}, Z_{43}, Z_{24}, Z_{15}, \bar{Z}_{12}, \bar{Z}_{31}, \bar{Z}_{14}, \bar{Z}_{53}, \bar{Z}_{25}, \bar{Z}_{54}\}.$$

Obviously, this new Lie algebra is isomorphic to so(5), the metric tensor being the unity:

$$\text{sp}(2) \simeq \text{so}(5).$$

In the same way, it is easy to prove a third isomorphism of the same type:

$$\text{sp}(1, 1) \simeq \text{so}(4, 1).$$

3. For completeness we give without proof a list of isomorphisms of Lie algebrae associated to special linear groups SL(n, Q) and to quaternionic orthogonal groups SO(n, Q):

$$\text{sl}(1, \text{Q}) \simeq \text{so}(3)$$
$$\text{sl}(2, \text{Q}) \simeq \text{so}(5, 1)$$
$$\text{so}(2, \text{Q}) \simeq \text{so}(3) \oplus \text{so}(2, 1)$$
$$\text{so}(3, \text{Q}) \simeq \text{su}\ (3, 1)$$
$$\text{so}(4, \text{Q}) \simeq \text{so}(6, 2).$$

CHAPTER XIV

TOPOLOGICAL PROPERTIES

14.1. Compactness

1. *Definition*: In a compact space, any infinite sequence has its limit in the space.

2. Let us now consider an unitary matrix $AA^* = A^*A = I$ and let us call its matrix elements a_{ij}. By definition, we have:

$$\sum_s \bar{a}_{sr} a_{st} = \sum_s a_{rs} \bar{a}_{ts} = \delta_{rt}.$$

In the particular case $t = r$ we obtain:

$$\sum_s |a_{sr}|^2 = 1.$$

All the coefficients of a unitary matrix are bounded in modulus by the unity.

3. The compactness of the unitary group follows immediately by using the Weierstrass procedure. The limit of an infinite sequence of unitary matrices is a unitary matrix.

4. The spaces SU(n), O(n), SO(n) are closed subsets of U(n). It follows that all these groups are compact Lie groups. The symplectic group Sp(n) is a closed subset of U($2n$) and therefore is compact.

5. All the other classical groups we have previously studied are non compact groups.

1.42. Connected Lie groups

We give, in this section, some definitions and properties in order to characterize a Lie group from a topological point of view.

1. *Path*. Let us consider two points a and b in the topological space G. A path from a to b in G can be described by a continuous function $f(t)$,

defined on the closed interval $0 \leqq t \leqq 1$ and such that:

$$f(0) \Rightarrow a \qquad f(1) \Rightarrow b$$
$$f(t) \Rightarrow r \qquad \text{with } r \in G \text{ for all } 0 \leqq t \leqq 1.$$

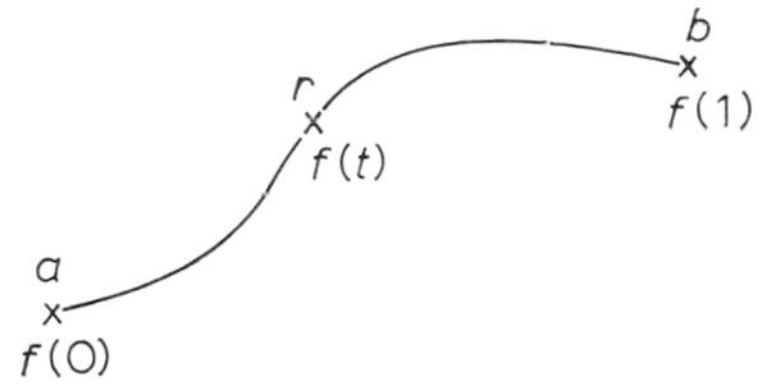

Fig. 14.1.

2. *Homotopy*. Let us consider two paths $f_1(t)$ and $f_2(t)$ joining two points a and b of G.

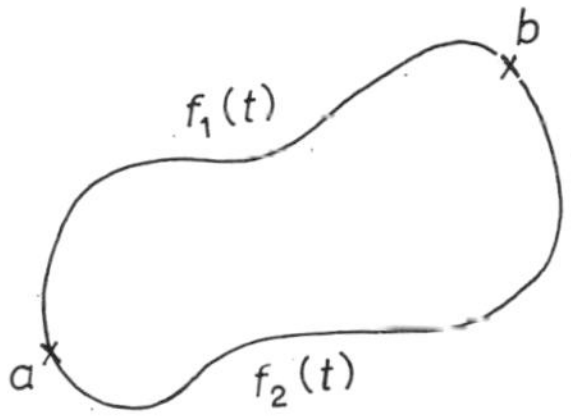

Fig. 14.2.

The paths f_1 and f_2 are said to be homotopic if f_1 can be continuously deformed into f_2, the end points a and b remaining fixed.

3. *Equivalence of two points*. The existence of a path between a and b is a symmetric reflexive and transitive property which can be used to define, in G, an equivalence. Two points are said equivalent if they can be joined by a path. In an evident way, the space G is divided into a direct sum of cosets $S_a, S_b, \ldots, S_m$. In a coset S_a all the points are equivalent and we will call S_a the component of a. Of course only the identity component S_e is a topological invariant subgroup of G and the factor group G/S_e is the group of the classes of equivalence.

4. *Connected Lie groups*. A topological space is connected if and only if it cannot be considered as the union of two non empty disjoined open subsets. It is easy to prove that the cosets for an analytic manifold are open and it follows that the S_a's are open sets. We then obtain the following sufficient and necessary condition: a Lie group is connected if and only if G/S_e is equivalent to the identity. It follows that in a connected Lie group two arbitrary points a and b can always be joined by a path.

5. *Examples*: as an illustration of the previous definition we give some results on the classical groups. We will call Z_n the additive group of real integers modulo n. Of course Z_n is isomorphic to the cyclic group of the nth roots of the unity.

a) *Linear groups.* The general linear group $\mathrm{GL}(n, \mathrm{R})$ is submitted to the condition $\det A \neq 0$. It is then possible to define two disjoined open subsets $\det A > 0$ and $\det A < 0$. It follows that the group $\mathrm{GL}(n, \mathrm{R})$ has two connected components. The connected component of $\mathrm{GL}(n, \mathrm{R})$ is the factor group $\mathrm{GL}(n, \mathrm{R})/\mathrm{Z}_2$ of regular $n \times n$ matrices of positive determinant.

The general linear group $\mathrm{GL}(n, \mathrm{C})$ has only one connected component because of the possibility to use complex values for $\det A$.

The special linear groups $\mathrm{SL}(n, \mathrm{R})$ and $\mathrm{SL}(n, \mathrm{C})$ are also connected Lie groups.

b) *Orthogonal groups.* The orthogonal group $\mathrm{O}(n)$ has two connected components respectively associated to $\det A = \pm 1$. Only the special linear group $\mathrm{SO}(n) \simeq \mathrm{O}(n)/\mathrm{Z}_2$ is a connected group.

It is well known that the Lorentz group has four connected components. The usual notation is:

$$\mathrm{L} \begin{cases} \det A = +1 & \mathrm{L}_+ \begin{cases} A_{00} \geqq 1 & \mathrm{L}_+^\uparrow \\ A_{00} \leqq -1 & \mathrm{L}_+^\downarrow \end{cases} \\ \det A = -1 & \mathrm{L}_- \begin{cases} A_{00} \geqq 1 & \mathrm{L}_-^\uparrow \\ A_{00} \leqq -1 & \mathrm{L}_-^\downarrow . \end{cases} \end{cases}$$

The connected component of the Lorentz group is $\mathrm{L}_+^\uparrow$. We can also define three groups which have two connected components:

$$\begin{array}{lll} \mathrm{L}_+^\uparrow \oplus \mathrm{L}_+^\downarrow \simeq \mathrm{L}_+ : & \text{proper group} \simeq \mathrm{SO}(3, 1) \\ \mathrm{L}_+^\uparrow \oplus \mathrm{L}_-^\uparrow \simeq \mathrm{L}^\downarrow : & \text{orthochronous group} \\ \mathrm{L}_+^\uparrow \oplus \mathrm{L}_-^\downarrow . & \end{array}$$

The factor group $\mathrm{L}/\mathrm{L}_+^\uparrow$ is isomorphic to the four element group of symmetries: $\{\mathrm{I}, \mathrm{S}, \mathrm{T}, \mathrm{ST}\}$ which has the structure $\mathrm{Z}_2 \otimes \mathrm{Z}_2$.

These results can be extended to the case of pseudo-orthogonal groups $\mathrm{O}(n-s, s)$ and $\mathrm{SO}(n-s, s)$. In particular, the special pseudo-orthogonal group $\mathrm{SO}(n-s, s)$ has two connected components.

The complex orthogonal group $\mathrm{O}(n, \mathrm{C})$ has two connected components and the special complex orthogonal group $\mathrm{SO}(n, \mathrm{C})$ is a connected Lie group.

c) *Unitary groups.* The pseudo-unitary groups $\mathrm{U}(n-s, s)$ and the special pseudo-unitary groups $\mathrm{SU}(n-s, s)$ are all connected Lie groups.

d) *Symplectic groups*. The symplectic group Sp(n) is connected for every $n \geqq 1$.

6. *Simply connected groups*. The notion of homotopy allows us to define an equivalence between two paths and to divide the paths into homotopy classes.

A connected Lie group is simply connected if the homotopy classes reduce to the identity. In a simply connected group, all the paths joining two points of G are homotopic.

7. *Examples*. The groups SU(n) and Sp(n) are simply connected. The group SO(n) is not simply connected.

14.3. Universal covering group

1. The Lie algebra of a Lie group is uniquely defined but the converse is not true.

If the Lie algebrae $\mathfrak{g}_1$ and $\mathfrak{g}_2$ of two Lie groups G_1 and G_2 are isomorphic, the Lie groups are only locally isomorphic.

2. To each Lie algebra of finite dimension on the real numbers, there corresponds a uniquely determined, connected, simply connected Lie group, called the universal covering group G*.

3. All connected Lie groups G, locally isomorphic to G* can be obtained from G* with a covering homomorphism. The kernel D of such a homomorphism is a discrete invariant subgroup of G* and G* being a connected group, D is a subgroup of the center Z of G*.

$$G^*/D \simeq G \quad \text{with} \quad D \subset Z(G^*).$$

4. *Ado's theorem*. A Lie algebra of finite dimension on the real numbers is isomorphic to a subalgebra of the Lie algebra of a general linear group GL(n, R) for a convenient value of n.

It follows that to each Lie algebra Λ of finite dimension on the real numbers corresponds a connected Lie group, of Lie algebra Λ, which is an analytic subgroup of GL(n, R).

5. Let us consider the direct sum $\mathfrak{g}$ of two Lie algebras $\mathfrak{g}_1$ and $\mathfrak{g}_2$

$$\mathfrak{g} = \mathfrak{g}_1 \oplus \mathfrak{g}_2 .$$

The universal covering group of $\mathfrak{g}$ is the direct product of the universal covering groups G_1^* and G_2^* of $\mathfrak{g}_1$ and $\mathfrak{g}_2$:

$$G^* = G_1^* \otimes G_2^* .$$

The center of G* contains the direct product of the centers of G_1^* and G_2^*

but in general, Z(G*) is much larger than this direct product:

$$Z(G^*) \supset Z(G_1^*) \otimes Z(G_2^*).$$

6. *Examples*:

a) We consider the one parameter Lie algebra A_0. In an evident way its universal covering group is the abelian additive group of the real numbers R.

The mapping

$$\alpha \Rightarrow \exp 2i\pi\alpha,$$

where $\alpha \in R$ is a covering homomorphism of R into the one dimensional group of unimodular complex numbers T. Due to the property $\exp 2i\pi n = 1$ if n is an integer number $n \in N$, the kernel of the covering homomorphism is the discrete group N

$$R/N \simeq T.$$

It can be easily seen that R and T are the only non isomorphic connected Lie groups of Lie algebra A_0.

b) *Special unitary group*. The special unitary group SU(n) is the universal covering group of its Lie algebra.

The center of SU(n) is the set of all $n \times n$ unimodular unitary matrices which commutes with all the $n \times n$ unitary matrices. From the Schur lemma the general form is ωI_n where ω is a complex number and I_n the $n \times n$ unit matrix. The condition $\det A = +1$ implies the restriction $\omega^n = 1$ and it follows that the center of SU(n) is isomorphic to Z_n:

$$Z(SU(n)) \simeq Z_n.$$

If n is a prime number, Z_n has no subgroup besides the identity and itself. If n can be written as the product $n = pq$ of two integers p and q, the groups Z_p and Z_q are subgroups of Z_n.

c) *Special orthogonal group*. The special orthogonal group SO(n) is connected but not simply connected. The universal covering group of its Lie algebra is called the spin group Spin (n).

The center of SO(n) is the identity if n is odd and Z_2 if n is even. The proof is the same as that given for the special unitary group.

The groups SO(n) and Spin (n) are related by:

$$\mathrm{Spin}(n)/Z_2 \simeq SO(n).$$

The center of the universal covering group is given by:

$$\begin{aligned} &Z(\mathrm{Spin}\,(n)) \simeq Z_2 && \text{if } n \text{ is odd} \\ &Z(\mathrm{Spin}\,(n)) \simeq Z_4 && \text{if } n = 4m+2 \\ &Z(\mathrm{Spin}\,(n)) \simeq Z_2 \otimes Z_2 && \text{if } n = 4m. \end{aligned}$$

d) *Symplectic group.* The symplectic group Sp(n) is the universal covering group of its Lie algebra. The center of Sp(u) is Z_2 and we have only two connected groups locally isomorphic Sp(n) and Sp(n)/Z_2.

e) *Special linear group.* The Lie algebra sl(n, C) is the complex extension either of the Lie algebra sl(n, R) or of the Lie algebra of the special unitary group su(n).

The universal covering group of su(n) is the group SU(n) itself and the universal covering group of sl(n, C) is the group SL(n, C) and the center of SL(n, C) is also Z_n.

7. *Applications*:

a) We have given, in chapter XIII, some particular relations of isomorphism between Lie algebrae of the classical groups.

It is possible, now, to give more information about the corresponding Lie groups.

α) su(2) $\simeq$ so(3) $\simeq$ sp(1).

The universal covering group is SU(2) $\simeq$ Spin(3) $\simeq$ Sp(1) and we have, for the second connected group

$$SU(2)/Z_2 \simeq SO(3).$$

β) so(5) $\simeq$ sp(2).

The universal covering group is Spin (5) $\simeq$ Sp(2) and we have a second connected group:

$$Sp(2)/Z_2 \simeq SO(5).$$

γ) su(4) $\simeq$ so(6).

The universal covering group is Spin (6) $\simeq$ SU(4) and we have two other connected groups. The first is simply

$$SU(4)/Z_2 \simeq SO(6)$$

and for the second we have two equivalent expressions:

$$SU(4)/Z_2 \simeq SO(6)/Z_2.$$

δ) so(4) $\simeq$ so(3) $\oplus$ so(3).

The universal covering group is Spin (4) $\simeq$ SU(2) $\otimes$ SU(2). The center of Spin(4) is the direct product $Z_2 \otimes Z_2$. We then have the set of connected groups associated to the same Lie algebra:

$$SU(2) \otimes SU(2)$$

$$SU(2) \otimes SO(3) \quad \text{kernel} \quad Z_2$$

$$SO(4) \simeq \frac{SU(2) \otimes SU(2)}{Z_2}$$

$$SO(3) \otimes SO(3) \qquad \text{kernel} \quad Z_2 \otimes Z_2.$$

ε) so(3, 1) $\simeq$ sl(2, C).

The universal covering group of the connected component L_+ of the Lorentz group is the special linear group SL(2, C) and we have the simple relation:

$$SL(2, C)/Z_2 \simeq L_+^\uparrow .$$

b) We now study a Lie algebra of particular interest in physics:

$$u(2) \simeq su(2) \oplus A_0$$

where A_0 is always the one dimensional Lie algebra previously studied. The universal covering group is the direct product of the universal covering groups

$$G_2^* \simeq SU(2) \oplus R.$$

To define the connected Lie groups, of Lie algebra u(2), we study the various covering homomorphisms. Some of them are evident:

kernel	N	$SU(2) \otimes T$
kernel	Z_2	$SO(3) \otimes R$
kernel	$N \otimes Z_2$	$SO(3) \otimes T$.

The unitary group U(2) itself cannot be obtained in this way. The elements of G_2^* have the form $\{\Sigma_2, \alpha\}$ where Σ_2 is an unimodular 2×2 unitary matrix and α a real number. In G_2^* the multiplication law is given by

$$\{\Sigma_2, \alpha\}\{\Sigma_2, \alpha'\} = \{\Sigma_2 \Sigma_2', \alpha + \alpha'\}.$$

The covering homomorphism to go from G_2^* to U(2):

$$\{\Sigma_2, \alpha\} \Rightarrow e^{i\alpha}\Sigma_2$$

has a kernel Δ_2 generated by the element $\{-I_2, \pi\}$ of G_2^*.

We then have:

$$U(2) \simeq \frac{SU(2) \otimes R}{\Delta_2} \simeq \frac{SU(2) \otimes T}{\Delta_2}.$$

The center of U(2) is obviously the group T and we have

$$U(2)/T \simeq SU(2)/Z_2 \simeq SO(3).$$

The irreducible representations of SU(2) are well known and characterized by a positive integer number $2j$. The element $-I_2$ of SU(2) is represented, in the irreducible representation $D(j)$ by $(-1)^{2j} I_{2j+1}$ where I_{2j+1} is the $(2j+1) \times (2j+1)$ unit matrix. It follows that for SO(3), due to the covering homomorphism Z_2, we have the restriction for j itself to be an integer number.

The irreducible representations of R are described by the application $\alpha \Rightarrow e^{i\alpha r}$ where r is an integer number. For the group T, r must be an integer number.

For the groups locally isomorphic to G_2^*, we then have the following results:

SU(2) ⊗ R	$2j$ integer	r real
SU(2) ⊗ T	$2j$ integer	r integer
SO(3) ⊗ R	j integer	r real
SO(3) ⊗ T	j integer	r integer.

For the unitary group U(2) we have to study the kernel Δ_2. In the representation (j, r) of G_2^*, the element $\{-I_2, \pi\}$ which generates Δ_2, is represented by $(-1)^{2j+r}I_{2j+1}$. The representation (j, r) is a representation of U(2) if and only if $(-1)^{2j+r} = 1$ which is equivalent to:

$$2j+r \equiv 0 \qquad (2).$$

An application of this result can be found in physics by considering the group of isotopic spin and hypercharge. We have only to identify j with the isotopic spin I and r with the hypercharge Y. The electric charge Q is related to isotopic spin and hypercharge by the Gell-Mann Nishijima formula:

$$Q = I_3 + \tfrac{1}{2}Y.$$

In the five connected groups previously studied we have a characterization of the possible values of the isotopic spin and of the hypercharge. In particular, for the unitary group U(2) the restriction

$$2I+Y \equiv 0 \quad (2)$$

is equivalent to retaining only integer values for the electric charge Q (MICHEL [1962]).

14.4. General theorems

1. All the connected semi-simple groups can be obtained from connected simple groups in the following way: let us call G_j a sequence of connected simple groups and let us define as G the direct product:

$$G = G_1 \otimes G_2 \otimes \ldots \otimes G_n.$$

The group G is a connected semi-simple group so as the factor groups G/D where D is a discrete subgroup of the center Z of G.

2. All the connected compact Lie groups can be obtained from connected compact simple groups in the following way: let us call H_j a sequence of connected compact simple groups and let us define the direct product:

$$H = H_1 \otimes H_2 \otimes \ldots \otimes H_n$$

and the direct product:

$$H^{(p)} = H \otimes T^p$$

where T^p is a p-dimensional toroid, e.g. a p-parameter compact abelian group. The groups $H^{(p)}$ are connected compact groups as well as the factor groups $H^{(p)}/N$ where N is a discrete subgroup of the center of $H^{(p)}$.

CHAPTER XV

LIE ALGEBRA OF THE SEMI-SIMPLE GROUPS

15.1. Standard form

1. *The eigenvalue problem.* Let us call as X_σ the r infinitesimal generator of a Lie algebra. We define as $A = a^\sigma X_\sigma$ an infinitesimal operator and we consider the eigenvalue problem defined by the equation:

$$[A, X] = sX.$$

The eigenvector X associated to the eigenvalue s is an element of Λ: $X = x^\rho X_\rho$ and s is in general a complex number. The basic equation can then be written:

$$a^\sigma x^\rho [X_\sigma, X_\rho] = s x^\tau X_\tau.$$

Taking into account the commutation relations of the Lie algebra, we obtain:

$$[a^\sigma x^\rho C^\tau_{\sigma\rho} - s x^\tau] X_\tau = 0.$$

The bracket is zero, because of the completeness of the X_σ basis in Λ:

$$(a^\sigma C^\tau_{\sigma\rho} - s\delta^\tau_\rho) x^\rho = 0.$$

We have a system of r homogeneous linear equations with respect to the r quantities x^ρ. Besides the trivial solution $x^\rho = 0$, we have a non zero solution if and only if the determinant of the coefficient vanishes:

$$\det (a^\sigma C^\tau_{\sigma\rho} - s\delta^\tau_\rho) = 0.$$

This condition is an algebraic equation of degree r in the variable s and we have r roots, real or complex, degenerate or not. To each root corresponds an eigenvector.

For a semi-simple Lie algebra, E. Cartan has obtained extremely important results. If the operator is chosen so that the equation in s has the maximum number of different roots:

a) The root $s = 0$ is degenerate with the multiplicity l and l is called the rank of the semi-simple group. To this root correspond l linearly independent eigenvectors $H_1, H_2, \ldots, H_l$ which commute two by two.

b) All the non zero roots are non degenerate.

2. *Fundamental relations.* We first define our notations. A greek index ρ, σ, τ refers to an arbitrary component of the Lie algebra. For the generators E_α associated to non zero roots we use the Greek indices α, β, γ and for the generators H_j associated to zero root we use the Latin indices j, k.

We are now working with the two results obtained by Cartan for a rank l semi-simple group:

a) The root zero is degenerate with the multiplicity l:

$$[A, H_j] = 0 \qquad j = 1, 2, \ldots, l.$$

b) The non zero roots α are non degenerate:

$$[A, E_\alpha] = \alpha E_\alpha .$$

As an evident consequence of the first equality, A is an eigenvector with the eigenvalue zero; it can then be written as a linear combination of the H_j, $A = \lambda^j H_j$, and the generators H_j generate an abelian subalgebra, called the Cartan algebra, which is maximal:

$$[H_j, H_k] = 0 \qquad \text{or} \quad C^\rho_{jk} = 0.$$

We now use the Jacobi identity for the three operators A, H_j, E_α of the Lie algebra:

$$[[A, H_j], E_\alpha] + [[H_j, E_\alpha], A] + [[E_\alpha, A], H_j] = 0.$$

By using the properties a) and b) we obtain:

$$[A, [H_j, E_\alpha]] = \alpha[H_j, E_\alpha]$$

which shows that $[H_j, E_\alpha]$ is an eigenvector corresponding to the non degenerate eigenvalue α. It follows that this vector must be proportional to E_α,

$$[H_j, E_\alpha] = \alpha_j E_\alpha \qquad \text{or} \quad C^\rho_{j\alpha} = \alpha_j \delta^\rho_\alpha .$$

After comparison with the eigenvalues equation b), we deduce the relation:

$$\alpha = \lambda^j \alpha_j .$$

We now define an l-dimensional vector space ε_l associated to the Cartan subalgebra. The quantity α can be considered as a vector in ε_l with covariant components α_j; in the same way, λ can be considered as a vector in ε_l with contravariant component λ_l. It will also be useful in the following to consider the H_j's as the covariant components of a vector H in ε_l.

We apply again the Jacobi identity with the three generators A, E_α, E_β:

$$[[A, E_\alpha], E_\beta]+[[E_\alpha, E_\beta], A]+[[E_\beta, A], E_\alpha] = 0.$$

We use the eigenvalue equation b) and obtain:

$$[A, [E_\alpha, E_\beta]] = (\alpha+\beta)[E_\alpha, E_\beta].$$

Three cases are possible:

a) $(\alpha+\beta)$ is not a root: the operators E_α and E_β commute.

b) $(\alpha+\beta) \neq 0$ is a root: the commutator $[E_\alpha, E_\beta]$ is proportional to the operator $E_{\alpha+\beta}$:

$$[E_\alpha, E_\beta] = N_{\alpha\beta} E_{\alpha+\beta} \qquad \text{or} \quad C^\rho_{\alpha\beta} = N_{\alpha\beta}\delta^\rho_{\alpha+\beta}.$$

c) $\alpha+\beta = 0$: the commutator $[E_\alpha, E_{-\alpha}]$ is an eigenvector associated to the eigenvalue zero and can be written as a linear combination of the operators H_j:

$$[E_\alpha, E_{-\alpha}] = C^j_{\alpha\,-\alpha} H_j.$$

3. *Theorem.* To each root α, it corresponds the root $-\alpha$.

The proof of this theorem is based on the Cartan criterion for semisimple groups previously given.

We consider the element $g_{\alpha\tau}$ of the row α of the Cartan tensor

$$g_{\alpha\tau} = C^\sigma_{\alpha\rho}\, C^\rho_{\tau\sigma}\,.$$

With the previous expressions obtained for the structure constants, $g_{\alpha\tau}$ becomes

$$g_{\alpha\tau} = -\alpha_j C^j_{\tau\alpha} + N_{\alpha\beta} C^\beta_{\tau\,\alpha+\beta} + C^j_{\alpha\,-\alpha}\, C^\alpha_{\tau j}\,.$$

The three terms are non-vanishing if and only if τ can take the value $\tau = -\alpha$. The Cartan criterion is satisfied if and only if $-\alpha$ is a root and the only element of the row α different from zero is then $g_{\alpha-\alpha}$.

For a Lie algebra of rank l and dimension r, there exist $r-l$ non degenerate and non vanishing roots. From the previous result $r-l$ is an even integer.

4. *Cartan tensor.* The normalization of the operators E_α can be chosen so that:

$$g_{\alpha\,-\alpha} = 1$$

and the Cartan tensor takes the simple structure:

$$g_{\rho\sigma} = \left|\begin{array}{c:ccc} g_{jk} & & 0 & \\ \hdashline & \begin{matrix}0&1\\1&0\end{matrix} & & 0 \\ 0 & & \begin{matrix}0&1\\1&0\end{matrix} & \\ & 0 & & \begin{matrix}0&1\\1&0\end{matrix}\end{array}\right| .$$

We have

$$\det g_{\rho\sigma} = (-1)^{\frac{1}{2}(r-l)} \det g_{jk} .$$

From the Cartan criterion, it follows that g_{jk} is a regular matrix:

$$\det g_{jk} \neq 0.$$

Of course, such a result is independent of the normalization condition.

By using the definition of the Cartan tensor, we obtain an explicit expression for g_{jk}:

$$g_{jk} = C^{\alpha}_{j\alpha}\, C^{\alpha}_{k\alpha} = \sum_{\alpha} \alpha_j \alpha_k = g_{kj} .$$

The matrix g_{jk} is symmetrical and will be called simply g in the following.

5. *Vector space* ε_l. The matrix g is used to define, in ε_l, a linear symmetrical connection. We introduce the inverse matrix g^{jk}:

$$g^{jk} g_{km} = \delta^j_m$$

to write the scalar product into the form:

$$(\alpha, \beta) = g(\alpha, \beta) = g^{jk} \alpha_j \beta_k = (\beta, \alpha).$$

The contravariant components of a vector α are given by:

$$\alpha^j = g^{jk} \alpha_k$$

and the scalar product takes an equivalent form:

$$(\alpha, \beta) = \alpha^j \beta_j = \alpha_k \beta^k.$$

As an interesting consequence, we obtain:

$$g^{jk} g_{jk} = \sum_{\alpha} g^{jk} \alpha_j \alpha_k = \sum_{\alpha} (\alpha, \alpha)$$

and:

$$\sum_{\alpha} (\alpha, \alpha) = l.$$

6. *Commutation relations.* We now show that the contravariant components α^j are identical with the $C^j_{\alpha-\alpha}$. The proof uses essentially the antisymmetry property of the structure constants:

$$C^j_{\alpha\,-\alpha} = g^{jk}C_{\alpha\,-\alpha\,k} = g^{jk}C_{k\,\alpha\,-\alpha} = g^{jk}g_{-\alpha\,\beta}\,C^\beta_{k\alpha}$$

with the normalization condition $g_{-\alpha\beta} = \delta_{\beta\alpha}$, it follows immediately:

$$C^j_{\alpha\,-\alpha} = g^{jk}\alpha_k = \alpha^j.$$

The commutation relation becomes:

$$[E_\alpha, E_{-\alpha}] = \alpha^j H_j.$$

It is extremely easy to deduce now a Lie subalgebra, generated by E_α, $E_{-\alpha}$ and the linear combination $\alpha^j H_j$ one can write as a scalar product (α, H); we obtain:

$$[E_\alpha, E_{-\alpha}] = (\alpha, H)$$
$$[(\alpha, H), E_\alpha] = (\alpha, \alpha)E_\alpha.$$

This subalgebra is isomorphic to an SU(2) Lie algebra and corresponds to the sequence α, 0, $-\alpha$ of the roots.

7. *Lemma.* If α, β, γ are three non zero roots such that $\alpha+\beta+\gamma = 0$, we have $N_{\alpha\beta} = N_{\beta\gamma} = N_{\gamma\alpha}$.

We use the Jacobi identity:

$$[E_\alpha, [E_\beta, E_\gamma]]+[E_\beta, [E_\gamma, E_\alpha]]+[E_\gamma, [E_\alpha, E_\beta]] = 0$$

and the commutation relations allow us to transform this equality into:

$$(\alpha, H)N_{\beta\gamma}+(\beta, H)N_{\gamma\alpha}+(\gamma, H)N_{\alpha\beta} = 0.$$

The operators of the Cartan subalgebra are linearly independent and each component j of α, β, γ are solutions of the system:

$$\alpha^j N_{\beta\gamma}+\beta^j N_{\gamma\alpha}+\gamma^j N_{\alpha\beta} = 0$$
$$\alpha^j+\beta^j+\gamma^j = 0.$$

It can easily be seen that the only possibility to obtain non zero roots α, β, γ is:

$$N_{\alpha\beta} = N_{\beta\gamma} = N_{\gamma\alpha}.$$

8. *Structure constants.* The structure constants $N_{\alpha\beta}$ are antisymmetric in the exchange of the two indices:

$$N_{\alpha\beta}+N_{\beta\alpha} = 0.$$

Let us apply the previous lemma for three non vanishing roots $-\alpha$, $\alpha+\beta$ and $-\beta$:

$$N_{-\alpha\,\alpha+\beta} = N_{\alpha+\beta\,-\beta} = N_{-\beta\,-\alpha}.$$

Because of the symmetry $\alpha \Leftrightarrow -\alpha$ in the set of the roots, it is always possible to choose, for the operators E_α, a normalization so that:

$$-N_{-\beta\,-\alpha} = N_{\alpha\beta}.$$

Another relation between the structure constants is given by the normalization condition of the Cartan tensor. By using the previous symmetries on the structure constants, we easily deduce:

$$g_{\alpha-\alpha} = 1+2(\alpha, \alpha)+\sum_{\beta\neq-\alpha} N_{\alpha\beta}^2.$$

15.2. Properties of the roots

1. *Theorem*: if α and β are two arbitrary roots,

a) the number $2(\alpha, \beta)/(\alpha, \alpha)$ is an integer called a Cartan integer;

b) the vector $\beta-2((\alpha, \beta)/(\alpha, \alpha))\alpha$ is also a root deduced from β by symmetry with respect to the hyperplane through the origin perpendicular to α.

The proof of this fundamental theorem will be given into two steps. Let us consider a root γ such that $\alpha+\gamma$ is not a root:

$$[E_\gamma, E_\alpha] = 0.$$

We introduce the sequence:

$$\begin{aligned} X_{\gamma-\alpha} &= [E_\gamma, E_{-\alpha}] \\ X_{\gamma-2\alpha} &= [X_{\gamma-\alpha}, E_{-\alpha}] \\ &\dots\dots\dots \\ X_{\gamma-p\alpha} &= [X_{\gamma-(p-1)\alpha}, E_{-\alpha}] \\ &\dots\dots\dots \end{aligned}$$

There is only a finite number of generators E_α and the sequence of the X operators must also be finite:

$$X_{\gamma-(g+1)\alpha} = 0 = [X_{\gamma-g\alpha}, E_{-\alpha}].$$

These formula can be inverted as follows

$$\begin{aligned} [X_{\gamma-(p+1)\alpha}, E_\alpha] &= \mu_{p+1} X_{\gamma-p\alpha} \\ &\dots\dots\dots \\ [X_{\gamma-\alpha}, E_\alpha] &= \mu_1 E_\gamma \end{aligned}$$

and, with the previous assumptions $\mu_0 = 0$.

We now write the Jacobi identity for the three operators E_α, $E_{-\alpha}$ and $X_{\gamma-p\alpha}$:

$$[[E_\alpha, E_{-\alpha}], X_{\gamma-p\alpha}]+[[E_{-\alpha}, X_{\gamma-p\alpha}], E_\alpha]+[[X_{\gamma-p\alpha}, E_\alpha], E_{-\alpha}] = 0.$$

By using the commutation relations, this relation becomes:

$$\alpha^j[H_j, X_{\gamma-p\alpha}]-[X_{\gamma-(p+1)\alpha}, E_\alpha]+\mu_p[X_{\gamma-(p-1)\alpha}, E_{-\alpha}] = 0$$

and finally:

$$(\alpha, \gamma-p\alpha)X_{\gamma-p\alpha}-\mu_{p+1}X_{\gamma-p\alpha}+\mu_p X_{\gamma-p\alpha} = 0.$$

We have obtained a recurrence formula for μ_p:

$$\mu_{p+1} = \mu_p+(\alpha, \gamma)-p(\alpha, \alpha).$$

Taking into account $\mu_0 = 0$, we deduce the explicit expression for μ_p:

$$\mu_p = p(\alpha, \gamma)-\tfrac{1}{2}p(p-1)(\alpha, \alpha).$$

The quantity g is defined by $\mu_{g+1} = 0$ and with the previous relation we find the value of g:

$$g = 2\frac{(\alpha, \gamma)}{(\alpha, \alpha)}.$$

The theorem is now proved in the particular case where the sum $\alpha+\gamma$ of two roots is not a root. The quantity g is an integer and there exists a set of roots:

$$\gamma, \gamma-\alpha, \gamma-2\alpha, \ldots, \gamma-g\alpha = \gamma-2\frac{(\alpha, \gamma)}{(\alpha, \alpha)}\alpha.$$

We go back to the general case where $\alpha+\beta$ can be a root.

We define as m and n, two positive integers such that $\beta+k\alpha$ is a root if and only if the algebraic integer k satisfies $-m \leqq k \leqq n$.

The previous results can be used with the root $\gamma = \beta+n\alpha$. The value of g is simply $g = m+n$ and we obtain:

a) $2(\alpha, \beta) = 2(\alpha, \gamma)-2n(\alpha, \alpha) = (m+n)(\alpha, \alpha)-2n(\alpha, \alpha) = (m-n)(\alpha, \alpha)$

$$2\frac{(\alpha, \beta)}{(\alpha, \alpha)} = m-n.$$

b) The vector $\beta-2((\alpha, \beta)/(\alpha, \alpha))\alpha = \beta+(n-m)\alpha$ is a root of the form $\beta+k\alpha$ because of the property: $-m \leqq n-m \leqq n$.

2. *Consequences.* Let us consider the possible roots β proportional to a given root $\alpha : \beta = k\alpha$. From the previous theorem, the quantity $2(\beta, \alpha)/(\alpha, \alpha) = 2k$ is a Cartan integer.

The operator E_α commutes with itself and both 2α and $\frac{1}{2}\alpha$ cannot be roots.

As an immediate consequence, the only allowed values of k are $k = \pm 1, 0$. This case is realized in the Lie algebra of the SU(2) group.

3. *Structure constants.* The operators $X_{\gamma - p\alpha}$ and $E_{\gamma - p\alpha}$ are related to each other by a product of structure constants:

$$X_{\gamma - p\alpha} = N_{\gamma\, -\alpha} \cdot N_{\gamma - \alpha\, -\alpha} \cdots N_{\gamma - (p-1)\alpha\, -\alpha} E_{\gamma - p\alpha}$$

and we immediately obtain an expression of μ_{p+1} in terms of these constants:

$$\mu_{p+1} = N_{\gamma - p\alpha\, -\alpha} \cdot N_{\gamma - (p+1)\alpha\, \alpha} \cdot$$

We now use the notations introduced in § 1: $\gamma = \beta + n\alpha$, $g = m + n$.

$$\mu_{p+1} = N_{\beta + (n-p)\alpha\, -\alpha} \cdot N_{\beta + (n-p-1)\alpha\, \alpha}$$

and we can compare this expression with the explicit ones given in § 1:

$$\mu_{p+1} = \tfrac{1}{2}(p+1)(m+n-p)(\alpha, \alpha).$$

We consider the particular case $p = n-1$. The properties of the structure constants allow us to write:

$$\mu_n = N_{\beta+\alpha\, -\alpha} N_{\beta\, \alpha} = N_{-\alpha\, \alpha+\beta} N_{\alpha\beta} = N_{\alpha\beta} N_{-\beta\, -\alpha} = N_{\alpha\beta}^2$$

and finally:

$$N_{\alpha\beta}^2 = \tfrac{1}{2} n(\beta)[m(\beta)+1](\alpha, \alpha)$$

where for a given root α, the positive integers m and n are functions of β.

The elements $g_{\alpha - \alpha}$ of the Cartan tensor will then give the normalization of the root α,

$$g_{\alpha\, -\alpha} = 1 = (\alpha, \alpha)\{2 + \tfrac{1}{2} \sum_{\beta \neq -\alpha} n(\beta)[m(\beta)+1]\}.$$

4. *Root diagram.* The roots can be considered as vectors in the vector space ε_l. The root diagram is the graphical representation of the roots in ε_l.

Let us apply the previous theorem for the roots α and β:

$$p = 2\frac{(\alpha, \beta)}{(\alpha, \alpha)} \qquad q = 2\frac{(\alpha, \beta)}{(\beta, \beta)}.$$

The two quantities p and q are algebraic integers. We have:

$$(\alpha, \beta)^2 = \tfrac{1}{4} pq(\alpha, \alpha)(\beta, \beta)$$

and by using the Schwartz inequality:

$$(\alpha, \beta)^2 \leqq (\alpha, \alpha)(\beta, \beta)$$

we can define a real angle ϕ by:

$$\cos^2 \phi = \tfrac{1}{4}pq.$$

Because of the symmetry $\alpha \Leftrightarrow -\alpha$ in the roots set, it is sufficient to study the angle ϕ between 0 and $\frac{1}{2}\pi$. In order to simplify the discussion, we call as β, the root of larger norm $(\beta, \beta) \geqq (\alpha, \alpha)$ and it follows immediatcly $p \geqq q$.

The numbers p and q being integers, the angle ϕ is restricted to the following values: 0, $\frac{1}{6}\pi$, $\frac{1}{4}\pi$, $\frac{1}{3}\pi$ and $\frac{1}{2}\pi$.

a) *Case* $\phi = 0$ *or* $pq = 4$. The first evident solution is $p = q = 2$ corresponding to $\beta = \alpha$. A second possibility, $p = 4, q = 1$, leads to $\beta = 2\alpha$ and must be rejected.

b) *Case* $\phi = \frac{1}{6}\pi$ *or* $pq = 3$. We have only one solution $p = 3$, $q = 1$ and $(\beta, \beta) = 3(\alpha, \alpha)$.

c) *Case* $\phi = \frac{1}{4}\pi$ *or* $pq = 2$. We have only one solution $p = 2$, $q = 1$ and $(\beta, \beta) = 2(\alpha, \alpha)$.

d) *Case* $\phi = \frac{1}{3}\pi$ *or* $pq = 1$. We have only one solution $p = 1$, $q = 1$ and $(\beta, \beta) = (\alpha, \alpha)$.

c) *Case* $\phi = \frac{1}{2}\pi$ *or* $pq = 0$. The only physical possibility is $p = 0$, $q = 0$. Of course the ratio p/q is undetermined.

15.3. Simple Lie algebrae

We first study in some details the particular cases of simple Lie algebrae of rank one and two. The results are generalized after to arbitrary rank simple Lie algebrae.

15.3.1. Simple Lie algebrae of rank one

This Lie algebra is well known but it seems to us useful to deduce its properties in the general framework previously given.

The simple Lie algebra of rank one corresponds to the three roots α, 0, $-\alpha$ and the one dimensional root diagram is simply:

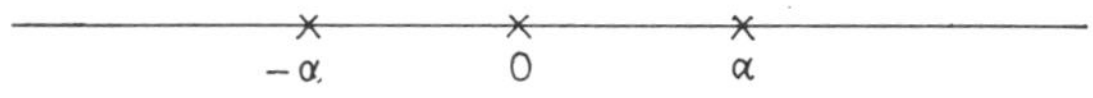

Fig. 15.1.

The commutation relations are given by:

$$[E_\alpha, E_{-\alpha}] = (\alpha, H) \qquad [(\alpha, H), E_\alpha] = (\alpha, \alpha)E_\alpha .$$

The normalization condition given: $(\alpha, \alpha) = \frac{1}{2}$. The covariant and the contravariant components are both equal to $1/\sqrt{2}$ and the Cartan tensor can be written as:

$$g_{\rho\sigma} = \left|\begin{array}{c:cc} 1 & 0 & 0 \\ \hdashline 0 & 0 & 1 \\ 0 & 1 & 0 \end{array}\right| .$$

With the convenient change of notations $E_\pm = E_\alpha$, $E_\mp = E_{-\alpha}$, $\alpha = \pm 1/\sqrt{2}$, we obtain the commutation rules in a more familiar form:

$$[E_\pm, E_\mp] = \pm \frac{1}{\sqrt{2}} H \qquad [H, E_\pm] = \pm \frac{1}{\sqrt{2}} E_\pm .$$

The Lie algebra of the special unitary group SU(2) can be written in the form:

$$\boldsymbol{J} \times \boldsymbol{J} = \mathrm{i}\boldsymbol{J}$$

or equivalently:

$$[J_1 \pm \mathrm{i}J_2, J_1 \mp \mathrm{i}J_2] = \pm 2J_3 \qquad [J_3, J_1 \pm \mathrm{i}J_2] = \pm(J_1 + \mathrm{i}J_2).$$

The identification is obtained by:

$$E_\pm = \tfrac{1}{2}(J_1 + \mathrm{i}J_2) \qquad H = \frac{1}{\sqrt{2}} J_3 .$$

15.3.2. Simple Lie algebrae of rank two

The root diagrams are two dimensional and we explore all allowed possibilities for the angle ϕ in order to construct all rank two simple Lie algebrae. It is only necessary to consider two roots α and β with the angle ϕ and to deduce all other roots simply by symmetry with respect to the straight line through the origin perpendicular to a root. All these reflections generate the Weyl group.

1. *Diagram* A_2. We consider two roots of equal norm α and γ, with the angle $\phi = \frac{1}{3}\pi$. After application of the Weyl reflections, we obtain: a regular hexagon and the Lie algebra is eight-dimensional.

The six non vanishing roots have the same norm: $(\alpha, \alpha) = \frac{1}{3}$. From fig. 15.2, it can be easily seen that if α, β, γ are there non zero roots such that $\gamma = \beta + \alpha$, then $\beta - \alpha$ and $\beta + 2\alpha$ are not roots. In the previously defined language, $m = 0$ and $n = 1$. All the non vanishing structure constants have the same modulus: $N^2_{\alpha\beta} = \frac{1}{6}$ and are known from one of them by using the symmetry properties.

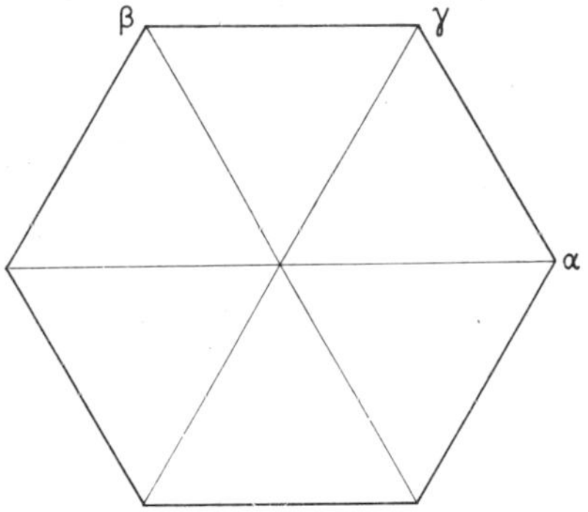

Fig. 15.2. Root diagram A_2.

2. *Diagram* B_2. We consider two roots α and β with the angle $\phi = \frac{1}{4}\pi$: from the previous results $(\beta, \beta) = 2(\alpha, \alpha)$. After application of the Weyl reflection we obtain 4 roots of the type α and 4 roots of the type β. The Lie algebra is ten-dimensional.

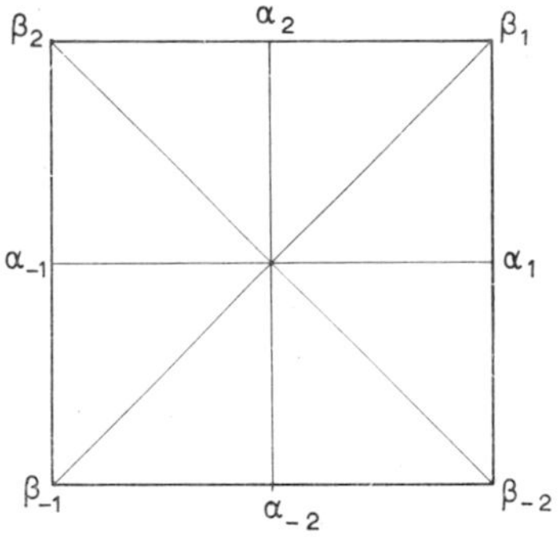

Fig. 15.3. Root diagram B_2.

The norm of the roots is given by the normalization condition $\sum_\alpha(\alpha, \alpha) + \sum_\beta(\beta, \beta) = 2$ and we obtain:

$$(\alpha, \alpha) = \tfrac{1}{6} \qquad (\beta, \beta) = \tfrac{1}{3}.$$

In order to determine the non vanishing structure constants, we calculate the values of m and n associated to a given system of two roots:

a) $\beta_i\beta_j$: $\beta_i+\beta_j$ can never be a root and $N_{\beta_i\beta_j} = 0$;

b) $\alpha_i\alpha_j$: there exists a sequence of three roots $\alpha_i-\alpha_j$, α_i, $\alpha_i+\alpha_j$ with $i \neq j$ corresponding to $m = n = 1$ and $N^2_{\alpha_i\alpha_j} = \frac{1}{6}$;

c) $\alpha_i\beta_j$: the two types of sequences of three roots are:

$$\beta_j, \beta_j+\alpha_{-j}, \beta_j+2\alpha_{-j} \quad \text{and} \quad \beta_j, \beta_j+\alpha_{-i}, \beta_j+2\alpha_{-i};$$

in both cases $m = 0$, $n = 2$ and it follows immediately:

$$N^2_{\beta j, \alpha-j} = N^2_{\beta j, \alpha-i} = \tfrac{1}{6}.$$

All the non vanishing structure constants have the same magnitude and the phases are known from two of them $N_{\alpha_i\alpha_j}$ and $N_{\beta j, \alpha-j}$ by using the symmetry properties.

3. *Diagram* G_2. We consider two roots α and β with the angle $\phi = \frac{1}{6}\pi$: from the previous results $(\beta, \beta) = 3(\alpha, \alpha)$. After application of the Weyl reflections, we obtain 6 roots of the type α and 6 roots of the type β. The Lie algebra is 14-dimensional.

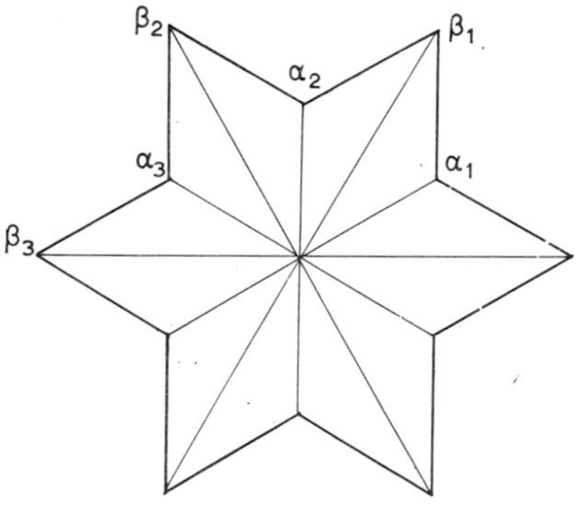

Fig. 15.4. Root diagram G_2.

The norm of the roots is given by the normalization condition: $\sum_\alpha(\alpha, \alpha)+\sum_\beta(\beta, \beta) = 2$ and we obtain:

$$(\alpha, \alpha) = \tfrac{1}{12} \qquad (\beta, \beta) = \tfrac{1}{4}.$$

It is easy to determine the structure constants by using the same method as in the previous section. All the non vanishing structure constants are known from three of them by using the symmetries properties and we have:

$$N^2_{\alpha_1\alpha_3} = \tfrac{1}{6} \qquad N^2_{\alpha_1\beta_3} = \tfrac{1}{8} \qquad N^2_{\beta_1\beta_3} = \tfrac{1}{8}.$$

15.3.3. Simple Lie algebrae of rank l

We try to extend the previous results to an l dimensional space ε_l.

1. *Lie algebra* A_l. The root diagram A_2 exhibits a hexagonal symmetry. It is then convenient to introduce a three dimensional space and to represent the root diagram A_2 in the plane $X_1+X_2+X_3=0$, in this way, we define the triangular coordinates X_1, X_2, X_3 of sum zero and the non vanishing roots have the generate form: $a_{ij} = e_i - e_j$.

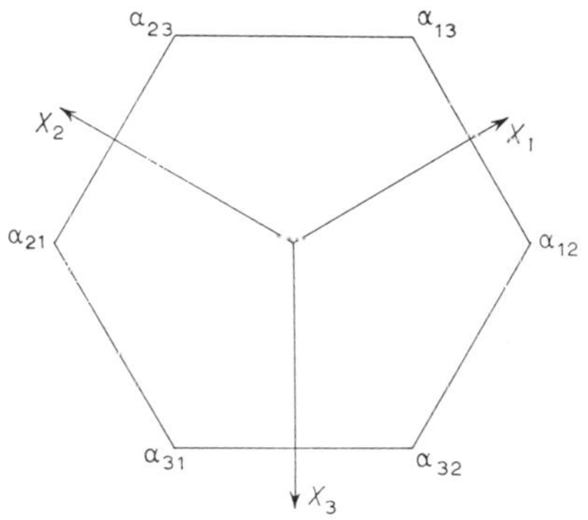

Fig. 15.5. Root diagram A_2 and triangular coordinates.

The natural generalization is to introduce a $(l+1)$ dimensional space and $(l+1)$ orthogonal vectors of equal norm e_j. The $l(l+1)$ vectors:

$$\alpha_{ij} = l_i - l_j$$

are located in the l dimensional hyperplane $X_1+X_2+\ldots+X_{l-1} = 0$. The Lie algebra A_l of rank l has the dimension $r = l(l+2)$.

All the non vanishing roots α_{ij} have the same norm $(\alpha, \alpha)=1/(l+1)$ and all the non-vanishing structure constants the same magnitude $N^2=1/2(l+1)$.

2. *Lie algebra* B_l. We introduce in the l dimensional space ε_l a system of l orthogonal vectors of equal norm e_j.

We first consider the following generalization of the Lie algebra B_2 by defining two sets of roots

a) *Roots of type* α: $2l$ roots given by $\pm e_j$

b) *Roots of type* β: $2l(l-1)$ roots given by $\pm e_i \pm e_j$.

As previously, we have, of course, $(\beta, \beta) = 2(\alpha, \alpha)$ and the norms are given by:

$$(\alpha, \alpha) = \frac{1}{2(2l-1)} \qquad (\beta, \beta) = \frac{1}{2l-1}.$$

The Lie algebra B_l, of rank l, has the dimension $r = l(2l+1)$. All the non-vanishing structure constants have the same magnitude $N^2 = 1/2(2l-1)$.

3. *Lie algebra* C_l. A different generalization of B_2 can be obtained by defining two sets of roots in the following way:

a) *Roots of type* α: $2l(l-1)$ roots given by $\pm e_i \pm e_j$

b) *Roots of type* β: $2l$ roots given by $\pm 2e_j$.

The values of the norms are given by:

$$(\alpha, \alpha) = \frac{1}{2(l+1)} \qquad (\beta, \beta) = \frac{1}{l+1}.$$

The Lie algebra C_l of rank l has the dimension $r = l(2l+1)$.

The structure constants can be divided into two classes following their magnitude:

$$(C^{\alpha_3}_{\alpha_1\alpha_2})^2 = \frac{1}{4(l+1)}, \qquad (C^{\beta_3}_{\alpha_1\alpha_2})^2 = (C^{\alpha_3}_{\alpha_1\beta_2})^2 = \frac{1}{2(l+1)}.$$

In an evident way, the Lie algebra C_2 is isomorphic to B_2.

4. *Lie algebra* D_l. A new Lie algebra of rank l can be constructed with the following set of roots of equal norm: $\pm e_i \pm e_j$. We obtain in this way a Lie algebra of dimension $r = l(2l-1)$. The norm of the roots is given by: $(\alpha, \alpha) = 1/2(l-1)$ and all non vanishing structure constants have the same norm: $N^2 = 1/4(l-1)$.

For $l = 2$, the Lie algebra D_2 is not simple and can be represented by the root diagram of the fig. 15.6.

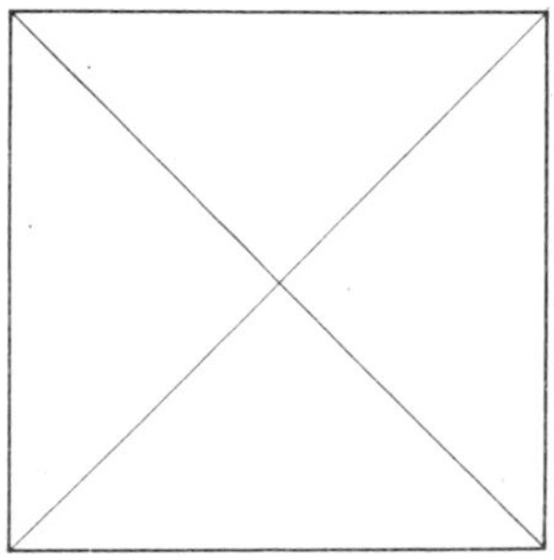

Fig. 15.6. Root diagram D_2.

D_2 is a semi-simple Lie algebra, direct sum of two rank one simple Lie algebrae, A_1:

$$D_2 \simeq A_1 \oplus A_1.$$

In the particular case $l = 3$, it can be easily shown that the two Lie algebrae D_3 and A_3 are isomorphic by superposition of the root diagrams after rotation in ε_3:

$$D_3 \simeq A_3 .$$

5. *Exceptional groups.* The following results will be given without proof and we refer to the original papers of Cartan and to the subsequent works of Van der Waerden and Dynkin.

A_l, B_l, C_l, D_l constitute the only four general classes of simple Lie algebrae. To the four series, there can be added five exceptional groups characterized in table 15.1:

TABLE 15.1

Exceptional simple Lie algebrae

Name	Rank	Dimension
G_2	2	14
F_4	4	52
E_6	6	78
E_7	7	133
E_8	8	248

15.4. Compact forms associated to simple Lie algebrae

1. The determination of the standard form for a Lie algebra Λ on the real numbers R is obtained by resolving an eigenvalue problem which introduces the field of complex number C. In reality, the standard forms are defined as Lie algebrae on the complex numbers. The various real Lie algebrae which have the same complex extension have also the same standard form.

Cartan has shown that only one compact group can be associated to a standard form and all other groups associated with the same standard form are non compact groups.

2. *Lie algebra* A_n. We want to prove that the Lie algebra A_n on C is isomorphic to sl$(n+1, \mathrm{C})$. We consider the special linear group SL$(n+1, \mathrm{R})$ and its Lie algebra sl$(n+1, \mathrm{R})$ is defined by n^2-1 infinitesimal generators X_{ij} of trace zero: $\sum_j X_{jj} = 0$. The commutation laws are given by:

$$[X_{rs}, X_{tu}] = \delta_{st} X_{ru} - \delta_{ur} X_{ts} .$$

It is convenient to write explicitly some particular relations

$$[X_{rr}, X_{tt}] = 0$$
$$[X_{rr}, X_{tu}] = (\delta_{rt} - \delta_{ru}) X_{tu}$$
$$[X_{rs}, X_{sr}] = X_{rr} - X_{ss}$$

in order to clearly exhibit the standard form of the Lie algebra.

By putting now:

$$X_{rr} = \lambda_n H_r \qquad X_{rs} = \lambda_n E_{rs}$$

the roots components are given by:

$$\alpha_{[rs]j} = \alpha^{j}_{[rs]} = \frac{1}{\lambda_n} (\delta_{jr} - \delta_{js})$$

and the non-vanishing structure constants by:

$$N^2 = \frac{1}{\lambda_n}.$$

Obviously the standard form is A_n and the normalization condition for the roots and the structure constants determines λ_n to be $\lambda_n = \sqrt{\{2(n+1)\}}$. From the Cartan theorem, only one compact group of complex Lie algebra $sl(n+1, C)$ has the standard form A_n. It is the unimodular unitary group $SU(n+1)$.

3. *Lie algebrae* B_n *and* D_n. We want to prove that the Lie algebrae B_n and D_n are the standard form of the Lie algebrae of the orthogonal groups.

We consider an N-dimensional space on the complex number and choose in C^N a convenient basis where the linear symmetric connection g has a completely non diagonal form. We first define an index j with the following range of variation:

a) $N = 2n+1 \qquad -n \leqq j \leqq n$

b) $N = 2n \qquad -n \leqq j \leqq n \quad$ but $\; j \neq 0$.

The matrix elements of g are defined by $g_{jk} = \delta_{j-k}$ and the scalar product becomes

$$g(x, y) = \sum_j x_j y_{-j}.$$

The general form of the commutation laws is given by:

$$[Z_{jk}, Z_{lm}] = g_{kl} Z_{jm} - g_{jl} Z_{km} - g_{km} Z_{jl} + g_{jm} Z_{kl}.$$

It is convenient to write explicitly some particular relations:

$$[Z_{j\,-j}, Z_{k\,-k}] = 0$$
$$[Z_{j\,-j}, Z_{kl}] = (\delta_{jk}+\delta_{jl}-\delta_{j\,-k}-\delta_{j\,-l})Z_{kl}$$
$$[Z_{kl}, Z_{-l\,-k}] = Z_{k\,-k}+Z_{l\,-l}$$

in order to exhibit the standard form of the Lie algebra.

We now restrict j to positive values only, $j = 1, 2, \ldots, n$. The standard form is easily obtained by putting:

$$Z_{j\,-j} = \lambda_N H_j \qquad Z_{rs} = \lambda_N E_{rs}.$$

The root components are given by:

$$\beta_{[rs]j} = \beta^j_{[rs]} = [\delta_{jr}+\delta_{js}-\delta_{j\,-r}-\delta_{j\,-s}]\,\frac{1}{\lambda_N}$$

and, in the case $N = 2n+1$ where r or s can take the value zero, we have a second sequence of roots:

$$\alpha_{[0r]j} = \alpha^j_{[0r]} = (\delta_{jr}-\delta_{j\,-r})\,\frac{1}{\lambda_N}.$$

The non-vanishing structure constants are all equal in magnitude to $N^2 = 1/\lambda_N^2$.

The normalization condition for the roots and the structure constants give the value $\lambda_N^2 = 2N-4$.

The Lie algebra B_n on the field C is isomorphic to so$(2n+1$, C) and the Lie algebra D_n on C is isomorphic to so($2n$, C). It follows that the orthogonal groups SO($2n+1$) and SO($2n$) are respectively the real compact realizations B_n and D_n.

4. *Lie algebra* C_n. We want to prove that the Lie algebra C_n on the field C is isomorphic to Sp(n, C). We consider the real symplectic group Sp(n, R) and its Lie algebra sp(n, R) is defined by $n(2n+1)$ infinitesimal generators R, S, T with the commutations laws

$$[R_{ij}, R_{kl}] = \delta_{jk}R_{il}-\delta_{li}R_{kj}$$
$$[S_{ij}, S_{kl}] = 0 = [T_{ij}, T_{kl}]$$
$$[R_{ij}, S_{kl}] = \delta_{jk}S_{il}+\delta_{jl}S_{ik}$$
$$[R_{ij}, T_{kl}] = -\delta_{ik}T_{jl}-\delta_{il}T_{jk}$$
$$[S_{ij}, T_{kl}] = \delta_{jk}R_{il}+\delta_{ik}R_{jl}+\delta_{jl}R_{ik}+\delta_{il}R_{jk}.$$

It is convenient to write explicitly some particular relations:

$$
\begin{aligned}
[R_{jj}, R_{kk}] &= 0 \\
[R_{jj}, S_{kk}] &= 2\delta_{jk} S_{kk} \\
[R_{jj}, T_{kk}] &= -2\delta_{jk} T_{kk} \\
[R_{jj}, R_{kl}] &= (\delta_{jk} - \delta_{jl}) R_{kl} \\
[R_{jj}, S_{kl}] &= (\delta_{jk} + \delta_{jl}) S_{kl} \\
[R_{jj}, T_{kl}] &= -(\delta_{jk} + \delta_{jl}) T_{kl}
\end{aligned}
$$

in order to exhibit clearly the standard form of the Lie algebra. By putting:

$$
\begin{aligned}
R_{jj} &= \lambda_n H_j \qquad & S_{jj} &= \mu_n E_j \qquad & T_{jj} &= \mu_n E_{-j} \\
S_{jk} &= \lambda_n E_{jk} \qquad & T_{jk} &= \lambda_n E_{-j-k} \qquad & R_{jk} &= \lambda_n E_{j-k}
\end{aligned}
$$

the roots components are given by

$$
\alpha_{[\pm k \pm l]j} = \alpha^j_{[\pm k \pm l]} = \frac{1}{\lambda_n}(\pm\delta_{jk} \pm \delta_{jl})
$$

$$
\beta_{[\pm k]j} = \beta^j_{[\pm k]} = \frac{2}{\lambda_n}(\pm\delta_{jk}).
$$

The normalization condition for the roots give $\lambda_n = 2\sqrt{(n+1)}$ and $\mu_n = 2\sqrt{\{2(n+1)\}}$:

The Lie algebra C_n on the field C is isomorphic to sp(n, C). It follows that the symplectic group is the compact realization of C_n.

TABLE 15.2

Compact and non compact simple classical groups

Standard form	Classical group	Compactness	Number of groups	Dimensionality
	SU(n+1)	C	1	
	SU(n+1−s, s)	NC	[$\frac{1}{2}$(n+1)]	
A_n	SL(n+1, R)	NC	1	$n(n+2)$
	SL($\frac{1}{2}$(n+1), Q) if n+1 is even	NC	1	
B_n	SO(2n+1)	C	1	$n(2n+1)$
	SO(2n+1−s, s)	NC	n	
	Sp(n)	C	1	
	Sp(n−s, s)	NC	[$\frac{1}{2}n$]	$n(2n+1)$
C_n	Sp(n, R)	NC	1	
	SO(2n)	C	1	
D_n	SO(2n−s, s)	NC	n	$n(2n-1)$
	SO(n, Q)	NC	1	

TABLE 15.3

Isomorphisms of classical simple Lie algebrae associated to the isomorphisms of the standard forms

Standard form	Classical simple Lie algebrae
$A_1 \simeq B_1 \simeq C_1$	su(2) $\simeq$ so(3) $\simeq$ sp(1) $\simeq$ sl(1, Q) su(1, 1) $\simeq$ so(2, 1) $\simeq$ sl(2, R) $\simeq$ sp(1, R)
$B_2 \simeq C_2$	so(5) $\simeq$ sp(2) so(4, 1) $\simeq$ sp(1, 1) so(3, 2) $\simeq$ sp(2, R)
$D_2 \simeq A_1 \oplus A_1$	so(4) $\simeq$ su(2) $\oplus$ su(2) so(3, 1) $\simeq$ sl(2, C) so(2, 2) $\simeq$ sl(2, R) $\oplus$ sl(2, R) so(2, Q) $\simeq$ su(2) $\oplus$ sl(2, R)
$A_3 \simeq D_3$	su(4) $\simeq$ so(6) su(3, 1) $\simeq$ so(3, Q) sl(2, Q) $\simeq$ so(5, 1) su(2, 2) $\simeq$ so(4, 2) sl(4, R) $\simeq$ so(3,3)

CHAPTER XVI

REPRESENTATIONS

16.1. Generalities

1. *Definition.* Let us introduce an N dimensional vector space V_N and an abstract group G. We consider the group G_N of linear transformations of V_N represented by $N \times N$ matrices U and such that G_N is isomorphic to G. By definition, G_N is a representation of dimension N of G. As a consequence:

$$U(a)U(b) = U(ab)$$

for all $a, b \in G$ and $U(a), U(b) \in G_N$.

If the homomorphism between G_N and G is an isomorphism, the representation is said faithful. It can be shown that all the representations of simple Lie algebrae, except the identity, are faithful representations.

2. *Equivalent representations.* Two representations $U_1(a)$ and $U_2(a)$ of G are equivalent if there exists a constant matrix A, independent of the group elements and such that

$$U_2(a) = AU_1(a)A^{-1} \qquad \text{for all} \quad a \in G.$$

3. *Reducibility.* A representation $U(a)$ of G in a vector space V_N is reducible if it leaves invariant a subspace V_1 of V_N. After a convenient change of basis, the matrix U can then be written in the form:

$$U = \begin{vmatrix} U_1 & 0 \\ U_3 & U_2 \end{vmatrix}$$

where the matrix U_1 has the same dimension as the vector space V_1.

If now $U_3 = 0$, there exist two invariant subspaces V_1 and V_2 of V_N such that the sum is precisely V_N, the representation U is said fully reducible into two representations U_1 and U_2:

$$U = \begin{vmatrix} U_1 & 0 \\ 0 & U_2 \end{vmatrix}.$$

A representation with unitary matrices is always fully reducible. Let us consider the matrix representation U written in the form:

$$U = \begin{vmatrix} U_1 & 0 \\ U_3 & U_2 \end{vmatrix}.$$

The conditions of unitarity, $UU^* = I = UU^*$ give immediately:

$$U_1 U_1^* = I \qquad U_3 U_3^* + U_2 U_2^* = I$$
$$U_1 U_3^* = 0 \qquad U_3 U_1^* = 0.$$

The matrix U_1 is a regular matrix: $|\det U_1|^2 = 1$ and its inverse is well defined. It follows that $U_3 = 0$ and the two submatrices U_1 and U_2 are unitary matrices also.

4. *Contragradient representation*: We consider an N dimensional representation of G with the complex matrices U:

$$U(a)U(b) = U(ab) \qquad a, b \in \mathrm{G}.$$

The complex conjugate matrices U^t constitute an N dimensional representation of G:

$$U^t(a)U^t(b) = U^t(ab).$$

The representations U and U^t are called contragradient representations.

5. The Lie algebra of a Lie group G is defined by a set of r infinitesimal generators X_σ. It is possible to find, in the group G_N, a set of r $(N \times N)$ matrices also denoted X_σ, which have the commutations laws of the Lie algebra:

$$[X_\sigma, X_\rho] = C^\tau_{\sigma\rho}\, X_\tau.$$

6. *Compact Lie groups.* The following important theorem can be proved: any real (complex) representation of a compact Lie group is equivalent to a representation with orthogonal (unitary) matrices. From this result it follows that every representation of a compact Lie group is semi-simple and fully reducible.

7. We restrict ourselves now to the particular case of semi-simple compact groups. The Lie algebra of a semi-simple group is defined, in its standard form by the infinitesimal generators H_j and E_α. In the unitary representation, the operators of the Cartan subalgebra can be represented by hermitian matrices; by using the commutation relation:

$$[E_\alpha, E_{-\alpha}] = (\alpha, H)$$

it is possible to choose a representation satisfying:

$$E_\alpha^* = E_{-\alpha}.$$

16.2. Weights

We study the case of compact semi-simple groups for which the representations can be taken as unitary.

1. *Definition.* We consider the l-dimensional abelian Cartan subalgebra. The operators H_j can be simultaneously diagonalized; in the vector space V_N we have the eigenvalue equation for each operator H_j,

$$H_j|\Omega\rangle = m_j|\Omega\rangle.$$

The numbers m_j can be considered as the covariant components of a vector m in the vector space ε_l previously considered. The vector m is called a weight and ε_l the weight space.

2. A simple weight is associated to one eigenvalue only. For the rank $l > 1$ groups, the weights are not, in general, simple.

3. *Properties.* We now give, without proof, two elementary properties:

a) there exists, at least, one weight in each representation;

b) the eigenvectors associated to different weights are linearly independent. As a consequence, the maximum number of weights for an N-dimensional representation is precisely N.

4. *Theorem* 1. If $|\Omega\rangle$ is an eigenvector associated to the weight m, the vector $E_\alpha|\Omega\rangle$ is either zero, or an eigenvector associated to the weight $m+\alpha$.

By definition, we have:

$$H_j|\Omega\rangle = m_j|\Omega\rangle.$$

Let us consider the vector $E_\alpha|\Omega\rangle$. By using the relation

$$H_j E_\alpha = E_\alpha H_j + [H_j, E_\alpha] = E_\alpha H_j + \alpha_j E_\alpha$$

we immediately obtain:

$$H_j E_\alpha|\Omega\rangle = E_\alpha H_j|\Omega\rangle + \alpha_j E_\alpha|\Omega\rangle = (m+\alpha)_j E_\alpha|\Omega\rangle.$$

If $E_\alpha|\Omega\rangle$ is not zero, it is an eigenvector associated to the weight $(m+\alpha)$.

5. *Theorem* 2. If m is a weight and α a root:

a) the number $2(m, \alpha)/(\alpha, \alpha)$ is an integer;

b) the vector $m-2\{(m, \alpha)/(\alpha, \alpha)\}\alpha$ is also a weight deduced from m by a reflection of the Weyl group.

The proof of this fundamental theorem is extremely similar to that given for the corresponding theorem with the roots in section 15.2.

6. *Equivalent weights.* Two weights deduced from each other by an operation of the Weyl group are called equivalent. They have the same multiplicity.

16.3. Weyl group

The Weyl group has been defined as the set of reflections with respect to the hyperplanes through the origin perpendicular to the roots. We are now concerned with the determination of the Weyl group for the simple Lie groups by applying the fundamental theorem 2.

1. *Lie algebra* A_l. The roots can be written $\alpha_{ij} = e_i - e_j$ and we expand the weight m on the basis of the vectors e_k:

$$m = \sum m_k e_k \qquad \text{with} \quad \sum_1^{l+1} m_k = 0.$$

We immediately find:

$$2\frac{(\alpha_{ij}, m)}{(\alpha, \alpha)} = m_i - m_j.$$

We now use the theorem 2. From the part a), the differences $m_i - m_j$ are integer numbers. From the part b), the weight m' obtained by reflection from m is given by:

$$\sum m'_k e_k = \sum m_k e_k - (m_i - m_j)(e_i - e_j) = \sum m_k e_k - m_i e_i - m_j e_j + m_i e_j + m_j e_i.$$

The Weyl group is the group of permutations of the components of the weights. It follows that the maximum number of equivalent weights is $(l+1)!$.

2. *Lie algebra* B_l. We have two series of roots:

$$\begin{aligned} \alpha_I &= \varepsilon(I)e_i & I &= \pm i & i &= 1, 2, \ldots, l \\ \beta_{IJ} &= \varepsilon(I)e_i + \varepsilon(J)e_j & I &= \pm i, J = \pm j & i, j &= 1, 2, \ldots, l \end{aligned}$$

and $\varepsilon(I)$ is the sign of I.

It follows immediately:

$$2\frac{(\alpha_I, m)}{(\alpha_I, \alpha_I)} = 2\varepsilon(I)m_i \qquad 2\frac{(\beta_{IJ}, m)}{(\beta_{IJ}, \beta_{IJ})} = \varepsilon(I)m_i + \varepsilon(J)m_j.$$

From the part a) of the theorem 2, the components of a weight m must be either all integer numbers or all half integer numbers.

The weights m' equivalent to m are defined from the part b) by:

$$\begin{aligned} \sum m'_k e_k &= \sum m_k e_k - [2\varepsilon(I)m_i][\varepsilon(I)m_i] = \sum m_k e_k - 2m_i e_i \\ \sum m'_k e_k &= \sum m_k e_k - [\varepsilon(I)m_i + \varepsilon(J)m_j][\varepsilon(I)e_i + \varepsilon(J)e_j] \\ \sum m'_k e_k &= \sum m_k e_k - m_i e_i - m_j e_j - \varepsilon(I)\varepsilon(J)[m_i e_j + m_j e_i]. \end{aligned}$$

The Weyl group is the group of permutations of the components of the weights with an arbitrary number of changes of sign. It follows that the maximum number of equivalent weights is $2^l l!$.

3. *Lie algebra* C_l. We have two series of roots:

$$\beta_I = 2\varepsilon(I)e_i \qquad \alpha_{IJ} = \varepsilon(I)e_i + \varepsilon(J)e_j$$

and it follows immediately:

$$2\frac{(\beta_I, m)}{(\beta_I, \beta_I)} = \varepsilon(I)m_i \qquad 2\frac{(\alpha_{IJ}, m)}{(\alpha_{IJ}, \alpha_{IJ})} = \varepsilon(I)m_i + \varepsilon(J)m_j .$$

From the part a) of theorem 2, the components of a weight m must be integer numbers. The weights m' equivalent to m are defined from the part b) by:

$$\sum m'_k e_k = \sum m_k e_k - [\varepsilon(I)m_i][2\varepsilon(I)e_i] = \sum m_k e_k - 2m_i e_i$$
$$\sum m'_k e_k = \sum m_k e_k - (m_i e_i + m_j e_j) - \varepsilon(I)\varepsilon(J)(m_i e_j + m_j e_i).$$

The Weyl group is the same in B_l and C_l.

4. *Lie algebra* D_l. The roots of the Lie algebra D_l have the general form:

$$\alpha_{IJ} = \varepsilon(I)e_i + \varepsilon(J)e_j$$

and it follows immediately:

$$2\frac{(\alpha_{IJ}, m)}{(\alpha_{IJ}, \alpha_{IJ})} = \varepsilon(I)m_i + \varepsilon(J)m_j .$$

From the part a) of theorem 2, the two quantities $m_i \pm m_j$ must be integer numbers. The weights m' equivalent to m are given by:

$$\sum m'_k e_k = \sum m_k e_k - (m_i e_i + m_j e_j) - \varepsilon(I)\varepsilon(J)(m_i e_j + m_j e_i).$$

The Weyl group is the group of permutations of the components of the weights with an *even* number of changes of sign.

16.4. Fundamental weights

1. We first introduce in the weight space ε_l an order relation. A vector is called a positive vector if its first non vanishing component is a positive number. We then have m_2 higher than m_1 if $m_2 - m_1$ is a positive vector. Of course, such a property depends on the basis in ε_l but the consequences are intrinsically true by means of the Weyl group reflections.

For a semi-simple Lie algebra of rank l and dimension r, there exist

$(r-l)$ non vanishing, non degenerate roots and $\frac{1}{2}(r-l)$ positive roots symbolically denoted α^+.

2. *Dominant weight.* In a set of equivalent weights, the dominant weight is higher than another weight of the set.

The highest weight of a representation is the highest dominant weight of the representation.

3. *Properties.* We give now, without proof, two important properties:

a) The highest weight of an irreducible representation is simple. It follows that the set of equivalent weights to the highest weight of an irreducible representation is a set of simple weights.

b) Two irreducible representations with the same highest weight are equivalent and conversely.

4. *Fundamental dominant weight.* Cartan has proved the following results: for a simple Lie group of rank l, there exist l fundamental dominant weights $L^1, L^2, \ldots, L^l$, with the following properties:

a) Every dominant weight L can be written as a linear combination of the L^j's with non-negative integer coefficients:

$$L(\lambda_1, \lambda_2, \ldots, \lambda_l) = \sum_{j=1}^{l} \lambda_j L^j \qquad \lambda_j \geqq 0.$$

b) To each L^j corresponds a fundamental irreducible representation for which L^j is the highest weight.

16.5. Character

1. *Definition*: Let us consider the representation $U(a)$ of G in the N dimensional vector space V_N. The trace of the $N \times N$ matrix $U(a)$ is called the character $\chi(a)$ of the representation:

$$\chi(a) = \mathrm{Tr}\, U(a).$$

2. The trace of a product of matrices is invariant under a cyclic permutation of the factors in the product. It follows that the character of two equivalent representations are identical:

$$\mathrm{Tr}\, U(a) = \mathrm{Tr}\, [AV(a)A^{-1}].$$

The character is independent of the basis choosen in V_N for the matrix representation.

3. Let us now consider two elements a and b in G such that:

$$b = mum^{-1} \qquad \text{where} \quad m \in \mathrm{G}.$$

The elements a and b are called conjugate elements in G. From the previous properties they have the same character:

$$\chi(b) = \chi(a).$$

The character is not a function of the elements of the group but simply of the classes of conjugate elements.

It can be proved that for a semi-simple rank l group, the classes depend on l parameters only which we will call in the following $\varphi_1, \varphi_2, \ldots, \varphi_l$.

4. The theory of the character has been studied by Weyl. We want to give here only some important results without proof. The notion of character is extremely useful because of the following theorem: two representations are equivalent if and only if they have the same characters.

5. We now introduce, in the weight space ε_l, two vectors which are used in the practical calculation of the character and of the dimensionality of a representation. The first one is:

$$R = \tfrac{1}{2}\sum_{\alpha^+} \alpha$$

where the sum is extended over the positive roots only and the second depends on the representation as the highest weight $L(\lambda_j)$:

$$K(\lambda_j) = R + L(\lambda_j).$$

The elements of the Weyl group are noted by S and the vector SK is the result of the operation of S on K.

6. For a compact semi-simple group, the character χ is given by the general formula:

$$\chi(\lambda, \varphi) = \frac{\xi(\lambda, \varphi)}{\xi(0, \varphi)}$$

where

$$\xi(\lambda, \varphi) = \sum_S \delta_S \exp \mathrm{i}(SK(\lambda), \varphi);$$

δ_S is the parity of S and φ a vector of the weight space ε_l.

If all the weights m of a representation are known with their multiplicity γ_m, an extremely simple expression can be used

$$\chi(\lambda, \varphi) = \sum_m \gamma_m \exp \mathrm{i}(m, \varphi).$$

7. *Dimension.* The dimension of the representation is given by:

$$N(\lambda) = \chi(\lambda, 0).$$

Weyl has shown the useful formula:

$$N(\lambda) = \prod_{\alpha^+} \frac{(\alpha, K(\lambda))}{(\alpha, R)} = \prod_{\alpha^+} \left(1 + \frac{(\alpha, L(\lambda))}{(\alpha, R)}\right)$$

where the product is extended to all the positive roots α^+.

8. *Contragradient representations.* The characters of two contragradient representations are complex conjugate. This result is simply a consequence of the definition of the contragradient representations with complex conjugate matrices.

It follows that the weight diagrams of two contragradient representations can be deduced from each other by a symmetry with respect to the origin in the weight space.

The character of a representation equivalent to its contragradient is real and there is a necessary and sufficient condition. In an equivalent way the weight diagram is symmetric with respect to the origin in the weight space and there is also a necessary and sufficient condition.

16.6. Application to simple Lie groups

16.6.1. Lie algebra A_l

1. The components m_j of any weight satisfy the two following requirements: all the differences $m_i - m_j$ are integer numbers and the sum of all the components vanish. The general structure of m_j is then a fraction with denominator $l+1$, and all the numerators are equivalent modulo $l+1$.

2. The l fundamental dominant weights of A_l can be written as:

$$L^j = \frac{1}{l+1}\left[(l+1-j)\sum_{k=1}^{j} e_k - j \sum_{k=j+1}^{l+1} e_k\right].$$

The number of weights equivalent to L^j is given by the number of independent permutations of the components of L^j, e.g.; the number of combinations C^j_{l+1}:

$$C^j_{l+1} = C^{l+1-j}_{l+1} = \frac{(l+1)!}{j!(l+1-j)!}.$$

3. All the weights of a fundamental representation F^j are equivalent to the highest weight which is the fundamental dominant weight L^j. It follows that all the weights are simple and the dimension of F^j is given by:

$$\dim F^j = C^j_{l+1}.$$

4. The two fundamental representations F^j and F^{l+1-j} have the same dimension. It is easy to verify that the weight diagrams can be deduced to each other by a symmetry with respect to the origin in the weight space. The fundamental representations F^j and F^{l+1-j} are contragradient representations.

In the case where l is odd: $l+1 = 2l_1$, the fundamental representation F_{l_1} is equivalent to its contragradient and can be choosen as real.

5. We define as S_α a permutation, element of the Weyl group:

$$S_\alpha = \frac{(1, 2, \ldots, l+1)}{(\alpha_1, \alpha_2, \ldots, \alpha_{l+1})}.$$

All the equivalent simple weights of a fundamental representation F^j are deduced from L^j by an operation S_α of the Weyl group. We then obtain, for the character $\chi_j(\varphi)$ of F^j:

$$\chi_j(\varphi) = \sum_{S_\alpha} \exp \mathrm{i}[\sum_{k=1}^{j} \varphi_{\alpha_k}]$$

where the vector φ satisfies the usual condition $\sum_{k=1}^{l+1} \varphi_k = 0$. It is then easy to verify on the explicit expression the relation:

$$\chi_{l+1-j}(\varphi) = \chi_j^*(\varphi).$$

6. We now consider an irreducible representation, characterized by its highest weight:

$$L(\lambda) = \sum_{j=1}^{l} \lambda_j L^j \qquad \lambda_j \geqq 0.$$

In order to calculate the dimension of the representation, we are first interested with the positive roots $\alpha_{mn} (n > m)$ and the vector R, previously defined is given by:

$$R = \tfrac{1}{2} \sum_{k=0}^{[\frac{1}{2}l]} (l-2k)(e_{k+1} - e_{l+1-k}).$$

We have successively:

$$(\alpha_{mn}, R) = (n-m)(e, e)$$

$$(\alpha_{mn}, L) = (\sum_{j=m}^{n-1} \lambda_j)(e, e).$$

The dimension of the irreducible representation $D^N(\lambda_1, \lambda_2, \ldots, \lambda_l)$ is obtained by using the Weyl formula:

$$N(\lambda_1, \lambda_2, \ldots, \lambda_l) = \prod_{m<n} \left(1 + \frac{\sum_{j=m}^{n-1} \lambda_j}{n-m}\right).$$

7. A particular interesting case corresponds to all λ_j's equal to zero except two $\lambda_1 = \lambda_l = 1$. The highest weight is simply:

$$L(1, 0, \ldots, 0, 1) = L^1 + L^l = e_1 - e_{l+1} = \alpha_{1\,l+1}.$$

All the equivalent weights of the highest weight are the $l(l+1)$ non vanishing roots α_{ij} of the A_l Lie algebra.

The dimension of the representation is obtained from the previous formula:

$$N(1, 0, \ldots, 0, 1) = l(l+2)$$

and turns out to be equal to the dimension of the A_l Lie algebra.

Such a representation is called the *adjoint* representation of the Lie algebra and the weight diagram is simply the root diagram.

The character of the adjoint representation is given by

$$\chi_A(\varphi) = l + 2 \sum_{m<n} \cos(\varphi_m - \varphi_n).$$

8. It is easy to show, by using the definition of the highest weights, that the representations $D^N(\lambda_1, \lambda_2, \ldots, \lambda_{l-1}, \lambda_l)$ and $D^N(\lambda_l, \lambda_{l-1}, \ldots, \lambda_2, \lambda_1)$ are contragradient representations.

It follows that only symmetric representations, defined by $\lambda_{l+1-j} = \lambda_j$ are equivalent to their contragradient representations.

9. *Lie algebra* A_1. From a pedagogical point of view, it is interesting to use the general language for the well known results of the A_1 Lie algebra.

We have one fundamental 2-dimensional representation, the spinor representation of the Lie algebra, and the fundamental weight is:

$$L^1 = \tfrac{1}{2}(e_1 - e_2).$$

In fig. 16.1, we have represented the weight diagram of the fundamental representation and the three roots of the A_1 Lie algebra.

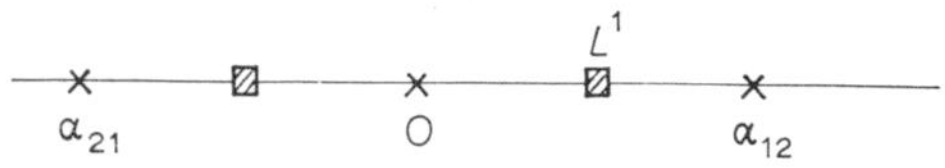

Fig. 16.1. Fundamental representation $D^{(2)}(1)$.

The irreducible representation $D^N(\lambda)$, of highest weight $L = \lambda L^1$ has the dimension:

$$N(\lambda) = 1 + \lambda.$$

All the weights are simple and of the general form $L = \mu L^1$ with $\mu = \lambda$, $\lambda-2, \ldots, -\lambda$. The character of the representation $D^N(\lambda)$ is given by:

$$\chi(\lambda, \varphi) = \frac{\sin(\lambda+1)\varphi}{\sin \varphi}.$$

In the usual language, $\lambda = 2J$ where J is the spin associated to the irreducible representation of the rotation group.

10. *Lie algebra* A_2. There exist two 3-dimensional contragradient fundamental representations. The fundamental dominant weights are given by:

$$L^1 = \tfrac{1}{3}[2e_1-(e_2+e_3)]$$
$$L^2 = \tfrac{1}{3}[(e_1+e_2)-2e_3].$$

The corresponding two-dimensional weight diagrams are drawn in figs. 16.2 and 16.3 and located with respect to the root diagram of the adjoint representation.

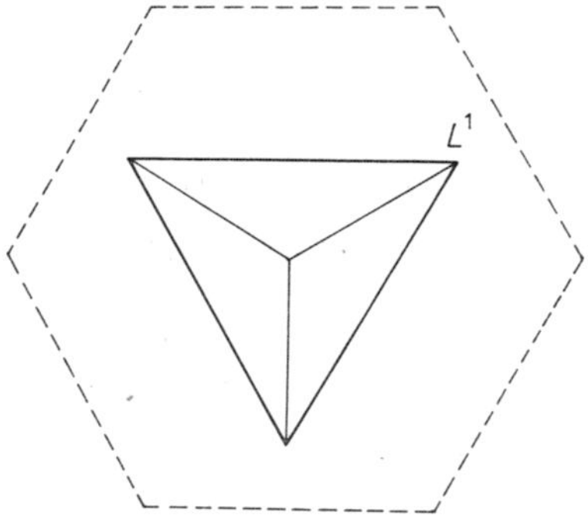

Fig. 16.2.

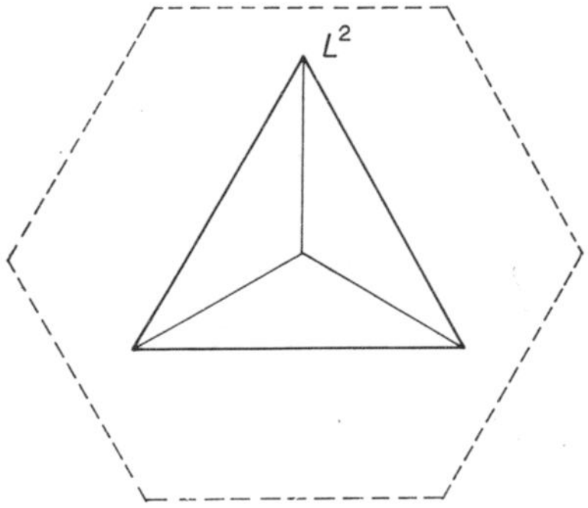

Fig. 16.3.

We will denote, in the following, the two fundamental representations by 3 and $\bar{3}$ and the adjoint representation by 8. The characters of these three representations are given by:

$$\chi(3, \varphi) = e^{i\varphi_1}+e^{i\varphi_2}+e^{i\varphi_3}$$
$$\chi(\bar{3}, \varphi) = e^{-i\varphi_1}+e^{-i\varphi_2}+e^{-i\varphi_3}$$
$$\chi(8, \varphi) = 2+2[\cos(\varphi_1-\varphi_2)+\cos(\varphi_2-\varphi_3)+\cos(\varphi_3-\varphi_1)]$$

with $\varphi_1+\varphi_2+\varphi_3 = 0$.

The dimension of the irreducible representation $D^N(\lambda_1, \lambda_2)$ is given by the symmetric formula:

$$N(\lambda_1, \lambda_2) = (1+\lambda_1)(1+\lambda_2)(1+\tfrac{1}{2}(\lambda_1+\lambda_2)).$$

Only the representations $D(\lambda, \lambda)$ are equivalent to their contragradient and the dimension is then given by:

$$N(\lambda, \lambda) = (1+\lambda)^3.$$

11. *Lie algebra* A_3. There exist three fundamental representations associated to the following fundamental dominant weights:

$$L^1 = \tfrac{1}{4}[3e_1-(e_2+e_3+e_4)]$$
$$L^2 = \tfrac{1}{2}[(e_1+e_2)-(e_3+e_4)]$$
$$L^3 = \tfrac{1}{4}[(e_1+e_2+e_3)-3e_4].$$

The representations F^1 and F^3 are two 4-dimensional contragradient representations and F^2 is a 6-dimensional representation equivalent to its contragradient.

The adjoint representation $D(1, 0, 1)$ is 15-dimensional as the Lie algebra A_3.

The dimension of the irreducible representation $D^N(\lambda_1, \lambda_2, \lambda_3)$ is given by:

$$N(\lambda_1, \lambda_2, \lambda_3) =$$
$$=(1+\lambda_1)(1+\lambda_2)(1+\lambda_3)(1+\tfrac{1}{2}(\lambda_1+\lambda_2))(1+\tfrac{1}{2}(\lambda_2+\lambda_3))(1+\tfrac{1}{3}(\lambda_1+\lambda_2+\lambda_3)).$$

12. *Lie algebra* A_5. There exist five fundamental representations associated to the following fundamental dominant weights:

$$L^1 = \tfrac{1}{6}[5e_1-(e_2+e_3+e_4+e_5+e_6)]$$
$$L^2 = \tfrac{1}{3}[2(e_1+e_2)-(e_3+e_4+e_5+e_6)]$$
$$L^3 = \tfrac{1}{2}[(e_1+e_2+e_3)-(e_4+e_5+e_6)]$$
$$L^4 = \tfrac{1}{3}[(e_1+e_2+e_3+e_4)-2(e_5+e_6)]$$
$$L^5 = \tfrac{1}{6}[(e_1+e_2+e_3+e_4+e_5)-5e_6].$$

The representations F^1 and F^2 are two 6-dimensional contragradient representations. The representations F^2 and F^4 are two 15-dimensional contragradient representations. The representation F^3 is a 20-dimensional representation equivalent to its contragradient.

The adjoint representation $D(1, 0, 0, 0, 1)$ is 35-dimensional. The dimension of the irreducible representation $D^N(\lambda_1, \lambda_2, \lambda_3, \lambda_4, \lambda_5)$ is given by

$$N(\lambda_1, \lambda_2, \lambda_3, \lambda_4, \lambda_5) =$$
$$= (1+\lambda_1)(1+\lambda_2)(1+\lambda_3)(1+\lambda_4)(1+\lambda_5)(1+\tfrac{1}{2}(\lambda_1+\lambda_2))(1+\tfrac{1}{2}(\lambda_2+\lambda_3))$$
$$\times(1+\tfrac{1}{2}(\lambda_3+\lambda_4))(1+\tfrac{1}{2}(\lambda_4+\lambda_5))(1+\tfrac{1}{3}(\lambda_1+\lambda_2+\lambda_3))(1+\tfrac{1}{3}(\lambda_2+\lambda_3+\lambda_4))$$
$$\times(1+\tfrac{1}{3}(\lambda_3+\lambda_4+\lambda_5))(1+\tfrac{1}{4}(\lambda_1+\lambda_2+\lambda_3+\lambda_4))(1+\tfrac{1}{4}(\lambda_2+\lambda_3+\lambda_4+\lambda_5))$$
$$\times(1+\tfrac{1}{5}(\lambda_1+\lambda_2+\lambda_3+\lambda_4+\lambda_5)).$$

16.6.2. Lie algebra B_l

1. The l fundamental dominant weights of B_l can be written as

$$L^j = \sum_{k=1}^{j} e_k \qquad j = 1, 2, \ldots, l-1$$

$$L^l = \tfrac{1}{2}\sum_{k=1}^{l} e_k .$$

We then have l fundamental representations, F^j, with the L^j's as highest weights.

2. The Weyl group is the set of permutations of the components of a weight with an arbitrary number of changes of sign. It follows that all weight diagrams are invariant under a symmetry with respect to the origin in the weight space and all representations are equivalent to their contragradiant representation. As another consequence, all the characters are real numbers.

3. We now calculate the dimension of the irreducible representation $D^N(\lambda_1, \lambda_2, \ldots, \lambda_l)$.

The vector R is given by:

$$R = \tfrac{1}{2}\sum_{k=1}^{l}(2l+1-2k)e_k .$$

The positive roots are α_j, β_{ij} and β_{i-j} with $0 < i < j$. We have successively:

$$(\alpha_j, L(\lambda)) = \tfrac{1}{2}\lambda_l + \sum_{k=j}^{l-1} \lambda_k$$

$$(\beta_{ij}, L(\lambda)) = \lambda_l + \sum_{k=i}^{l-1} \lambda_k + \sum_{k=j}^{l-1} \lambda_k$$

$$(\beta_{i-j}, L(\lambda)) = \sum_{k=i}^{j-1} \lambda_k$$

and the dimension $N(\lambda_1, \lambda_2, \ldots, \lambda_l)$ is finally given by:

$$N(\lambda_1, \lambda_2, \ldots, \lambda_l) =$$

$$\prod_{m=1}^{l} \left\{ \left(1+\frac{\lambda_l + 2\sum_{m}^{l-1} \lambda_k}{2l+1-2m}\right) \prod_{n=m+1}^{l} \left[\left(1+\frac{\lambda_l + \sum_{m}^{n-1} \lambda_k + 2\sum_{n}^{l-1} \lambda_k}{2l+1-m-n}\right) \left(1+\frac{\sum_{m}^{n-1} \lambda_k}{n-m}\right) \right] \right\}.$$

4. The fundamental representation F^1 is called the vector representation of the Lie algebra B_l. The dimension of F^1 is given by the general formula:

$$\dim F^1 = 2l+1.$$

The weights of the vector representation are the $2l$ simple weights equivalent to L^1 and the simple weight $m = 0$.

The character of the vector representation is then given by:

$$\chi_V(\varphi) = 1 + 2\sum_{k=1}^{l} \cos \varphi_k .$$

5. The fundamental representation F^l is called the spinor representation of the Lie algebra B_l. The dimension of F^l is given by the general formula:

$$\dim F^l = 2^l.$$

The weights of the spinor representation are the 2^l simple weights equivalent to L^l.

6. The fundamental representation F^2 has its weight diagram identical to the root diagram of the Lie algebra B_l and it follows that F^2 is the adjoint representation. The dimension is given by the general formula:

$$\dim F^2 = l(2l+1)$$

and the character of the adjoint representation is simply:

$$\chi_A(\varphi) = l + 2\sum_{k=1}^{l} \cos \varphi_k + 4\sum_{j<k} \cos \varphi_j \cos \varphi_k .$$

7. *Lie algebra* B_2. The fundamental weights of the vector and spinor representations are given by:

$$L^1 = e_1$$
$$L^2 = \tfrac{1}{2}(e_1+e_2).$$

The corresponding two dimensional weight diagrams are drawn in figs. 16.4 and 16.5 and located with respect to the root diagram of the adjoint representation.

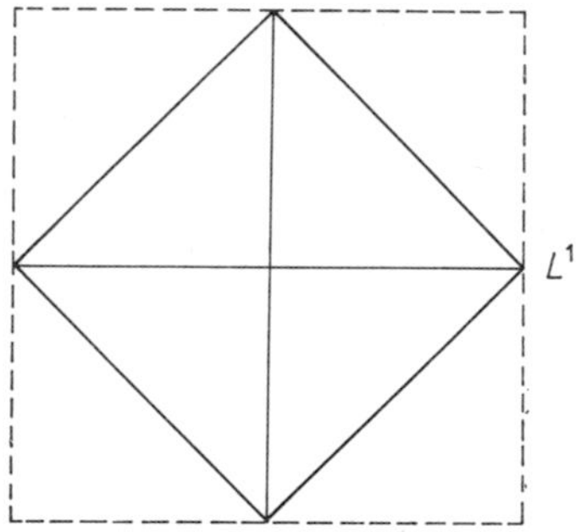

Fig. 16.4.

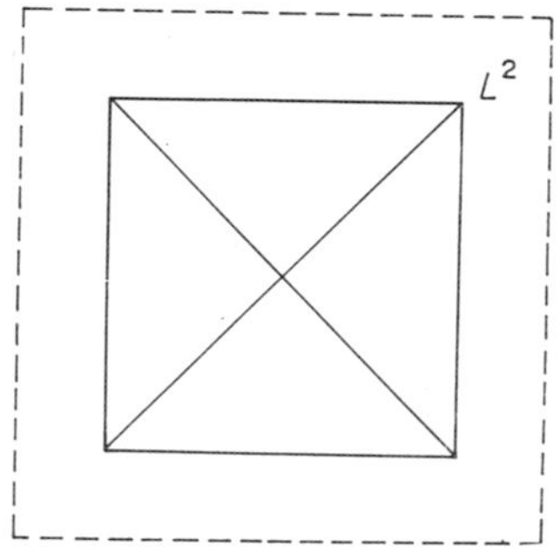

Fig. 16.5.

The characters of the fundamental and adjoint representations are given by:

$$\chi_V(\varphi) = 1+2(\cos\varphi_1+\cos\varphi_2)$$
$$\chi_S(\varphi) = 4\cos\tfrac{1}{2}\varphi_1\cos\tfrac{1}{2}\varphi_2$$
$$\chi_A(\varphi) = 2+2(\cos\varphi_1+\cos\varphi_2)+4\cos\varphi_1\cos\varphi_2\,.$$

The dimension of the irreducible representation $D^N(\lambda_1, \lambda_2)$ is given by the formula:

$$N(\lambda_1, \lambda_2) = (1+\lambda_1)(1+\lambda_2)(1+\tfrac{1}{2}(\lambda_1+\lambda_2))(1+\tfrac{1}{3}(2\lambda_1+\lambda_2)).$$

16.6.3. Lie algebra C_l

1. The l fundamental dominant weights of C_l can be written as:

$$L^j = \sum_{k=1}^{j} e_k \qquad j = 1, 2, \ldots, l.$$

We then have l fundamental representations, F^j, with the L^j's as their heighest weights.

2. As in the case of the B_l Lie algebra, all the representations are equivalent to their contragradient representation and all the characters are real numbers.

3. We now calculate the dimension of the irreducible representation $D^N(\lambda_1, \lambda_2, \ldots, \lambda_l)$. The vector R is given by:

$$R = \sum_{k=1}^{l} (l+1-k)e_k.$$

The positive roots are $\alpha_{ij} = e_i+e_j$, $\alpha_{i-j} = e_i-e_j$, $\beta_j = 2e_j$ with $0 < j \leqq l$.

We have successively:

$$(\alpha_{ij}, L(\lambda)) = \sum_{i}^{j-1} \lambda_k + 2\sum_{j}^{l} \lambda_k$$

$$(\alpha_{i-j}, L(\lambda)) = \sum_{i}^{j-1} \lambda_k$$

$$(\beta_j, L(\lambda)) = 2\sum_{j}^{l} \lambda_k.$$

The dimension $N(\lambda_1, \lambda_2, \ldots, \lambda_l)$ is given by:

$$N(\lambda_1, \lambda_2, \ldots, \lambda_l) =$$

$$= \prod_{m=1}^{l} \left\{ \left(1 + \frac{\sum_{m}^{l} \lambda_k}{l+1-m} \right) \prod_{n=m+1}^{l} \left[\left(1 + \frac{\sum_{m}^{n-1} \lambda_k + 2\sum_{n}^{l} \lambda_k}{2l+2-m-n} \right) \left(1 + \frac{\sum_{m}^{n-1} \lambda_k}{n-m} \right) \right] \right\}.$$

4. The dimension of the fundamental representation F^1 is given by the general formula to be:

$$\dim F^1 = 2l.$$

The weights are the $2l$ simple weights equivalents to L^1. The character of

F^1 is given by:

$$\chi_1(\varphi) = 2\sum_{k=1}^{l} \cos \varphi_k .$$

5. The dimension of the fundamental representation F^2 is obtained using the general formula:

$$\dim F^2 = (l-1)(2l+1).$$

For the fundamental representation F^3, we have:

$$\dim F^3 = \tfrac{1}{3}l(4l^2-1).$$

6. The adjoint representation has its highest weight given by $L_A = 2e_1$. It is the irreducible representation $D(2, 0, 0, \ldots, 0)$ for which the weight diagram coincides with the root diagram of the Lie algebra C_l. The dimension is calculated with the general formula:

$$N(2, 0, 0, \ldots, 0) = l(2l+1).$$

The character of the adjoint representation is given by:

$$\chi_A(\varphi) = l+2\sum_{k} \cos \varphi_k + 4\sum_{j<k} \cos \varphi_j \cos \varphi_k .$$

7. *Lie algebra* C_3. The fundamental weights are:

$$\begin{aligned} L^1 &= e_1 \\ L^2 &= e_1+e_2 \\ L^3 &= e_1+e_2+e_3 . \end{aligned}$$

The first fundamental representation is six dimensional: the second one 14-dimensional and the third one 35-dimensional.

The adjoint representation $D(2, 0, 0)$ is 21-dimensional.

The dimension of an irreducible representation $D^N(\lambda_1, \lambda_2, \lambda_3)$ is given by:

$$\begin{aligned} N(\lambda_1, \lambda_2, \lambda_3) &= \\ &= (1+\lambda_1)(1+\lambda_2)(1+\lambda_3)\big(1+\tfrac{1}{2}(\lambda_1+\lambda_2)\big)\big(1+\tfrac{1}{2}(\lambda_2+\lambda_3)\big)\big(1+\tfrac{1}{3}(\lambda_1+\lambda_2+\lambda_3)\big) \\ &\times \big(1+\tfrac{1}{3}(\lambda_2+2\lambda_3)\big)\big(1+\tfrac{1}{4}(\lambda_1+\lambda_2+2\lambda_3)\big)\big(1+\tfrac{1}{5}(\lambda_1+2\lambda_2+2\lambda_3)\big). \end{aligned}$$

16.6.4. Lie algebra D_l

1. The fundamental dominant weights of D_l can be written as:

$$L^j = \sum_{k=1}^{j} e_k \qquad j = 1, 2, \ldots, l-2$$
$$L^{l-1} = \tfrac{1}{2}(e_1 + e_2 + \ldots + e_{l-1} + e_l)$$
$$L^l = \tfrac{1}{2}(e_1 + e_2 - \ldots + e_{l-1} - e_l).$$

We have l fundamental representations F^j with the L^j's as the highest weights.

2. The Weyl group is the set of all permutations of the components of the weights with an even number of changes of sign. The fundamental representations $F^1, F^2, \ldots, F^{l-2}$ are all equivalent to their contragradient representations. The same result is also true for F^{l-1} and F^l if l is an even number. But if l is an odd number, the fundamental representations F^{l-1} and F^l are cnntragradient representations.

3. We now calculate the dimension of the irreducible representation $D^N(\lambda_1, \lambda_2, \ldots, \lambda_l)$. The vector R is given by:

$$R = \sum_{k=1}^{l} (l-k)e_k.$$

The positive roots are $\alpha_{ij} = e_i + e_j$ and $\alpha_{ij} = e_i - e_j$ with $0 < i < j \leqq l$. We have successively:

$$(\alpha_{ij}, L(\lambda)) = \sum_{i}^{l-2} \lambda_k + \sum_{j}^{l-2} \lambda_k + \lambda_{l-1} + \tfrac{1}{2}(1+\delta_{jl})\lambda_l$$
$$(\alpha_{i-j}, L(\lambda)) = \sum_{i}^{j-1} \lambda_k + \delta_{jl}\lambda_l$$

and the dimension $N(\lambda_1, \lambda_2, \ldots, \lambda_l)$ is finally given by:

$$N(\lambda_1, \lambda_2, \ldots, \lambda_l) = \prod_{m=1}^{l} \left\{ \left(1 + \frac{\lambda_l + \sum_{m}^{l-2} \lambda_k}{l-m}\right)\left(1 + \frac{\lambda_{l-1} + \sum_{m}^{l-2} \lambda_k}{l-m}\right) \times \right.$$
$$\left. \times \prod_{n=m+1}^{l-1} \left[\left(1 + \frac{\sum_{m}^{n-1} \lambda_k + 2\sum_{k}^{l-2} \lambda_k + \lambda_{l-1} + \lambda_l}{2l-m-n}\right)\left(1 + \frac{\sum_{m}^{n-1} \lambda_k}{n-m}\right)\right]\right\}.$$

4. The fundamental representation F^1 is called the vector representation of the Lie algebra D_l. The dimension of F^1 is given by the general formula:

$$\dim F^1 = 2l.$$

The weights of the vector representation are the $2l$ simple weights equivalent to L^1.

The character of the vector representation is given by:

$$\chi_V(\varphi) = 2\sum_{k=1}^{l} \cos \varphi_k .$$

5. The fundamental representations F^{l-1} and F^l are called the two spinor representations of the Lie algebra D_l and they are inequivalent representations. The dimension of F^{l-1} and F^l is the same, due to the symmetry of $N(\lambda_1, \lambda_2, \ldots, \lambda_{l-1}, \lambda_l)$ in the exchange of λ_{l-1} and λ_l:

$$\dim F^{l-1} = \dim F^l = 2^l.$$

The weights of the spinor representations are the simple weights equivalent to the highest weights L^{l-1} and L^l.

6. The fundamental representation F^2 has a weight diagram identical to the root diagram of the Lie algebra D_l and it follows that F^2 is the adjoint representation. The dimension is given by the general formula

$$\dim F^2 = l(2l-1).$$

The character of the adjoint representation is:

$$\chi_A(\varphi) = l+4\sum_{j<k} \cos \varphi_j \cos \varphi_k .$$

7. *Lie algebra* D_4. The fundamental representations are defined by the fundamental dominant weights:

$$\begin{aligned} L^1 &= e_1 \\ L^2 &= e_1+e_2 \\ L^3 &= \tfrac{1}{2}(e_1+e_2+e_3+e_4) \\ L^4 &= \tfrac{1}{2}(e_1+e_2+e_3-e_4). \end{aligned}$$

The vector representation F^1 and the two spinor representations F^3 and F^4 are 8-dimensional representations. The adjoint representation is 28-dimensional.

The characters of the fundamental representations are given by:

$$\chi_V(\varphi) = 2[\cos \varphi_1+\cos \varphi_2+\cos \varphi_3+\cos \varphi_4]$$

$$\chi_A(\varphi) = 4[1+\cos \varphi_1 \cos \varphi_2+\cos \varphi_1 \cos \varphi_3+\cos \varphi_1 \cos \varphi_4+ +\cos \varphi_2 \cos \varphi_3+\cos \varphi_2 \cos \varphi_4+\cos \varphi_3 \cos \varphi_4]$$

$$\chi_s(\varphi) = 8[\cos \tfrac{1}{2}\varphi_1 \cos \tfrac{1}{2}\varphi_2 \cos \tfrac{1}{2}\varphi_3 \cos \tfrac{1}{2}\varphi_4+\sin \tfrac{1}{2}\varphi_1 \sin \tfrac{1}{2}\varphi_2 \sin \tfrac{1}{2}\varphi_3 \sin \tfrac{1}{2}\varphi_4]$$

$$\chi_{s'}(\varphi) = 8[\cos \tfrac{1}{2}\varphi_1 \cos \tfrac{1}{2}\varphi_2 \cos \tfrac{1}{2}\varphi_3 \cos \tfrac{1}{2}\varphi_4-\sin \tfrac{1}{2}\varphi_1 \sin \tfrac{1}{2}\varphi_2 \sin \tfrac{1}{2}\varphi_3 \sin \tfrac{1}{2}\varphi_4].$$

The representation $D^N(\lambda_1, \lambda_2, \lambda_3, \lambda_4)$ has the following dimension:

$$N(\lambda_1, \lambda_2, \lambda_3, \lambda_4) =$$
$$= (1+\lambda_1)(1+\lambda_2)(1+\lambda_3)(1+\lambda_4)\left(1+\tfrac{1}{2}(\lambda_1+\lambda_2)\right)\left(1+\tfrac{1}{2}(\lambda_2+\lambda_3)\right)$$
$$\times\left(1+\tfrac{1}{2}(\lambda_2+\lambda_4)\right)\left(1+\tfrac{1}{3}(\lambda_1+\lambda_2+\lambda_3)\right)\left(1+\tfrac{1}{3}(\lambda_1+\lambda_2+\lambda_4)\right)\left(1+\tfrac{1}{3}(\lambda_2+\lambda_3+\lambda_4)\right)$$
$$\times\left(1+\tfrac{1}{4}(\lambda_1+\lambda_2+\lambda_3+\lambda_4)\right)\left(1+\tfrac{1}{5}(\lambda_1+2\lambda_2+\lambda_3+\lambda_4)\right).$$

This formula exhibits a complete symmetry in the three variables λ_1, λ_3, λ_4 associated to the three 8-dimensional fundamental representations.

16.7. The Schur-Frobenius classification

1. We consider an unitary representation $U(a)$ of a compact semi-simple group G. If $U(a)$ is equivalent to its contragradient representation $U^+(a)$, there exists a constant matrix C such that:

$$U^+(a) = CU(a)C^{-1} \qquad \text{for all} \quad a \in \mathrm{G}.$$

Taking into account the unitarity property written as $U^+ = U^{-1\mathrm{T}}$, we also obtain:

$$C = U^{\mathrm{T}}(a)CU(a).$$

The U transformations leave invariant a bilinear form C in the N-dimensional representation space V_N.

2. By using a representation of the Lie algebra with $N \times N$ hermitian matrices, the transformation $U(a)$ can be written as:

$$U(a) = \exp \mathrm{i}\, a^\sigma X_\sigma$$

and the a^σ's are real parameters.

For the contragradient representation, we have:

$$U^+(a) = \exp \mathrm{i}\, a^\sigma X'_\sigma$$

with:

$$X'_\sigma = -X^{\mathrm{T}}_\sigma.$$

If the representations U and U^+ are equivalent, there exists a matrix C such that:

$$X^{\mathrm{T}}_\sigma = -CX_\sigma C^{-1}$$

for all the generators X_σ of the Lie algebra.

The properties of the matrix C can be obtained by iterating the basic relation. Without loss of generality, C can be choosen as unitary and using the Schur lemma, we can easily prove the following relations:

$$C^{\mathrm{T}} = \varepsilon_1 C \qquad C^{+} = \varepsilon_2 C$$

$$CC^{*} = I \qquad CC^{\mathrm{T}} = \varepsilon_2 I \qquad C^2 = \varepsilon_1 \varepsilon_2 I$$

where $\varepsilon_1 = \pm 1$ and $\varepsilon_2 = \pm 1$.

If a real representation can be used for $U(a)$, the matrix C can be choosen as real ($\varepsilon_2 = 1$) and is an orthogonal matrix:

$$C^{\mathrm{T}} = \pm C \qquad C^{+} = C$$

$$CC^{*} = I \qquad CC^{\mathrm{T}} = I \qquad C^2 = \pm I.$$

4. *The Schur-Frobenius classification.* An irreducible representation belongs to the class $\lambda = 1$, $\lambda = 0$, $\lambda = -1$ if it leaves invariant respectively:

a) $\lambda = 1$ a symmetrical bilinear form ($\varepsilon_1 = +1$);
b) $\lambda = 0$ no bilinear form;
c) $\lambda = -1$ an antisymmetrical bilinear form ($\varepsilon_1 = -1$).

5. *Application.* As a consequence of the properties of the fundamental representations of the simple Lie groups obtained in the previous sections, all the irreducible representations of B_l, C_l, D_{2l} belong to the classes $\lambda = \pm 1$.

CHAPTER XVII

TENSOR ALGEBRA OF THE LINEAR GROUP

17.1. Generalities

1. If H is a subgroup of G, the irreducible representations of G can be either irreducible representations of H or reducible into a direct sum of irreducible representations of H.

2. The irreducible representations of a compact semi-simple group G can be taken as unitary. The unitary matrices of an N dimensional representation of G generate a subgroup of the unitary group $U(N)$.

3. It follows that the irreducible representations of a compact semi-simple group G can be studied from the irreducible representations of the unitary groups.

The importance of the tensor algebra of the unitary group is essentially due to this property.

4. It is convenient for simplicity to speak the language of the general linear group $GL(n, R)$ instead of that of the unitary group $U(n)$. As it has been shown in the previous chapter, the two languages are equivalent from the point of view of irreducible representations.

17.2. Irreducible representations of GL(n, R)

1. We consider an n-dimensional real vector space $E(n, R)$ and the dual real vector space $E^*(n, R)$, which is the space of the linear forms on E. The elements of E are called contravariant vectors and the elements of E^* covariant vectors:

$$\bar{x} \in E \qquad \underline{x} \in E^*.$$

2. A contravariant tensor ξ_p is an element of the tensorial power of order p of E:

$$\xi_p \in E^{\otimes p} \qquad \xi_1 \in E \qquad \xi_0 \in R.$$

In the same way, it is easy to introduce covariant tensors as the elements of $E^{*\otimes q}$ and mixed tensors as the elements of $E^{\otimes p} \otimes E^{*\otimes q}$.

3. We now consider the general linear group GL(n, R) and the unimodular linear transformations SL(n, R).

The irreducible tensors can be associated in a one-to-one correspondance to the irreducible representations of the permutation group. We do not give the proof of this important result.

4. The irreducible representation of the permutation group of p elements G_p are easily described by using the Young tables and the Young diagrams.

A Young table is a set of n non-negative integer numbers such that:

$$f_1 \geqq f_2 \geqq \ldots \geqq f_n \geqq 0$$

with the restriction:

$$\sum_{j=1}^{n} f_j = p.$$

In other terms, it is a partition of the number p.

The associated Young diagram is a set of p boxes divided in n rows with f_j boxes in the jth row:

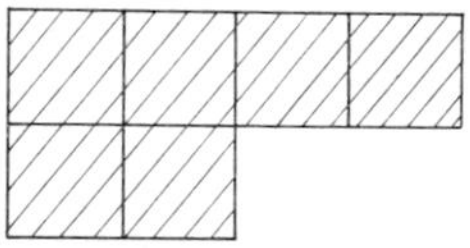

[4, 2, 0, 0]
$p = 6, n = 4$

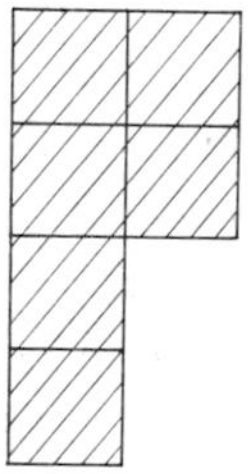

[2, 2, 1, 1]
$p = 6, n = 4$

Fig. 17.1. Young diagrams.

5. We now go back to a contravariant tensor of order p, the dimension of E being precisely n. The Young table describes a symmetry of the tensor and the properties are the following:

a) the indices associated to each box of a horizontal row are symmetrized;

b) the indices associated to each box of a vertical column are antisymmetrized.

For instance, a completely symmetrized tensor of rank p is associated to the partition $f_1 = p, f_2 = f_3 = \ldots = f_n = 0$ and the corresponding Young diagram has only one row:

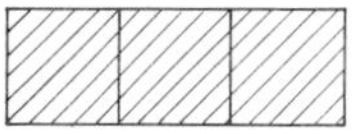

[3, 0, 0, 0]
$p = 3, \quad n = 4$
Fig. 17.2.

Such a tensor is an element of the vector sub-space $SE^{\otimes p}$ of the completely symmetrical tensors. The dimension of $SE^{\otimes p}$ is the combination number C^p_{n+p-1}.

A completely antisymmetrized tensor of rank p is associated to the partition: $f_1 = f_2 = \ldots = f_p = 1$, $f_{p-1} = f_{p-2} = \ldots = f_n = 0$ and the corresponding Young diagram has only one column:

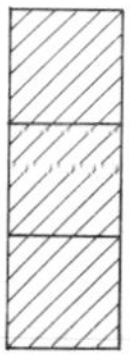

[1, 1, 1, 0]
$p = 3, \quad n = 4$
Fig. 17.3.

Such a tensor is an element of the vector sub-space $AE^{\otimes p}$ of the completely antisymmetrical tensors. The dimension of $AE^{\otimes p}$ is the combination number C^p_n. Of course it is not possible to construct a completely antisymmetrical tensor of order $p > n$ and the maximum number of rows of a Young diagram is precisely n.

6. For a covariant tensor of order q, element of $E^{*\otimes q}$, the previous results can be extended in the following way. To each partition of the number q, we associate a set of non-positive integer numbers:

$$0 \geqq f_1 \geqq f_2 \geqq \ldots \geqq f_n$$

with the restriction:

$$\sum_{j=1}^{n} f_j = -q.$$

The corresponding Young diagram is a set of q boxes divided into n rows with $-f_j$ boxes in the jth row:

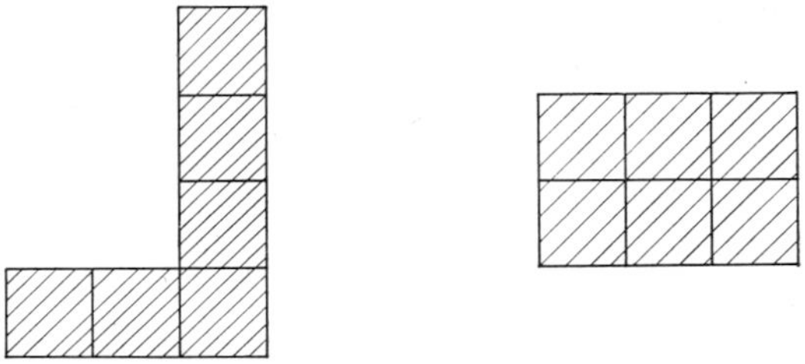

[−1, −1, −1, −3]　　　　[0, 0, −3, −3]

$q = 6, \quad h = 4$　　　　$q = 6, \quad n = 4$

Fig. 17.4.

For a mixed tensor, element of $E^{\otimes p} \otimes E^{*\otimes q}$ one associates to each partition of p and q, a set of n algebraic integer numbers

$$f_1 \geqq f_2 \geqq \ldots \geqq f_j \geqq 0 \geqq f_{j+1} \geqq \ldots \geqq f_n$$

such that:

$$\sum_{k=1}^{j} f_k = p \qquad \sum_{k=j+1}^{n} f_k = -q.$$

The corresponding Young diagram is then immediately drawn by using the previous results:

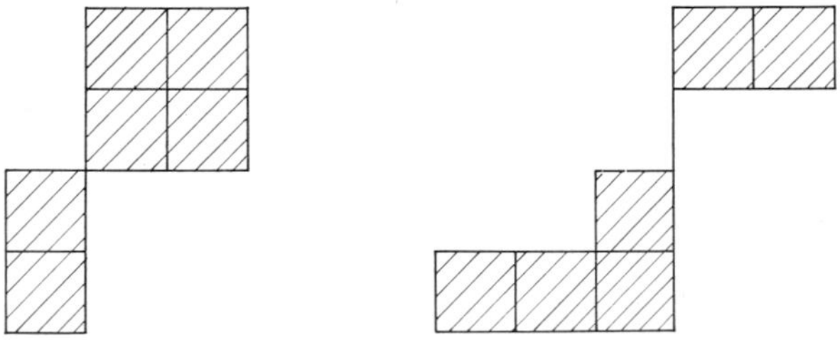

[2, 1, −1, −1]　　　　[2, 0, −1, −3]

$p = 4, \quad q = 2, \quad n = 4$　　　　$p = 2, \quad q = 4, \quad n = 4$

Fig. 17.5. Young diagrams for mixed tensors.

7. We are now interested with the completely antisymmetrized one component tensor of order n.

Let us introduce in E a basis $\bar{e}_j$; the corresponding basis in $AE^{\otimes n}$ can be written with exterior tensorial products as:

$$\bar{e}_1 \wedge \bar{e}_2 \wedge \ldots \wedge \bar{e}_n$$

We consider n linearly independent vectors $\bar{x}_{(j)}$ of E; the completely anti-symmetrized product:

$$\bar{x}_{(1)} \wedge \bar{x}_{(2)} \wedge \ldots \wedge \bar{x}_{(n)}$$

is the only linearly independent element of $AE^{\otimes n}$. By using the coordinates:

$$\bar{x}_{(j)} = x^k_{(j)} \bar{e}_k$$

we immediately obtain:

$$\bar{x}_{(1)} \wedge \bar{x}_{(2)} \wedge \ldots \wedge \bar{x}_{(n)} = [\sum_{[\sigma]} \chi(\sigma) x^{\sigma_1}_{(1)} x^{\sigma_2}_{(2)} \ldots x^{\sigma_n}_{(n)}] \bar{e}_1 \wedge \bar{e}_2 \wedge \ldots \wedge \bar{e}_n$$

where $[\sigma]$ is the permutation $\begin{pmatrix} 1 & 2 & \ldots n \\ \sigma_1 & \sigma_2 & \ldots \sigma_n \end{pmatrix}$ of parity $\chi(\sigma)$.

The bracket is simply the determinant $D(\bar{x}_{(1)}, \bar{x}_{(2)}, \ldots, \bar{x}_{(n)})$

$$\bar{x}_{(1)} \wedge \bar{x}_{(2)} \wedge \ldots \wedge \bar{x}_{(n)} = D(\bar{x}_{(1)}, \bar{x}_{(2)}, \ldots, \bar{x}_{(n)}) = \bar{e}_1 \wedge \bar{e}_2 \wedge \ldots \wedge \bar{e}_n.$$

We now perform a regular linear transformation in E, represented by the element A of GL(n, R):

$$\bar{x}'_{(k)} = \bar{x}_{(j)} A^j_k.$$

By using the previous results we find

$$\bar{x}'_{(1)} \wedge \bar{x}'_{(2)} \wedge \ldots \wedge \bar{x}'_{(n)} = \operatorname{Det} A \bar{x}_{(1)} \wedge \bar{x}_{(2)} \wedge \ldots \wedge \bar{x}_{(n)}$$

and finally:

$$\operatorname{Det}(\bar{x}'_{(1)}, \bar{x}'_{(2)}, \ldots, \bar{x}'_{(n)}) = \operatorname{Det} A \operatorname{Det}(\bar{x}_{(1)}, \bar{x}_{(2)}, \ldots, \bar{x}_{(n)}).$$

If now, A is an unimodular matrix, element of the special linear group SL(n, R), the quantity Det $(\bar{x}_{(1)}, \bar{x}_{(2)}, \ldots, \bar{x}_{(n)})$ is an invariant.

17.3. Irreducible representations of SL(n, R)

1. We have just seen that for the unimodular linear transformations of E(n, R) the one component representation [1, 1, . . ., 1] is invariant. In other terms, the two representations [1, 1, . . ., 1] and [0, 0, . . ., 0] are equivalent. In a more general way, the two equivalent representations of GL(n, R):

$$[f_1, f_2, \ldots, f_n] \quad \text{and} \quad [f'_1, f'_2, \ldots, f'_n]$$

are equivalent in SL(n, R) if and only if:

$$f'_j = f_j + s \qquad j = 1, 2, \ldots, n$$

where s is an algebraic integer number independent of j.

In particular, in SL(n, R), the representations

$$[f_1, f_2, \ldots, f_{n-1}, f_n] \quad \text{and} \quad [f_1-f_n, f_2-f_n, \ldots, f_{n-1}-f_n, 0]$$

are equivalent and, with respect to unimodular transformations, any tensor is equivalent to a contravariant tensor with $f_n = 0$.

2. It is convenient to introduce the completely antisymmetrical tensor of order n, element of $AE^{*\otimes n}$, $\varepsilon_{\sigma_1\sigma_2\ldots\sigma_n}$ defined by

$$\varepsilon_{12\ldots n} = 1 \qquad \varepsilon_{\sigma_1\sigma_2\ldots\sigma_n} = \chi(\sigma).$$

In this language, we have:

$$\operatorname{Det}(\bar{x}_{(1)}, \bar{x}_{(2)}, \ldots, \bar{x}_{(n)}) = \sum_{[\sigma]} \varepsilon_{\sigma_1\sigma_2\ldots\sigma_n} x_{(1)}^{\sigma_1} x_{(2)}^{\sigma_2} \ldots x_{(n)}^{\sigma_n}.$$

The determinant is invariant under unimodular transformations but transforms with a factor Det A for all $A \in$ GL(n, R).

In the same way, the quantity:

$$\varepsilon_{\sigma_1\sigma_2\ldots\sigma_n} x_{(2)}^{\sigma_2} \ldots x_{(n)}^{\sigma_n}$$

transforms like a covariant vector of E* under unimodular transformations. A straight forward generalization of this result is the following: the two irreducible representations of GL(n, R):

$$[f_1, f_2, \ldots, f_n] \quad \text{and} \quad [f_1+s, f_2+s, \ldots, f_n+s]$$

are equivalent for unimodular transformations but we have to add an extra factor (Det $A)^s$ if now A is an element of the general linear group.

3. As a consequence, an irreducible representation of GL(n, R) is also an irreducible representation of SL(n, R). It is then sufficient to study the irreducible representation of SL(n, R) and with the previous statement we are able to deduce all the irreducible representations of GL(n, R).

Such a result was expected because of the homomorphism from GL(n, R) into SL(n, R) is a central homomorphism.

Of course, the representations $[f_1+s, f_2+s, \ldots, f_n+s]$ have the same dimension independent of s.

4. The irreducible representations of SL(n, R) can then be characterized by a set of $(n-1)$ non-negative integer numbers.

It is convenient to work with the representation $[f_1, f_2, \ldots, f_{n-1}, 0]$ and to define:

$$\lambda_j = f_j - f_{j+1} \qquad j = 1, 2, \ldots, n-1$$

and conversely:

$$f_j = \sum_{k=j}^{n-1} \lambda_k .$$

The representation $(\lambda_1, \lambda_2, \ldots, \lambda_{n-1})$ can be associated to a contravariant tensor of order p given by:

$$p = \sum_{j=1}^{n-1} f_j = \sum_{k=1}^{n-1} k\lambda_k .$$

The representations R^k with all the λ_j's equal to zero, except $\lambda_k = 1$, corresponds to a completely antisymmetrical tensor of order k:

$$f_1 = f_2 = \ldots = f_k = 1 \qquad f_{k+1} = f_{k+2} = \ldots = f_{n-1} = f_n = 0.$$

The dimension of this representation is C_n^k, as the dimension of the fundamental representation F^k of the A_{n-1} Lie algebra discussed in Chapter XV. It can be shown that R^k and F^k are isomorphic and more generally, the highest weight of the irreducible representation $[f_1, f_2, \ldots, f_{n-1}, 0]$ is simply given by:

$$L = \sum_{j=1}^{n-1} \left(f_j - \frac{p}{n}\right) e_j .$$

For instance, the n dimensional fundamental representation of A_{n-1}, F^1 is associated to the vectors of E and the contragradient representation to the vectors of E*, considered also as completely antisymmetrized contravariant tensors of order $n-1$.

17.4. Adjoint representation

1. The Lie algebra of the general linear group GL(n, R) is the set of n^2 infinitesimal generators X_σ. It has been shown that the linear combination $X = \mathrm{Tr}\, X_\sigma$ commutes with all the generators.

The n^2-1 generators X_σ of trace zero generate the simple Lie algebra of type A_{n-1} of the special linear group SL(n, R).

We also consider a sub-algebra of A_{n-1}, with infinitesimal generators L_σ and the commutation laws:

$$[L_\rho, L_\tau] = C^\tau_{\rho\sigma} L_\tau .$$

Of course, this subalgebra can be A_{n-1} itself.

2. The adjoint representation of the Lie algebra A_{n-1}, $D(1, 0, \ldots, 0, 1)$ can be associated, from the previous results, of section 17.3, to an irreducible

mixed tensor of order 2, or, equivalently, to a covariant tensor of order $n+1$. We now study the mixed tensors of order two.

3. The second order mixed tensors ξ_j^k are the elements of E $\otimes$ E*. Let us now consider the representation with unitary matrices of the Lie algebra A_{n-1}

$$UU^* = I.$$

The infinitesimal generators can be represented by hermitic matrices following:

$$U \simeq I + i\varepsilon^\rho X_\rho \qquad U^* \simeq I - i\varepsilon^\rho X_\rho$$

where ε^ρ is a set of real infinitesimal parameters and $X_\rho^* = X_\rho$.

The tensor ξ is transformed, according to:

$$\xi' = U^* \xi U$$

and, for infinitesimal transformations, we obtain:

$$\xi_j'^k = \{\delta_j^m - i\varepsilon^\rho [X_\rho]_j^m\} \xi_m^n \{\delta_n^k + i\varepsilon^\sigma [X_\sigma]_n^k\}$$

and, after reduction:

$$\xi_j'^k = \xi_j^k - i\varepsilon^\rho \{[X_\rho]_j^m \delta_n^k - [X_\rho]_n^k \delta_j^m\} \xi_m^n .$$

From the previous expression, we immediately verify the invariance of the trace of ξ:

$$\operatorname{Tr} \xi' = \operatorname{Tr} \xi.$$

4. We now consider the quantities:

$$\phi_\sigma = [L_\sigma]_k^j \xi_j^k .$$

The transformation laws of the ϕ_σ's are deduced from those of the ξ_j^k's; taking into account the commutation laws of the Lie subalgebra we obtain:

$$\phi'_\sigma = \phi_\sigma + i\varepsilon^\rho C_{\rho\sigma}^\tau \, \phi_\tau .$$

In the basis of the ϕ_σ's the infinitesimal generators of the Lie algebra $[L_\sigma]$ are represented by the structure constants of this Lie algebra,

$$[L_\sigma]_\rho^\tau = C_{\rho\sigma}^\tau .$$

This result can also be interpreted as a consequence of the Jacobi identity satisfied by the structure constants. The dimension of the representation is the dimension of the Lie algebra and we have extracted the adjoint representation of the Lie algebra.

The adjoint representation is irreducible if and only if the Lie algebra is simple. For instance, the n^2-1 quantities:

$$\Phi_\sigma = [X_\sigma]^j_k \xi^k_j$$

are a basis of the adjoint representation of SL(n, R).

5. The n^2 components of the second order mixed tensor ξ^k_j have been reduced in the following way:

a) the invariant trace $\delta^j_k \xi^k_j$;

b) the n^2-1 components of trace zero $\xi^k_j-(1/n)\delta^k_j \operatorname{Tr} \xi$.

17.5. Product of representations

The reduction of a product of representations is the determination of the irreducible components of a tensor.

1. *Second order tensors.* We first consider the case of a contravariant tensor. The indices can be symmetrized and antisymmetrized, following the decomposition of the tensorial product into a symmetrical and an exterior product

$$\bar{x}_1 \otimes \bar{x}_2 = \bar{x}_1 \vee \bar{x}_2 \oplus \bar{x}_1 \wedge \bar{x}_2 .$$

In terms of Young diagrams, we have:

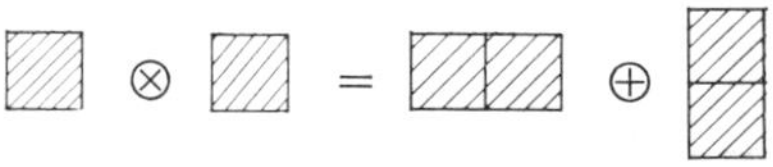

and the correspondance is the following:

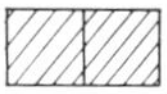 corresponds to $\bar{x}_1 \vee \bar{x}_2$ with $\frac{1}{2}n(n+1)$ components

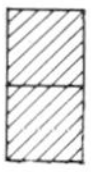 corresponds to $\bar{x}_1 \wedge \bar{x}_2$ with $\frac{1}{2}n(n-1)$ components.

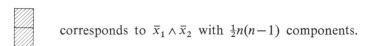

In the general linear group the product of representations is written as:

$$[1, 0, 0, \ldots, 0] \otimes [1, 0, 0, \ldots, 0] = [2, 0, 0, \ldots, 0] \oplus [1, 1, 0, \ldots, 0]$$

and in the special linear group, the corresponding expression is:

$$D(1, 0, 0, \ldots, 0) \otimes D(1, 0, 0, \ldots, 0) = D(2, 0, 0, \ldots, 0) \oplus D(0, 1, 0, \ldots, 0).$$

The same results can easily be obtained for covariant second order tensors using

$$x_1 \otimes x_2 = x_1 \vee x_2 \oplus x_1 \wedge x_2$$

and we obtain the same expressions for the product of the contragradient representations:

$$[0, \ldots, 0, 0, -1] \otimes [0, \ldots, 0, 0, -1] = [0, \ldots, 0, 0, -2] \oplus [0, \ldots, 0, -1, -1]$$

in GL(n, R) and for SL(n, R):

$$D(0, \ldots, 0, 0, 1) \otimes D(0, \ldots, 0, 0, 1) = D(0, \ldots, 0, 0, 2) \oplus D(0, \ldots, 0, 1, 0).$$

The case of a mixed second order tensor has been studied with some details in the previous section. In terms of product of representations, we obtain simply in GL(n, R):

$$[1, 0, \ldots, 0, 0] \otimes [0, 0, \ldots, 0, -1] = [0, 0, \ldots, 0, 0] \oplus [1, 0, \ldots, 0, -1]$$

and in SL(n, R):

$$D(1, 0, \ldots, 0, 0) \otimes D(0, 0, \ldots, 0, 1) = D(0, 0, \ldots, 0, 0) \oplus D(1, 0, \ldots, 0, 1).$$

2. *Third order contravariant tensor.* We use the method of the Young diagrams and we have only three possibilities:

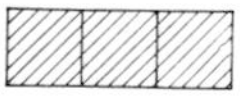 with $\frac{1}{6}n(n+1)(n+2)$ components

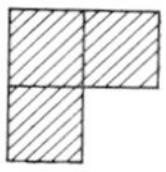 with $\frac{1}{3}n(n^2-1)$ components

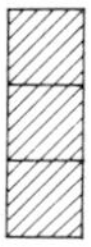 with $\frac{1}{6}n(n-1)(n-2)$ components.

The second possibility can be reached in two different ways and we obtain the following reduction in GL(n, R):

$$[1, 0, \ldots, 0]^{\otimes 3} = [3, 0, 0, \ldots, 0] \oplus 2[2, 1, 0, \ldots, 0] \otimes [1, 1, 1, 0, \ldots, 0]$$

and in SL(n, R) we have:

$$D(1, 0, 0, \ldots, 0) \otimes D(1, 0, 0, \ldots, 0) \otimes D(1, 0, 0, \ldots, 0) =$$
$$= D(3, 0, 0, \ldots, 0) \oplus 2D(1, 1, 0, \ldots, 0) \oplus D(0, 0, 1, 0, \ldots, 0).$$

3. *General case.* Let us consider two irreducible representations $[\bar{f}]$ and $[\bar{f}']$ of GL(n, R). It is always possible to introduce the representations, $[f]$ and $[f']$, equivalent in SL(n, R), respectively to $[\bar{f}]$ and $[\bar{f}']$ and such that $f_n = f_n' = 0$.

We are then working with representations $[f]$ and $[f']$ associated to contravariant tensors where all the f_j's and f_j''s are positive. The best way to reduce the product $[f] \otimes [f']$ is to use the Young diagrams following the Littlewood method.

The $[f]$ diagram has f_1 boxes α, f_2 boxes β, f_3 boxes γ, etc. The boxes of the diagram $[f]$ are added to the diagram $[f']$ in the following way:

a) with the α's, we form a new Young diagram, excluding the case where two boxes α are in the same column;

b) with the β's ,we form a new Young diagram, excluding the first row and the case where two boxes β are in the same column;

c) with the γ's ,we form a new Young diagram, excluding the first and the second rows and the case where two boxes γ are in the same column and so on with all the boxes of the diagram $[f]$.

Finally, we have also to take into account the last restriction: the added symbols, read from right to left in the first row, then the second row, etc. . . must form a lattice permutation of the α's, β's, γ's, etc. . . .

4. As an example, the Littlewood method can be used to reduce the product of two adjoint representations of the Lie algebra A_{n-1}. The result, written in GL(n, R) is the following:

$$[1, 0, \ldots, 0, -1] \otimes [1, 0, \ldots, 0, -1] = [0, \ldots, 0] \oplus 2[1, 0, \ldots, 0, -1] \oplus \oplus [2, 0, \ldots, 0, -1, -1] \oplus [1, 1, 0, \ldots, 0, -2] \oplus [1, 1, 0, \ldots, 0, -1, -1] \oplus \oplus [2, 0, \ldots, 0, -2]$$

and in SL(n, R) we obtain:

$$D(1, 0, \ldots, 0, 1) \otimes D(1, 0, \ldots, 0,1) = D(0, \ldots, 0) \oplus 2D(1, 0, \ldots, 0, 1) \oplus \oplus D(2, 0, \ldots, 0, 1, 0) \oplus D(0, 1, 0, \ldots, 0, 2) \oplus D(0, 1, 0, \ldots, 1, 0) \oplus \oplus D(2, 0, \ldots, 0, 2).$$

The dimension of these irreducible representations can be calculated using the general formula given in the Chapter XVI. We add the symbol S or A according as the representation enters in the symmetrical or in the antisymmetrical part of the product:

$$\begin{array}{rll}
N(0, \ldots, 0) = 1 & \text{S} & \\
N(1, 0, \ldots, 0, 1) = n^2-1 & \text{S and A} & \\
N(2, 0, \ldots, 0, 1, 0) = \frac{1}{4}(n^2-4)(n^2-1) & & \text{A} \\
N(0, 1, 0, \ldots, 0, 2) = \frac{1}{4}(n^2-4)(n^2-1) & & \text{A} \\
N(0, 1, 0, \ldots, 0, 1, 0) = \frac{1}{4}(n-3)n^2(n-1) & \text{S} & \\
N(2, 0, \ldots, 0, 2) = \frac{1}{4}(n-1)n^2(n+3) & \text{S.} &
\end{array}$$

The representations being denoted by their dimensionality, we obtain:

$$
\begin{array}{ll}
l = 1 & 3 \otimes 3 = 1 \oplus 3 \oplus 5, \\
l = 2 & 8 \otimes 8 = 1 \oplus 8_s \oplus 8_a \oplus 10 \oplus \overline{10} \oplus 27, \\
l = 3 & 15 \otimes 15 = 1 \oplus 15_s \oplus 15_a \oplus 45 \oplus \overline{45} \oplus 20 \oplus 84, \\
l = 4 & 24 \otimes 24 = 1 \oplus 24_s \oplus 24_a \oplus 126 \oplus \overline{126} \oplus 75 \oplus 200, \\
l = 5 & 35 \otimes 35 = 1 \oplus 35_s \oplus 35_a \oplus 280 \oplus \overline{280} \oplus 189 \oplus 405.
\end{array}
$$

Excepted the case $l = 1$, the adjoint representation is present in both the symmetrical and the antisymmetrical part of the product of two adjoint representations.

APPENDIX

Isometries

We give the explicit expressions of some useful isometries associated to the adjoint representation. The normalization is choosen as in the text and we take as examples of realization of the SU(3) multiplets the $J = \frac{1}{2}^+$ and $J = \frac{3}{2}^+$ baryons and the $J = 1^-$ mesons.

If X_ρ is an infinitesimal generator of the SU(3) Lie algebra and O_ρ an operator transformed like X_ρ under unitary transformation we have the following commutation relations:

$$[X_\rho, X_\sigma] = C^\tau_{\sigma\rho}\, X_\tau$$
$$[O_\rho, X_\sigma] = C^\tau_{\sigma\rho}\, O_\tau.$$

These equalities give a check of the consistency between the various isometries.

$$\underline{8 \otimes 8 \Rightarrow 8\text{a}}$$

The isometries are the infinitesimal generators of the Lie algebra.

$$\Omega^{(8a)}_{I+} = |\text{p}\rangle\langle\text{n}| - |\Xi^0\rangle\langle\Xi^-| + \sqrt{2}|\Sigma^0\rangle\langle\Sigma^-| - \sqrt{2}|\Sigma^+\rangle\langle\Sigma^0|$$

$$\Omega^{(8a)}_{I-} = |\text{n}\rangle\langle\text{p}| - |\Xi^-\rangle\langle\Xi^0| + \sqrt{2}|\Sigma^-\rangle\langle\Sigma^0| - \sqrt{2}|\Sigma^0\rangle\langle\Sigma^+|$$

$$\Omega^{(8a)}_{I_3} = \tfrac{1}{2}[|\text{p}\rangle\langle\text{p}| + |\Xi^0\rangle\langle\Xi^0| - |\text{n}\rangle\langle\text{n}| - |\Xi^-\rangle\langle\Xi^-|] + |\Sigma^+\rangle\langle\Sigma^+| - |\Sigma^-\rangle\langle\Sigma^-|$$

$$\Omega^{(8a)}_{Y} = |\text{p}\rangle\langle\text{p}| + |\text{n}\rangle\langle\text{n}| - |\Xi^0\rangle\langle\Xi^0| - |\Xi^-\rangle\langle\Xi^-|$$

$$\Omega^{(8a)}_{Q} = |\text{p}\rangle\langle\text{p}| + |\Sigma^+\rangle\langle\Sigma^+| - |\Sigma^-\rangle\langle\Sigma^-| - |\Xi^-\rangle\langle\Xi^-|$$

$$\Omega^{(8a)}_{V+} = |\Sigma^+\rangle\langle\Xi^0| - |\text{n}\rangle\langle\Sigma^-| + \frac{1}{\sqrt{2}}|\Sigma^0\rangle\langle\Xi^-| - \frac{1}{\sqrt{2}}|\text{p}\rangle\langle\Sigma^0| + $$
$$+ \sqrt{\tfrac{3}{2}}|\Lambda^0\rangle\langle\Xi^-| - \sqrt{\tfrac{3}{2}}|\text{p}\rangle\langle\Lambda^0|$$

$$\Omega^{(8a)}_{V-} = |\Xi^0\rangle\langle\Sigma^+| - |\Sigma^-\rangle\langle\text{n}| + \frac{1}{\sqrt{2}}|\Xi^-\rangle\langle\Sigma^0| - \frac{1}{\sqrt{2}}|\Sigma^0\rangle\langle\text{p}| + $$
$$+ \sqrt{\tfrac{3}{2}}|\Xi^-\rangle\langle\Lambda^0| - \sqrt{\tfrac{3}{2}}|\Lambda^0\rangle\langle\text{p}|$$

$$\Omega_{U+}^{(8a)} = |\Xi^-\rangle\langle\Sigma^-|-|\Sigma^+\rangle\langle p|+\frac{1}{\sqrt{2}}|\Sigma^0\rangle\langle n|-\frac{1}{\sqrt{2}}|\Xi^0\rangle\langle\Sigma^0|+ +\sqrt{\tfrac{3}{2}}|\Xi^0\rangle\langle\Lambda^0|-\sqrt{\tfrac{3}{2}}|\Lambda^0\rangle\langle n$$

$$\Omega_{U-}^{(8a)} = |\Sigma^-\rangle\langle\Xi^-|-|p\rangle\langle\Sigma^+|+\frac{1}{\sqrt{2}}|n\rangle\langle\Sigma^0|-\frac{1}{\sqrt{2}}|\Sigma^0\rangle\langle\Xi^0|+ +\sqrt{\tfrac{3}{2}}|\Lambda^0\rangle\langle\Xi^0|-\sqrt{\tfrac{3}{2}}|n\rangle\langle\Lambda^0|$$

$8 \otimes 8 \Rightarrow 8s$

$$\Omega_{I+}^{(8s)} = |p\rangle\langle n|+|\Xi^0\rangle\langle\Xi^-|+\sqrt{\tfrac{2}{3}}|\Lambda^0\rangle\langle\Sigma^-|+\sqrt{\tfrac{2}{3}}|\Sigma^+\rangle\langle\Lambda^0|$$

$$\Omega_{I-}^{(8s)} = |n\rangle\langle p|+|\Xi^-\rangle\langle\Xi^0|+\sqrt{\tfrac{2}{3}}|\Sigma^-\rangle\langle\Lambda^0|+\sqrt{\tfrac{2}{3}}|\Lambda^0\rangle\langle\Sigma^+|$$

$$\Omega_{I_3}^{(8s)} = \tfrac{1}{2}[|p\rangle\langle p|-|\Xi^0\rangle\langle\Xi^0|-|n\rangle\langle n|+|\Xi^-\rangle\langle\Xi^-|]+ +\frac{1}{\sqrt{3}}[|\Lambda^0\rangle\langle\Sigma^0|+|\Sigma^0\rangle\langle\Lambda^0|]$$

$$\Omega_{Y}^{(8s)} = -\tfrac{1}{3}[|p\rangle\langle p|+|n\rangle\langle n|+|\Xi^0\rangle\langle\Xi^0|+|\Xi^-\rangle\langle\Xi^-|] + +\tfrac{2}{3}[|\Sigma^+\rangle\langle\Sigma^+|+|\Sigma^-\rangle\langle\Sigma^-|+|\Sigma^0\rangle\langle\Sigma^0|-|\Lambda^0\rangle\langle\Lambda^0|]$$

$$\Omega_{Q}^{(8s)} = \tfrac{1}{3}[|p\rangle\langle p|+|\Sigma^+\rangle\langle\Sigma^+|+|\Sigma^-\rangle\langle\Sigma^-|+|\Xi^-\rangle\langle\Xi^-|+ +|\Sigma^0\rangle\langle\Sigma^0|-|\Lambda^0\rangle\langle\Lambda^0|]-\tfrac{2}{3}[|n\rangle\langle n|+|\Xi^0\rangle\langle\Xi^0|]+\frac{1}{\sqrt{3}}[|\Lambda^0\rangle\langle\Sigma^0|+|\Sigma^0\rangle\langle\Lambda^0|]$$

$$\Omega_{V+}^{(8s)} = |\Sigma^+\rangle\langle\Xi^0|+|n\rangle\langle\Sigma^-|+\frac{1}{\sqrt{2}}|\Sigma^0\rangle\langle\Xi^-|+\frac{1}{\sqrt{2}}|p\rangle\langle\Sigma^0|+ -\frac{1}{\sqrt{6}}|\Lambda^0\rangle\langle\Xi^-|-\frac{1}{\sqrt{6}}|p\rangle\langle\Lambda^0|$$

$$\Omega_{V-}^{(8s)} = |\Xi^0\rangle\langle\Sigma^+|+|\Sigma^-\rangle\langle n|+\frac{1}{\sqrt{2}}|\Xi^-\rangle\langle\Sigma^0|+\frac{1}{\sqrt{2}}|\Sigma^0\rangle\langle p|+ -\frac{1}{\sqrt{6}}|\Xi^-\rangle\langle\Lambda^0|-\frac{1}{\sqrt{6}}|\Lambda^0\rangle\langle p|$$

$$\Omega_{U+}^{(8s)} = |\Xi^-\rangle\langle\Sigma^-|+|\Sigma^+\rangle\langle p|-\frac{1}{\sqrt{2}}|\Sigma^0\rangle\langle n|-\frac{1}{\sqrt{2}}|\Xi^0\rangle\langle\Sigma^0|+ -\frac{1}{\sqrt{6}}|\Xi^0\rangle\langle\Lambda^0|-\frac{1}{\sqrt{6}}|\Lambda^0\rangle\langle n|$$

$$\Omega_{U-}^{(8s)} = |\Sigma^-\rangle\langle\Xi^-| + |p\rangle\langle\Sigma^+| - \frac{1}{\sqrt{2}}|n\rangle\langle\Sigma^0| - \frac{1}{\sqrt{2}}|\Sigma^0\rangle\langle\Xi^0| + \\ - \frac{1}{\sqrt{6}}|\Lambda^0\rangle\langle\Xi^0| - \frac{1}{\sqrt{6}}|n\rangle\langle\Lambda^0|.$$

The isometries $\Omega_Y^{(8s)}$ and $\Omega_Q^{(8s)}$ have been previously given, in Chapter VIII, as operations of the covering algebra but with a different normalization.

$$\Omega_Y^{(8s)} = \tfrac{1}{3}[2I(I+1) - \tfrac{1}{2}Y^2 - 2]$$
$$\Omega_Q^{(8s)} = \tfrac{1}{3}[2 + \tfrac{1}{2}Q^2 - 2U(U+1)].$$

$\underline{10 \otimes 8 \Rightarrow 8}$

$$\Omega_{I+}^{(8)} = \sqrt{6}|N^{*++}\rangle\langle p| - \sqrt{2}|N^{*+}\rangle\langle n| - \sqrt{3}|Y^{*+}\rangle\langle\Lambda^0| - |Y^{*+}\rangle\langle\Sigma^0| + \\ + |Y^{0*}\rangle\langle\Sigma^-| + \sqrt{2}|\Xi^{*0}\rangle\langle\Xi^-|$$

$$\Omega_{I-}^{(8)} = -\sqrt{6}|N^{*-}\rangle\langle n| - \sqrt{2}|N^{*0}\rangle\langle p| - \sqrt{3}|Y^{*-}\rangle\langle\Lambda^0| + |Y^{-*}\rangle\langle\Sigma^0| + \\ - |Y^{0*}\rangle\langle\Sigma^+| + \sqrt{2}|\Xi^{*-}\rangle\langle\Xi^0|$$

$$\Omega_{I_3}^{(8)} = \sqrt{2}|N^{*+}\rangle\langle p| - \sqrt{2}|N^{*0}\rangle\langle n| + \frac{1}{\sqrt{2}}|Y^{*+}\rangle\langle\Sigma^+| - \frac{1}{\sqrt{2}}|Y^{*-}\rangle\langle\Sigma^-| + \\ - \sqrt{\tfrac{3}{2}}|Y^{*0}\rangle\langle\Lambda^0| - \frac{1}{\sqrt{2}}|\Xi^{*0}\rangle\langle\Xi^0| + \frac{1}{\sqrt{2}}|\Xi^{*-}\rangle\langle\Xi^-|$$

$$\Omega_Y^{(8)} = \sqrt{2}\{|Y^{*+}\rangle\langle\Sigma^+| + |Y^{*-}\rangle\langle\Sigma^-| + |Y^{*0}\rangle\langle\Sigma^0| - |\Xi^{*0}\rangle\langle\Xi^0| - |\Xi^{*-}\rangle\langle\Xi^-|\}$$

$$\Omega_Q^{(8)} = \sqrt{2}\{|Y^{*+}\rangle\langle\Sigma^+| - |\Xi^{*0}\rangle\langle\Xi^0| + |N^{*+}\rangle\langle p| - N^{*0}\rangle\langle n|\} + \\ - \sqrt{\tfrac{3}{2}}|Y^{*0}\rangle\langle\Lambda^0| + \frac{1}{\sqrt{2}}|Y^{*0}\rangle\langle\Sigma^0|$$

$$\Omega_{V+}^{(8)} = -\sqrt{6}|N^{*++}\rangle\langle\Sigma^+| - \sqrt{2}|Y^{*+}\rangle\langle\Xi^0| - 2|N^{*+}\rangle\langle\Sigma^0| - |Y^{*0}\rangle\langle\Xi^-| + \\ + \sqrt{2}|N^{*0}\rangle\langle\Sigma^-|$$

$$\Omega_{V-}^{(8)} = \sqrt{6}|\Omega^-\rangle\langle\Xi^0| - \sqrt{2}|\Xi^{*0}\rangle\langle\Sigma^+| + |Y^{*0}\rangle\langle p| + \sqrt{3}|\Xi^*\rangle\langle\Lambda^0| + \\ + |\Xi^{*-}\rangle\langle\Sigma^0| + \sqrt{2}|Y_1^{*-}\rangle\langle n|$$

$$\Omega_{U+}^{(8)} = \sqrt{6}|\Omega^-\rangle\langle\Xi^-| + \sqrt{2}|\Xi^{*-}\rangle\langle\Sigma^-| - \sqrt{3}|\Xi^{*0}\rangle\langle\Lambda^0| - |\Xi^{*0}\rangle\langle\Sigma^0| + \\ + |Y^{*0}\rangle\langle n| - \sqrt{2}|Y^{*+}\rangle\langle p|$$

$$\Omega_{U-}^{(8)} = -\sqrt{6}|N^{*-}\rangle\langle\Sigma^-| + \sqrt{2}|Y^{*-}\rangle\langle\Xi^-| - 2|N^{*0}\rangle\langle\Sigma^0| - |Y^{*0}\rangle\langle\Xi^0| + \\ - \sqrt{2}|N^{*+}\rangle\langle\Sigma^+|.$$

$\overline{10} \otimes 10 \Rightarrow 8$

$$\Omega_{I+}^{(8)} = -\sqrt{3}|N^{*++}\rangle\langle N^{*+}|+\sqrt{3}|N^{*0}\rangle\langle N^{*-}|-2|N^{*+}\rangle\langle N^{*0}|+ \\ -\sqrt{2}|Y^{*+}\rangle\langle Y^{*0}|+\sqrt{2}|Y^{*0}\rangle\langle Y^{*-}|-|\Xi^{*0}\rangle\langle \Xi^{*-}|$$

$$\Omega_{I-}^{(8)} = -\sqrt{3}|N^{*+}\rangle\langle N^{*++}|+\sqrt{3}|N^{*-}\rangle\langle N^{*0}|-2|N^{*0}\rangle\langle N^{*+}|+ \\ -\sqrt{2}|Y^{*0}\rangle\langle Y^{*+}|+\sqrt{2}|Y^{*-}\rangle\langle Y^{*0}|-|\Xi^{*-}\rangle\langle \Xi^{*0}|$$

$$\Omega_{I_3}^{(8)} = \tfrac{3}{2}[|N^{*++}\rangle\langle N^{*++}|-|N^{*-}\rangle\langle N^{*-}|]+\tfrac{1}{2}[|N^{*+}\rangle\langle N^{*+}|-|N^{*0}\rangle\langle N^{*0}|+ \\ +|\Xi^{*0}\rangle\langle \Xi^{*0}|-|\Xi^{*-}\rangle\langle \Xi^{*-}|]+|Y^{*+}\rangle\langle Y^{*+}|-|Y^{*-}\rangle\langle Y^{*-}|$$

$$\Omega_{Y}^{(8)} = |N^{*++}\rangle\langle N^{*++}|+|N^{*+}\rangle\langle N^{*+}|+|N^{*0}\rangle\langle N^{*0}|+|N^{*-}\rangle\langle N^{*-}|+ \\ -|\Xi^{*0}\rangle\langle \Xi^{*0}|-|\Xi^{*-}\rangle\langle \Xi^{*-}|-2|\Omega^{-}\rangle\langle \Omega^{-}|$$

$$\Omega_{Q}^{(8)} = 2|N^{*++}\rangle\langle N^{*++}|+|N^{*+}\rangle\langle N^{*+}|-|N^{*-}\rangle\langle N^{*-}|+|Y^{*+}\rangle\langle Y^{*+}|+ \\ -|Y^{*-}\rangle\langle Y^{*-}|-|\Xi^{*-}\rangle\langle \Xi^{*-}|-|\Omega^{-}\rangle\langle \Omega^{-}|$$

$$\Omega_{V+}^{(8)} = -\sqrt{3}|\Xi^{0*}\rangle\langle \Omega^{-}|+\sqrt{3}|N^{*++}\rangle\langle Y^{*+}|-2|Y^{*+}\rangle\langle \Xi^{*0}|+ \\ -\sqrt{2}|Y^{*0}\rangle\langle \Xi^{*-}|+\sqrt{2}|N^{*+}\rangle\langle Y^{*0}|-|N^{*0}\rangle\langle Y^{*-}|$$

$$\Omega_{V-}^{(8)} = -\sqrt{3}|\Omega^{-}\rangle\langle \Xi^{*0}|+\sqrt{3}|Y^{*+}\rangle\langle N^{*++}|-2|\Xi^{*0}\rangle\langle Y^{*+}|+ \\ -\sqrt{2}|\Xi^{*-}\rangle\langle Y^{*0}|+\sqrt{2}|Y^{*0}\rangle\langle N^{*+}|-|Y^{*-}\rangle\langle N^{*0}|$$

$$\Omega_{U+}^{(8)} = -\sqrt{3}|Y^{*-}\rangle\langle N^{*-}|+\sqrt{3}|\Omega^{-}\rangle\langle \Sigma^{*-}|-2|\Xi^{*-}\rangle\langle Y^{*-}|+ \\ -\sqrt{2}|Y^{*0}\rangle\langle N^{*0}|+\sqrt{2}|\Xi^{*0}\rangle\langle Y^{*0}|-|Y^{*+}\rangle\langle N^{*+}|$$

$$\Omega_{U-}^{(8)} = -\sqrt{3}|N^{*-}\rangle\langle Y^{*-}|+\sqrt{3}|\Xi^{*-}\rangle\langle \Omega^{-}|-2|Y^{*-}\rangle\langle \Xi^{*-}|+ \\ -\sqrt{2}|N^{*0}\rangle\langle Y^{*0}|+\sqrt{2}|Y^{*0}\rangle\langle \Xi^{*0}|-|N^{*+}\rangle\langle Y^{*+}|.$$

$8 \otimes 1 \Rightarrow 8$

$$\Omega_{I+} = \sqrt{2}|\rho^{+}\rangle\langle\omega^{0}|$$

$$\Omega_{I-} = \sqrt{2}|\rho^{-}\rangle\langle\omega^{0}|$$

$$\Omega_{I_3} = |\rho^{0}\rangle\langle\omega^{0}|$$

$$\Omega_{Y} = \frac{2}{\sqrt{3}}|\varphi^{0}\rangle\langle\omega^{0}|$$

$$\begin{aligned}
\Omega_Q &= |\rho^0\rangle\langle\omega^0| + \frac{1}{\sqrt{3}}\,|\varphi^0\rangle\langle\omega^0| \\
\Omega_{V+} &= \sqrt{2}|\mathrm{K}^{*+}\rangle\langle\omega^0| \\
\Omega_{V-} &= \sqrt{2}|\mathrm{K}^{*-}\rangle\langle\omega^0| \\
\Omega_{U+} &= \sqrt{2}|\overline{\mathrm{K}}^{*0}\rangle\langle\omega^0| \\
\Omega_{U-} &= \sqrt{2}|\mathrm{K}^{*0}\rangle\langle\omega^0|.
\end{aligned}$$

GENERAL REFERENCES ON THE MATHEMATICAL INTRODUCTION

BOERNER, H., Representations of groups (North-Holland Publishing Company, Amsterdam, 1963)

CARTAN, E., Sur la structure des groups de transformations finis et continus (Thèse, Paris, 1894)

CHEVALLEY, C., Theory of Lie groups (Princeton Math. Series 8)

COHN, P., Lie groups (Cambridge, 1957)

HAMMERMESH, M., Group theory and its application to physical problems (New York, 1962)

HELGASON, S., Differential geometry and symmetric spaces (Academic Press, New York, 1962)

LITTLEWOOD, D. E., The theory of group characters and matrix representations of groups (Oxford, 1950)

MICHEL, L., Lectures given at the Istambul Summer School (1962)

MURNAGHAN, F. D., The theory of group representations (Baltimore, 1938)

PONTRJAGEN, L., Topological groups (Princeton, 1946)

RACAH, G., Group theory and spectroscopy (Princeton Lecture Notes, 1951)

VAN DER WAERDEN, B. L., Die Gruppen-theoretische Method in der Quantenmechanik Berlin, 1932);
Modern algebra I, II (New York, 1949, 1950)

WEYL, H., The theory of groups and quantum mechanics (New York, 1931);
The classical groups, their invariants and representations (Princeton, 1939)

WIGNER, E. P., Group theory and its application to the quantum mechanics of atomic spectra (New York, 1959)

SÉMINAIRE Sophus Lie. E.N.S. (1954/55)

REFERENCES

Abarbanel, H. and C. Callan, Phys. Letters **16**, 191 (1965)
Ademollo, M. and R. Gatto, Phys. Rev. Letters **13**, 264 (1964)
Adler, S. L., Phys. Rev. Letters **14**, 1051 (1965)
Alles, W. and D. Amati, Preprint CERN (1965)
Amati, D., C. Bouchiat and J. Nuyts, Preprint (1965)
Anderson, J. M. and F. S. Crawford, Jr., Phys. Rev. Letters **13**, 167 (1964)
Armenteros, R. et al., Phys. Letters **19**, 75 (1965)
Backer, M. and S. L. Glashow, Nuovo Cimento **26**, 803 (1962)
Bardakci, K., J. M. Cornwall, P. G. O. Freund and B. W. Lee, Phys. Rev. Letters **13**, 698 (1964)
Bardakci, K., J. M. Cornwall, P. G. O. Freund and B. W. Lee, Phys. Rev. Letters **14**, 48, 264 (1965)
Barret, B. and K. Tanaka, Nuovo Cimento **36**, 965 (1965)
Barton, G. and S. P. Prosen, Phys. Rev. Letters **8**, 414 (1962)
Bég, M. A. B., B. W. Lee and A. Pais, Phys. Rev. Letters **13**, 514 (1964)
Bég, M. A. B. and V. Singh, Phys. Rev. Letters **13**, 418 (1964)
Behrends, R. E., J. Dreitlein, C. Fronsdal and B. W. Lee, Rev. Mod. Phys. **34**, 1 (1962)
Behrends, R. E. and A. Sirlin, Phys. Rev. Letters **4**, 186 (1960)
Berman, S. M. and M. Veltman, Preprint (1964)
Block, M., Phys. Rev. Letters **12**, 262 (1964)
Borchi, E. and R. Gatto, Phys. Letters **14**, 352 (1965)
Bouchiat, C. and Ph. Meyer, Nuovo Cimento **34**, 1122 (1964)
Cabbibo, N., Phys. Rev. Letters **10**, 531 (1963)
Cabibbo, N., Phys. Rev. Letters **12**, 62 (1964)
Cabibbo, N. and R. Gatto, Nuovo Cimento **21**, 872 (1962)
Charriere, C. et al., Phys. Letters **15**, 66 (1965)
Christenson, J. H. et al. Phys. Rev. Letters **13**, 138 (1964)
Cini, M., Phys. Letters **19**, 251 (1965)
Coester, F., M. Hammermesh and W. D. McGlinn, Phys. Rev. **135**, B 451 (1964)
Coleman, S., Preprint CERN (1965a)
Coleman, S., Phys. Rev. **19**, 144 (1965b)
Coleman, S. and S. L. Glashow, Phys. Rev. Letters **6**, 423 (1961)
Cool, R. L. et al., Phys. Rev. **127**, 2232 (1962)
Dalitz, R. H. and D. G. Sutherland, Nuovo Cimento **38**, 1945 (1965)
Dalitz, R. H. and F. Von Hippel, Phys. Letters **10**, 153 (1964)
Dashen, R. F. and M. Gell-Mann. Phys. Letters **17**, 142 (1965a)
Dashen, R. F. and M. Gell-Mann, Phys. Letters **17**, 145 (1965b)
Dashen, R. F. and D. A. Sharp, Phys. Rev. **133**, B 1585 (1964)
Delbourgo, R., M. A. Rashid and J. Strathdee, Phys. Rev. Letters **14**, 719 (1965)
De Souza, P. D., G. A. Snow and S. Menshkov, Phys. Rev. **135**, 565 (1964)
d'Espagnat, B. and J. Prentki, Nuovo Cimento **24**, 497 (1962)
De Swart, J. J., Rev. Mod. Phys. **35**, 916 (1963)
De Swart, J. J., Nuovo Cimento **31**, 420 (1965)
Dietz, K. and W. Drechsler, Preprint (1965)
Diu, B., H. Rubinstein and J. L. Basdevant, Nuovo Cimento **35**, 460 (1965)
Dosch, H. G. and B. Stech, Preprint (1965)

EDMONDS, A. R., Proc. Roy. Soc. A **268**, 567 (1962)
FEENBERG, E. and E. P. WIGNER, Phys. Rev. **51**, 15 (1937)
FERMI, E., Ricerea Scientifica **4**, 491 (1933)
FERMI, E., Nuovo Cimento II, 1 (1934)
FEYNMAN, R. P. and M. GELL-MANN, Phys. Rev. **109**, 193 (1958)
FEYNMAN, R. P., M. GELL-MANN and G. ZWEIG, Phys. Rev. Letters **13**, 678 (1964)
FRANZINI, E. P. and L. A. RADICATI, Phys. Letters **6**, 322 (1963)
FUBINI, S. and G. FURLAN, Physics **1**, 229 (1965)
GASIOROWICZ, S., ANL 6729 (1963)
GELL-MANN, M., CTSL 20 (1961) unpublished.
GELL-MANN, M., Phys. Rev. **125**, 1067 (1962)
GELL-MANN, M., Phys. Letters **8**, 214 (1964a)
GELL-MANN, M., Physics **1**, 63 (1964b)
GELL-MANN, M., Phys. Rev. Letters **12**, 62 (1964c)
GELL-MANN, M., Phys. Rev. Letters **14**, 77 (1965)
GELL-MANN, M. and M. LÉVY, Nuovo Cimento **16**, 703 (1960)
GELL-MANN, M., D. SHARP and W. G. WAGNER, Phys. Rev. Letters **8**, 261 (1962)
GERNSTEIN, I. S., Preprint (1965)
GERNSTEIN, S. S. and J. B. ZELDOVITCH, Zum. Eksp. Teor. Fiz. **29**, 698 (1955)
GINIBRE, J., J. Math. Physics **4**, 720 (1963a)
GINIBRE, J., Nuovo Cimento **30**, 407 (1963b)
GLASHOW, S. L. and A. H. ROSENFELD, Phys. Rev. Letters **10**, 192 (1963)
GLASHOW, S. L. and R. H. SOCOLOW, Phys. Letters **10**, 142 (1964)
GOLDBERGER, M. L. and S. B. TREIMAN, Phys. Rev. **110**, 1178, 1478 (1958)
GOURDIN, M., TH/45 (Orsay, february 1964a) unpublished
GOURDIN, M., Unitary symmetry and weak interactions (Bordeaux, may 1964b) unpublished
GOURDIN, M., Ergebnisse der exakten Naturwissenschaften, 36 Band (1964c)
GOURDIN, M. and PH. SALIN, Nuovo Cimento **27**, 193 (1963a)
GOURDIN, M. and PH. SALIN, Nuovo Cimento **27**, 309 (1963b)
GREENBERG, O. W., Phys. Rev. **135** B, 1447 (1964)
GÜRSEY, F., A. PAIS and L. A. RADICATI, Phys. Rev. Letters **13**, 299 (1964)
GÜRSEY, F., T. D. LEE and M. NAUENBERG, Phys. Rev. **135** B, 467 (1964)
GÜRSEY, F. and L. A. RADICATI, Phys. Rev. Letters **13**, 173 (1964)
HARA, Y., Phys. Rev. Letters **12**, 378 (1964)
HARRARI, H. and H. LIPKIN, Phys. Rev. Letters **13**, 208 (1963)
HILL, D. A., K. K. LI, E. W. JENKINS, T. F. KYCRA and H. RUDERMAN, Phys. Rev. Letters **15**, 85 (1965)
HUWE, D. O., UCRL 11, 291 (1964)
ITABASHI, K., Phys. Rev. **136**, B 221 (1964)
JOHNSON, K. and S. B. TREIMAN, Phys. Rev. Letters **14**, 189 (1965)
KERMAN, W. et al., Phys. Rev. **129**, 870 (1963)
KONUMA, M. and Y. TOMOZAWA, Phys. Letters **10**, 347 (1964)
LEANSON, C. A., H. J. LIPKIN and S. MESHKOV, Phys. Letters **7**, 81 (1963)
LEE, B. W., Phys. Rev. Letters **12**, 83 (1964)
LEE, B. W., Phys. Rev. Letters **14**, 676 (1965)
LEVINSON, C. A. and I. J. MUZINICH, Phys. Rev. Letters **15**, 715 (1965)
LIPKIN, H. J., C. A. LEVINSON and S. MESHKOV, Phys. Letters **7**, 159 (1963)
LIPKIN, H. J. and S. MESHKOV, Phys. Letters **14**, 670 (1965)
LURÇAT, F. and L. MICHEL, Nuovo Cimento **21**, 574 (1961)
MACFARLANE, A. M. and E. C. G. SUDARSHAN, Nuovo Cimento **31**, 1176 (1964)
MARTIN, A. W. and K. C. WALI, Phys. Rev. **130**, 2455 (1963)

MAYER, M. E., H. T. SCHNITZER, E. C. G. SUDARSHAN, R. ACHARYA, M. Y. HAN, Phys. Rev. **136** B, 888 (1964)
MCGLINN, W. D., Phys. Rev. Letters **12**, 467 (1964)
MCINTURFF, A. D. and C. E. ROOS, Phys. Rev. Letters **13**, 246 (1964)
MCNAMEE, P. and F. CHILTON, Rev. Mod. Phys. **36**, 1005 (1964)
MESHKOV, S., C. A. LEVINSON and H. J. LIPKIN, Phys. Rev. Letters **10**, 361 (1963)
MESHKOV, S., G. A. SNOW and G. B. YODH, Phys. Rev. Letters **12**, 87 (1964)
MICHEL, L., Lectures given at the Istambul Summer School (1962)
MICHEL, L., Phys. Rev. **137**, B 405 (1965)
MURASKIN, M. and S. L. GLASHOW, Phys. Rev. **132**, 482 (1963)
NE'EMAN, Y., Nuclear Physics **26**, 222 (1961)
OKUBO, S., Progr. Theor. Phys. **27**, 949 (1962); **28**, 24 (1962)
OKUBO, S., Phys. Letters **4**, 14 (1963a)
OKUBO, S., Phys. Letters **5**, 165 (1963b)
OLSSON, M. G., Phys. Rev. Letters **14**, 118 (1965)
OTTOSON, U., A. KIHLBERG and J. NILSSON, Phys. Rev. **137**, B 658 (1965)
PAIS, A., Phys. Rev. Letters **13**, 175 (1964)
PJERROU, G. M., Phys. Rev. Letters **14**, 275 (1965)
RASHID, M. A., Nuovo Cimento **26**, 118 (1962)
RAYFEARTAIGH, L. O., Phys. Rev. Letters **14**, 332 575 (1965)
ROSENBERG, A. H., A. BARBARO–GALTIERI, W. H. BARKAS, P. L. BASTIEN, J. KIRZ and M. ROOS, UCRL 8030 (August 1965).
RUEGG, H., Preprint CERN (1965)
RUEGG, H., D. SPEISER and A. MORALES, Nuovo Cimento **25**, 307 (1962)
RUEGG, H. and D. V. VOLKOV, Preprint CERN (1965)
RÜHL, W., Phys. Letters **14**, 346; **15**, 101, 340 (1965a)
RÜHL, W., Nuovo Cimento **37**, 301, 319; **38**, 675; **39**, 307 (1965b)
SAKATA, S., Progr. Theor. Phys. **16**, 686 (1956)
SAKITA, B., Phys. Rev. Letters **13**, 643 (1964a)
SAKITA, B., Phys. Rev. **136** B, 1756 (1964b)
SAKITA, B. and K. C. WALI, Phys. Rev. **139** B, 1355 (1965)
SAKURAI, J. J., Ann. Phys. **11**, 1 (1960)
SAKURAI, J. J., Phys. Rev. Letters **9**, 472 (1962)
SAKURAI, J. J., Phys. Rev. Letters **12**, 79 (1964)
SALAM, A., R. DELBOURGO and J. STRATHDEE, Proc. Roy. Soc. **284**, 146 (1965)
SALAM, A., J. STRATHDEE, J. M. CHARAP and P. T. MATTHEWS, Phys. Letters **15**, 184 (1965)
SAWYER, R. F., Phys. Rev. **14**, 471 (1965)
SCHNITZER, H., Preprint (1965)
SCHÜLKE, L., Preprint (1965)
SCHWINGER, J., Phys. Rev. Letters **3**, 296 (1959)
SCHWINGER, J., Phys. Rev. Letters **12**, 237 (1964)
TARJANNE, P., Ann. Acad. Sci. Fennicae, Ser. A VI, 105 (1962)
TARJANNE, P., Carnegie Institute of Technology, N.Y.O. 9290-A (1963a)
TARJANNE, P., Preprint N.Y.O. 9290 (1963b)
VOLKOV, D. V., Soviet Phys. Letters **1**, 129 (1965)
VON DARDEL, G. et al., Phys. Letters **4**, 51 (1963)
WEISBERGER, W. I., Phys. Rev. Letters **14**, 1047 (1965)
WIGNER, E. P., Phys. Rev. **51**, 106 (1937)
WILLIS, H. et al., Phys. Rev. Letters **13**, 291 (1964)
ZACHARIASEN, F. and G. ZWEIG, Phys. Rev. Letters **14**, 794 (1965)
ZDANIS, R. A. et al., Phys. Rev. Letters **14**, 721 (1965)
ZWEIG, G., CERN reports

SUBJECT-INDEX